WITHDRAWN

Mechanical Properties
of Polymers and Composites

(IN TWO VOLUMES)

VOLUME 2

Mechanical Properties
of Polymers and Composites

(IN TWO VOLUMES)

VOLUME 2

LAWRENCE E. NIELSEN
Monsanto Company
St. Louis, Missouri

MARCEL DEKKER, INC. New York   1974

MARCEL DEKKER, INC.

305 East 45th Street, New York, New York 10017

LIBRARY OF CONGRESS CATALOG CARD NUMBER: 74-80758

ISBN: 0-8247-6208-8

Current printing (last digit);
10 9 8 7 6 5 4 3 2 1

PRINTED IN THE UNITED STATES OF AMERICA

To

Deanne

and

My Mother

CONTENTS

Contents of Volume 1   ix

Preface   xi

Chapter 5   STRESS-STRAIN BEHAVIOR AND STRENGTH   257

         I.   Stress Strain Behavior   257

              A. Introduction   257

              B. Models   258

              C. Compression and Shear Versus
                 Tensile Tests   260

              D. Effect of Temperature   262

              E. Rate of Testing and the Failure
                 Envelope   265

              F. Effect of Hydrostatic Pressure   270

              G. Effect of Molecular Weight and
                 Branching   271

              H. Effect of Crosslinking   275

              I. Effect of Crystallinity   280

              J. Effects of Plasticization and
                 Copolymerization   283

              K. Molecular Orientation   285

              L. Polyblends, Block, and Graft
                 Polymers   292

        II.   Brittle Fracture and Stress
              Concentrators   294

              A. Stress Concentrators   294

              B. Fracture Theory   296

       III.   Theories of Yielding and Cold-Drawing   299

IV.   Impact Strength and Tearing   308

       A. Nature of Impact Tests   308

       B. Effect of Notches   309

       C. Effect of Temperature   313

       D. Effects of Orientation   314

       E. Other Factors Affecting Impact
          Strength   317

       F. Impact Strength of Polyblends   318

       G. Tearing   320

V.   Summary   322

VI.   Problems   323

VII.   References   328

Chapter 6   OTHER MECHANICAL PROPERTIES   341

I.   Heat Distortion Temperature   341

II.   Fatigue   348

III.   Friction   353

IV.   Abrasion, Wear, and Scratch
       Resistance   359

V.   Hardness and Indentation Tests   363

VI.   Summary   369

VII.   Problems   370

VIII. References   371

Chapter 7   PARTICULATE-FILLED POLYMERS   379

I.   Introduction to Composite Systems   379

II.   Rheology of Suspensions   380

III.   Relation Between Viscosity and
       Sheer Modulus   386

IV.   Moduli of Filled Polymers   387

      A. Regular Systems   387

      B. Inverted Systems and Phase
         Inversion   394

      C. Errors in Composite Moduli   401

      D. Experimental Examples   405

V.   Strength and Stress-Strain Behavior   405

      A. Rigid Fillers   405

      B. Polyblends, Block Polymers, and
         Foams   415

VI.   Creep and Stress Relaxation   418

VII. Dynamic Mechanical Properties   422

VIII. Other Mechanical Properties   430

      A. Impact Strength   430

      B. Heat Distortion Temperature   431

      C. Hardness and Wear   433

      D. Coefficients of Thermal
         Expansion   434

IX.   Summary   437

X.   Problems   438

XI.   References   442

Chapter 8   FIBER-FILLED COMPOSITES AND OTHER
             COMPOSITES   453

      I.   Introduction   453

      II.   Moduli of Fiber-Filled Composites   454

      III. Strength of Fiber-Filled Composites   465

            A. Uniaxially Oriented Fibers   465

            B. Strength of Randomly Oriented
               Fiber Composites and Laminates   474

IV.   Other Properties   479

       A. Creep   479

       B. Fatigue   480

       C. Heat Distortion Temperature   481

       D. Impact Strength   483

       E. Coefficients of Thermal
          Expansion   487

V.   Ribbon-Filled Composites   490

VI.   Other Types of Composites   496

       A. Flake-Filled Polymers   496

       B. Composites with Thick Interlayers   497

       C. Interpenetrating Network
          Composites   499

VII.   Summary   500

VIII. Problems   501

IX.   References   503

Appendix I   CHEMICAL STRUCTURE OF COMMON POLYMERS   511

Appendix II   CONVERSION FACTORS FOR MODULI, STRESS
              AND VISCOSITY   513

Appendix III GLASS TRANSITION TEMPERATURE AND MELTING
              POINTS OF POLYMERS   515

Appendix IV   RELATIONS BETWEEN ENGINEERING MODULI AND
              TENSOR MODULI AND TENSOR COMPLIANCES FOR
              ANISOTROPIC MATERIALS   519

Appendix V   LIST OF SYMBOLS   525

Author Index   537

Subject Index   553

CONTENTS OF VOLUME 1

Mechanical Tests and Polymer Transitions. Elastic Moduli.
Creep and Stress Relaxation. Dynamic Mechanical Properties.

Polymers are relatively cheap, large volume structural
materials comparable in importance to metals. Their widespread
use and rapid growth result largely from their versatile
mechanical properties which cover the range from soft elastomers
to rigid materials. There is a need for a knowledge of mechanical properties of polymers by many groups of workers with widely
different backgrounds and interests. It has been about a
decade since an up to date book has been published on the
mechanical properties of polymers which is simple enough to be
easily understood by a scientist who is not a specialist in the
field but which has enough detail and depth to be useful for
those working with polymers. Many universities have established
departments in polymers or material sciences and are offering
more courses in polymer technology. This book, which includes
sections on problems, should be suitable for a one semester
course on mechanical properties of polymers. Much of the material in this book has already been tested in courses at Washington University. Industrial laboratories are putting more
emphasis on mechanical behavior and on applications involving
mechanical properties and less emphasis on synthesis of polymers
in recent years. Design engineers are being forced to gain
knowledge of viscoelasticity and the mechanical properties of

polymers as these newer materials displace metals and glass in
more and more applications. Fabricators are becoming more aware
of the importance of many factors (such as molecular weight,
heat treatments, and molecular orientation, etc.) that affect
the performance of their finished objects. Thus, there is a
need for a book which discusses the mechanical properties of
polymers at the elementary to intermediate level. It is the
purpose of this book to fulfill the needs of all these people
as far as the mechanical properties of polymers and composite
materials are concerned.

    This book outlines the general mechanical behavior of
polymers to both environmental and structural factors. Environmental factors include time, temperature, external pressure, and
magnitude of applied loads. Structural factors include molecular weight, branching, crosslinking, copolymerization, plasticization, crystallinity and crystallite morphology, molecular
orientation, and block copolymerization. In all cases, emphasis
is placed upon general principles, useful empirical rules, and
practical equations. However, there is extensive reference also
to the specific behavior of many common polymers. Developments,
both experimental and theoretical, which have occurred in recent
years are given the most attention.

    Composite materials are now a major field of research and
development activity. Composites are rapidly becoming important
and useful structural materials, and probably the next major
area for polymer applications is in the field of composite
materials. A second objective of this book is to present a
complete and unified picture of the mechanical properties

of composites in an easily understood manner. At present, no
comparable book exists which covers the entire field of the
mechanical behavior of composite materials, including particulate-filled polymers, fiber-filled materials, foams, and
high impact polymers and polyblends. Other books cover only
certain aspects of the field of composites or are too mathemati-
cal for most scientists and engineers who need a working knowledge of these materials. Many composite materials are entirely
different from materials used in the past because of their
anisotropy, that is, their mechanical properties may be entirely
different in different directions. For this reason, this book
discusses anisotropy in detail at an elementary level since most
scientists and engineers are familiar only with isotropic
materials.

Extensive reference is made to the literature. An attempt
has been made to select the most important references and those
that illustrate a point. Undoubtedly, a few important references
have been missed, but the author hopes he has performed a useful
service by culling out tens of thousands of references which
really add very little to our knowledge. Thus, for any given
topic, it should be easy for the reader to quickly acquaint
himself with what has been done by looking up the listed
references.

The author cannot acknowledge everyone who has helped in
the preparation of this book. Colleagues who have offered
numerous suggestions after reading the original manuscript
include Joseph Bergomi, Rolf Buchdahl, Melvin Hedrick, Myron Holm,

Allen Kenyon, James Kurz, Thomas Lewis, Eli Perry, and James Woodbrey. Mrs. Bobbie Kaplan had the formidable task of typing the manuscript. Deanne, my wife, not only helped with the proof reading, the literature, and the indexes, but she tolerated the author and his mass of papers for the three years required to write this book.

                                        Lawrence E. Nielsen

Mechanical Properties of Polymers and Composites

(IN TWO VOLUMES)

VOLUME 2

Chapter 5

Stress-Strain Behavior and Strength

I. Stress-Strain Tests

A. Introduction

The mechanics of the stress-strain test and the types of
stress-strain curves which are typical of high polymers have
been discussed in Chapter 1. The stress-strain test is the
most widely used of all mechanical tests. It is a very important
practical test and one which engineers have a feeling for.
However, the relationship of this test to use applications is not
as clear as is generally assumed. Because of the viscoelastic
nature of polymers with their sensitivity to many factors, the
stress-strain test is, at best, only a rough guide to how a
polymer will behave in a finished object. Often only a single
curve or datum point characteristic of one temperature and speed
of testing is published. To give the engineer or designer the
information he really needs requires tests at many temperatures,
rates of testing, and other conditions; this requires much time
and material. Often only tensile or flexural data are known, but
it would be desirable to have compression and shear data and also
biaxial data in addition to the uniaxial data. Thus, it is
obvious that in using the stress-strain data usually available,
the engineer must do a lot of guessing based on past experience

and often overdesign an object in order to be sure that it will fulfill its purpose.

Stress-strain tests not only give an indication of the strength of a material but also its toughness. The concept of toughness may be defined in several ways, one of which is in terms of the area under a stress-strain curve. Toughness, therefore, is an indication of the energy that a material can absorb before breaking. Thus, toughness and impact strength should be related in some manner. Brittle materials have low toughness while ductile materials which cold draw are very tough because of the large elongations to break.

B. Models

As an aid to the understanding of the shape of stress-strain curves, it is helpful to look at the curves of simple models. Four simple models are shown in Figure 1 along with their stress-strain curves for two rates of elongation (1). A spring has a constant modulus independent of the speed of testing, that is, Hooke's law holds, and the initial slope of the stress-strain curve is a constant proportional to the modulus. A dashpot, on the other hand, has no modulus, but the force resisting motion is proportional to the speed of testing, as shown in case B of Figure 1. The Voigt or Kelvin model (case C) has a stress-strain curve given by

$$\sigma = K\eta + E\varepsilon \tag{1}$$

where K is the speed of testing $d\varepsilon/dt$, η is the viscosity of the dashpot, and E is the modulus of the spring. Because of the dashpot, the stress starts at some value greater than zero, and as the spring stretches, the stress increases. The slope of

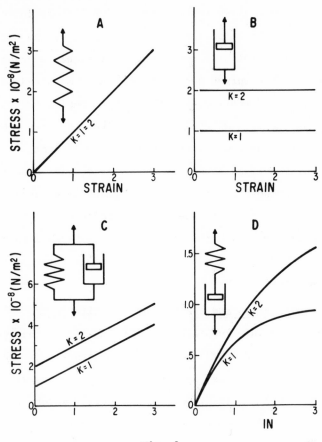

Fig. 1

The stress-strain behavior of simple models at two speeds of testing, K_1 and $K_2 = 2K_1$. $K = d\varepsilon/dt$.

---

the line is the modulus of the spring.

The Maxwell unit (case D) has a more complex stress-strain curve, which is given by (1):

$$\sigma = K\eta[1 - \exp(E\varepsilon/K\eta)]. \tag{2}$$

The initial slope gives the modulus, which is independent of
the speed of deformation since the first part of the curve
corresponds to stretching the spring. At higher elongations
the slopes of the curves decrease, and their magnitude depends
upon the speed of testing when the dashpot begins to relax out
part of the stress. Eventually the spring stops stretching, and
all the elongation comes from motion in the dashpot.

Actual materials generally show more complex behavior than
the models. However, very brittle polymers have curves similar
to springs (case A) up to the point of failure, and many less
brittle polymers show curves similar to the Maxwell unit (case D).
None of the models show yield points characteristic of many
ductile polymers.

C. Compression and Shear Versus Tensile Tests

Stress-strain curves are very dependent upon the type of
test. Tensile, flexural, and compression tests might be expected
to give the same results, but in general the curves will be quite
different. Even the first part of the curves which are
determined by the Young's modulus is different. The moduli
determined in compression are generally higher than those
determined in tension.

Comparison of the stress-strain curves in compression and
tension for a fairly brittle polymer such as polystyrene is
shown in Figure 2. In tension the polymer fails in a brittle
manner while in compression the material behaves as a ductile
polymer with a yield point and higher elongation to break (2).
The tensile properties of brittle materials are largely
determined by flaws and submicroscopic cracks. The cracks do not
play such an important role in compression because the stresses

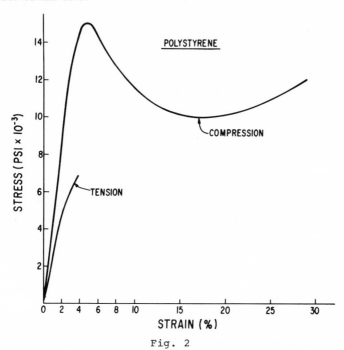

Fig. 2

The stress-strain behavior of a normally brittle polymer
such as polystyrene under tension and compression.

_____

tend to close the cracks rather than open them. Thus, compression

tests tend to be characteristic of the pure polymer while tension

tests are more characteristic of the flaws in the material. One

theory predicts that the compressive strength of a brittle

material should be six to twelve times its tensile strength; in

polymers this factor is much less — a ratio of 1.5 to 4 is more

common (3).

Flexural strengths tend to be greater than tensile strengths.

This is largely a result of the nonlinearity of the stress-strain

curve and the compressive strength being greater than the tensile

strength. In flexural tests part of the specimen is under tension

and part under compression. Flexural strengths are generally
somewhat in error because the classical equations used to
calculate them assume a linear stress-strain curve.

When a polymer fails in a brittle manner, it fails in tension,
while tough materials generally fail in shear even in a tensile
test (4). Under certain assumptions, the tensile strength
theoretically should be twice the shear strength. In actual
cases the tensile strength is generally less than twice the
shear strength. If a specimen is under a triaxial state of
stress or if it contains a notch, the material behaves in a more
brittle manner.

D. Effect of Temperature

Temperature has a great effect on all the stress-strain
properties. The effects on modulus in going through the glass
transition region have already been discussed. All the types
of stress-strain curves given in Chapter 1, Figure 3, can be
obtained from a single polymer by just changing the temperature
over wide enough range. When increasing the temperature from
well below T_g to above T_g or the melting point, the following
behavior is characteristic: The elongation to break ε_B is low at
low temperatures, and there is no yield point. At higher
temperatures there is a yield point and ε_B greatly increases.
Finally, at high temperatures where the material is extremely soft,
ε_B may again decrease. These effects of temperature are
illustrated in Figure 3 (5).

Yield points generally appear near the glass transition
temperature. The higher the speed of testing the higher must
the temperature be for the yielding to occur. Some polymers
with prominent secondary glass transitions become ductile and

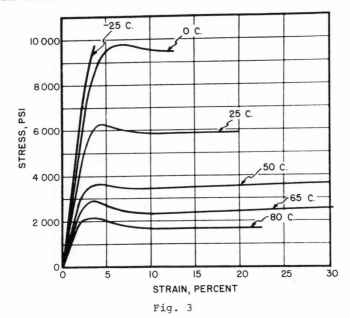

Fig. 3

The stress-strain behavior of cellulose acetate at different temperatures. [Reprinted from Carswell and Nason, Modern Plast., 21, 121 (June 1944).]

show yield points at the secondary transition temperature rather than at T_g. Yield strengths σ_y decrease as the temperature increases. The ε_y generally decreases with an increase in temperature for amorphous materials, but the opposite effect can be found with some crystalline polymers (6,7). Typical results on the effect of temperature on σ_y and ε_y are shown in Figures 4 and 5 (6). The curves for all polymers are brought much closer together if $(T-T_g)$ is used as the variable rather than the temperature T. In Figures 4 and 5 the T_g of the polymers differ by as much as 105°C since T_g of polymethyl methacrylate is 105°C and that of polyphenylene oxide is 210°C. Yet, all the polymers have the same curve near T_g when plotted on a $(T-T_g)$ scale.

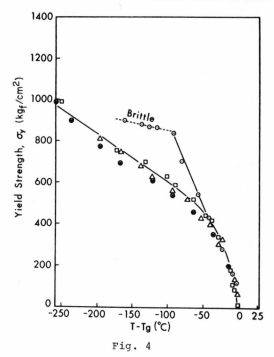

Fig. 4

Yield strength as a function of temperature for polymethyl
methacrylate, polycarbonate of bisphenol-A, polyphenylene
oxide, and polysulfone. [Reprinted from DiBenedetto and
Trachte, J. Appl. Polymer Sci., 14, 2249 (1970).]

The elongation to break of ductile polymers is large at all
temperatures above the temperature at which a yield point first
appears. However, for these materials, ε_B often decreases with
temperature. The general behavior of the stress-strain curves
at different temperatures in relation to the modulus-temperature
curve is shown in Figure 6.

At cryogenic temperatures nearly all polymers are very
brittle. However, a few such as biaxially oriented polyethylene
terephthalate film and fibers of polyethylene terephthalate and
nylon show elongations to break of ten percent or more even at

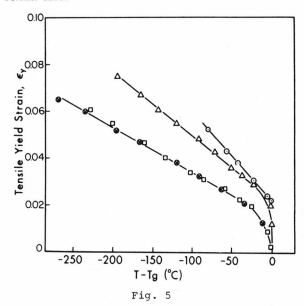

Fig. 5

Tensile yield strain as a function of temperature for
polymethyl methacrylate, bisphenol-A polycarbonate,
polyphenylene oxide, and polysulfone. [Reprinted from
DiBenedetto and Trachte, J. Appl. Polymer Sci., 14, 2249
(1970).]

---

these very low temperatures (8-10). At cryogenic temperatures
these polymers appear quite tough partly because the stress-
strain test causes a large rise in temperature since the heat
capacity is low near 0°K (10).

E.   Rate of Testing and the Failure Envelope

The effects of speed of testing are illustrated in
Figure 7(11). The behavior is about what one would expect on
the basis of the time-temperature superposition principle. The
modulus and the yield or ultimate strength increase, but the
elongation to break generally decreases for rigid polymers as
the rate of testing increases (11-18). The ε_B may increase with
speed for rubbers, however (19-21). For very brittle polymers

STRESS – STRAIN

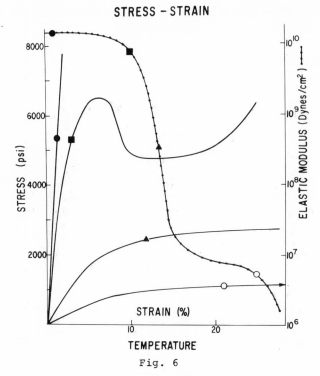

TEMPERATURE

Fig. 6

Stress-strain curves of a typical polymer taken at the temperatures shown on the superimposed modulus versus temperature curve.

---

the effects are small, but for rigid ductile materials and elastomers the effects can be large if the speed of testing is varied over several decades. The yield stress σ_y increases linearly with the logarithm of the strain rate $d\varepsilon/dt$ according to the equation

$$\sigma_y = \sigma_y^o + K \log(d\varepsilon/dt) \qquad (3)$$

where σ_y^o is the yield stress when $d\varepsilon/dt = 1$ at the specified temperature, and K is a constant at fixed temperatures.

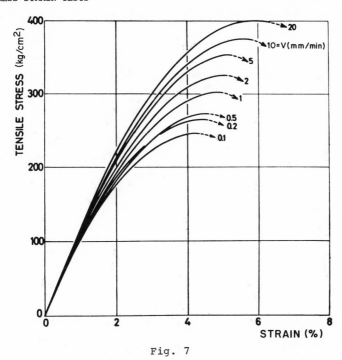

Fig. 7

Tensile stress-strain curves up to the yield point taken
at the strain rates shown on the curves. The polymer is
an epoxy resin. [Reprinted from Ishai, J. Appl. Polymer Sci.,
11, 963 (1967).]

Attempts have been made to superimpose the different stress-
strain parameters obtained over a range of speeds and temperatures
to produce master curves (17, 21-26). Moduli and yield strengths
obtained on rigid polymers from tensile, compression, and flexure
tests at different temperatures can all be superimposed by using
the same shift factors along the time or speed of testing
scale (17). Furthermore, the shift factors used for the modulus,
E, versus the reciprocal of the rate of testing, $(d\varepsilon/dt)^{-1}$, can
be used to predict stress relaxation, $E_r(t)$, versus time. Typical
results of superposition are shown in Figures 8 and 9 (24). The

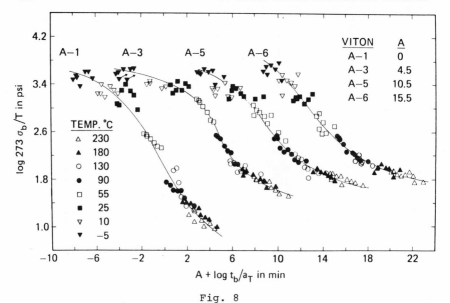

Fig. 8

Log $273\sigma_B/T$ versus log t_B/a_T for fluorinated rubber
vulcanizates. t_B = time to break. a_T = 1 at 90°C. Factor A
is used to displace curves along the abscissa for clarity;
amount of shift is shown in tables in upper right corner.
[Reprinted from Smith and Chu, J. Polymer Sci., A2, 10,
133 (1972).]

master curves for tensile strength decreases in a sigmoidal

manner as the rate of testing $(1/t_\ell)$ decreases. The curves for the

elongation to break go through a maximum as the speed of testing

is changed.

    Another type of superposition scheme for temperature and

speed of testing has been proposed by Smith (21-24) for elastomers

and is called the failure envelope. The failure envelope

compresses a great deal of information into a single curve. A

typical failure envelope is shown in Figure 10. The tensile

strength is reduced to a common reference temperature T_o (°K)

by multiplying σ_B obtained at temperature T by the factor T/T_o.

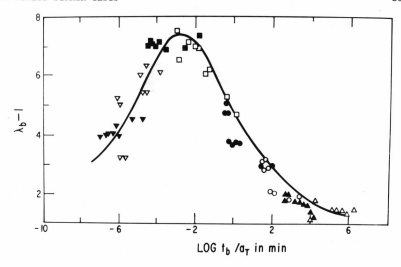

Fig. 9

Plots of elongation to break ($\lambda_B - 1$) versus log t_B/a_T
for fluorinated rubber vulcanizates. t_B = time to break.
a_T = 1 at 90°C. Symbols for different temperatures are
shown in Figure 8. [Modified from Smith and Chu, J. Polymer
Sci., A2, 10, 133 (1972).]

––––––––––––

Lowering the temperature or increasing the speed of testing $\frac{d\varepsilon}{dt}$

moves the experimental data counter-clockwise around the failure

envelope. For instance, the stress-strain curve OA of Figure 10

might become curve OB when the temperature is decreased. In the

figure, OA, OB, and OC are typical stress-strain curves, the

points of fracture being points on the failure envelope.

Elastomers are along the bottom part of the curve while rigid

polymers are at the top. The tensile strength is calculated on

the basis of the original cross-sectional area rather than upon

the actual area when failure occurs. The same failure envelope

for a material is obtained in constant load creep-rupture

tests as in stress-strain tests in which the load constantly

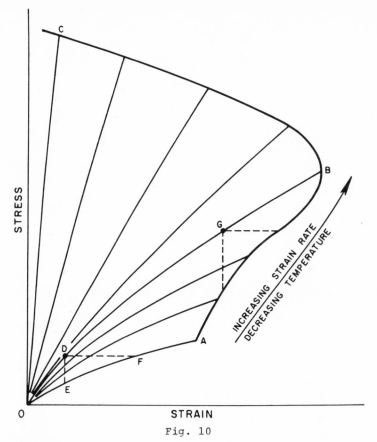

Fig. 10

Failure envelope for schematically representing the
dependence of stress-strain curves on strain rate and
temperature. [Reprinted from Smith, _J. Polymer Sci._, Al
3597 (1963).]

increases. This implies that above some critical load, failure
will always occur if enough time is allowed for the material to
creep until the elongation reaches a critical value.

F.   Effect of Hydrostatic Pressure

Within recent years the effect of hydrostatic pressure on
stress-strain behavior has been quite clearly established (27-38).

In all cases the modulus and the yield stress increase with
pressure. The elongation at yield also generally increases with
pressure but not in all cases. The tensile strength can either
increase or decrease depending upon the polymer; there is a
tendency for σ_B to increase for ductile materials and to decrease
with some brittle materials. The elongation to break can either
increase or decrease with pressure; ε_B increases with some
ductile polymers, but it decreases in the cases of polyethylene,
polytetrafluoroethylene, and most brittle polymers. Figure 11
presents data on polypropylene which are typical of the results
on the effect of pressure (30). The effect on the modulus and yield
stress are expected if the phenomena are associated with a free
volume in the polymer. The effect of the pressure is either to
reduce the amount of free volume or to increase the density of
packing. The pressure also tends to keep any cracks closed; this
effect would tend to increase σ_B and ε_B. The beneficial effect
of minimizing the effects of cracks and defects is counter-
balanced by the increased tendency for brittle behavior as a
result of the decrease in free volume.

G. Effect of Molecular Weight and Branching

Very low molecular weight polymers are viscous liquids
if T_g is below the ambient temperature. At higher molecular
weights these polymers become cheesy elastomers with low
strength and low elongation to break. At still higher molecular
weights (of the order of 10^5 and higher), the polymer molecules
become entangled enough to show true rubbery behavior to short
term deformations, and the elongation to break becomes of the
order of 1000 percent.

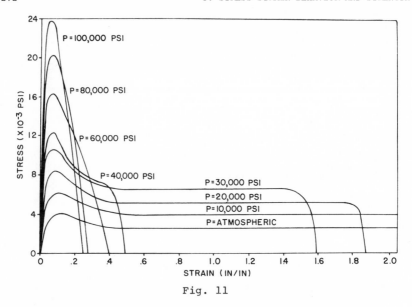

Fig. 11

The stress-strain behavior of polypropylene at different
pressures. [Reprinted from Mears, et al., J. Appl. Phys.,
40, 4229 (1969).]

Polymers of very low molecular weight which have glass
transition temperatures above the ambient temperature tend to
be extremely brittle (39). It may be impossible to prepare test
specimens of such materials because the thermal and shrinkage
forces involved in making a specimen are great enough to shatter
the polymer into small pieces of very low strength. For such
brittle materials there must be some molecular entanglements
before the polymer becomes strong enough to carry any load (40).
Chain ends act as imperfections in the structure which adversely
affect the strength properties, but chain ends have very little
effect on the elastic moduli.

Above the minimum molecular weight needed to form a specimen,
the strength and elongation increase toward a limiting value

at very high molecular weight (39,41-48). Polar polymers and
polymers with hydrogen bonding between chains reach their
maximum properties at lower molecular weights than do nonpolar
polymers.

The early work on the stress-strain behavior of polymers
indicated that the number average molecular weight was the
important variable (39,41,42,45-47). Later work has shown that
the molecular weight variable is a more complex function than
just $\bar{M}_n$. The weight average molecular weight also has some
effect (43). For rigid polystyrene, the tensile strength seems
to depend upon some molecular weight function between $\bar{M}_n$ and $\bar{M}_w$
(43). However, in most cases where mixtures of fractions were
studied rather than broad distributions of molecular weight,
the tensile strength follows an equation of the form:

$$\sigma_B = \sigma_{BO} - \frac{K}{\bar{M}_n} \tag{4}$$

where σ_{BO} is the limiting tensile strength for very high
molecular weight, and K is a constant. A similar equation also
holds for ε_B. In other cases the viscosity rather than the
molecular weight per se seems to be the important variable.
An indication of the importance of entanglements and of the
type of molecular weight average in determining stress-strain
properties is given by the works of Toggenburger (49), Boyer (50),
Goppel (51), and Wyman (52). Goppel found that the tensile
strength of polypropylene increased linearly with the inherent
viscosity; this would indicate that weight average molecular
weight is more important than number average molecular weight.

Boyer found the strength of polystyrene increased with melt
viscosity. Toggenburger studied both linear and branched
styrene copolymers. The tensile strength did not correlate well
with molecular weights because of the branching. However, all
polymers (linear and branched) gave the same curve when tensile
strength was plotted against the logarithm of the melt viscosity.
Similar results are reported by Wyman on linear and branched
polystyrene. Thus, entanglements not only strongly affect melt
viscosity but also the strength of polymers. Since the branched
polymers had fewer entanglements than the linear polymers for a
given molecular weight, the strength and the elongation to break
were lower for the branched polymers. It, thus, appears that
in general the simple relationship shown by equation 4 between
stress-strain properties and molecular weight is not accurate,
and the molecular weight dependence is more complex.

Molecular weight not only affects the stress-strain
properties of uncrosslinked rubbers, but the effects are carried
over into the vulcanized rubbers as well. Flory (45,46) and
Yanko (47) found that the tensile strength of crosslinked
rubbers increased with number average molecular weight of the
starting uncrosslinked polymer up to a limiting value. The
elongation to break also increased with molecular weight at
first, but at very high initial molecular weights before
crosslinking, the ε_B tended to decrease somewhat. The effect
of initial molecular weight on the properties of vulcanizates
is a result of fewer imperfections, such as dangling chain ends
in the network as molecular weight increases.

The stress-strain properties of crystalline polymers such
as polyethylene and polypropylene depend upon molecular weight

in a manner similar to amorphous polymers (44,48,53,54).
However, the dependence upon molecular weight tends to be less
apparent because the crystallites help hold the material together
in much the same way as chain entanglements do. The molecular
weight dependence of properties is further confused because in
general there is a decrease in degree of crystallinity as
molecular weight increases (54). Thus, at temperatures above T_g,
increasing the molecular weight tends to increase toughness. On
the other hand, low molecular weight polymer tends to collect at
the boundary between spherulites, and this low molecular weight
polymer reduces the number of "tie molecules," so low molecular
weight polymers tend to be brittle and to have low strengths (55).
The type of crystal morphology and extent of spherulitic structure
also may change with molecular weight. Thus, the behavior of
crystalline polymers is affected by both molecular weight and a
variable degree of crystallinity which may change with molecular
weight.

H. Effect of Crosslinking

The effects of crosslinking are most important and best
understood for elastomers. As a rough approximation, the kinetic
theory of rubber elasticity can be used as a guide to the stress-
strain properties of rubbers (56,57). This theory predicts for
tensile tests that

$$\sigma = \frac{\rho RT}{\overline{M}_c} \left(1 - \frac{2\overline{M}_c}{\overline{M}_n}\right) \left[\frac{L}{L_o} - \left(\frac{L_o}{L}\right)^2\right]. \tag{5}$$

The stress σ is based upon the original cross-sectional area of
the specimen in the unstretched state. In this equation ρ is

the density, R is the gas constant, T is the temperature in degrees Kelvin, $\overline{M}_c$ is the number average molecular weight of the polymer between crosslinks, $\overline{M}_n$ is the number average molecular weight of the polymer before it was crosslinked, L_O is the unstretched length of the specimen, and L is the stretched length of the polymer. For rubbers the proper definition of strain is given in the square brackets; this strain is three times the usual engineering strain at small deformations. The term $\dfrac{2\overline{M}_c}{\overline{M}_n}$ is the first approximation of a correction factor which takes into account the flaws in the network structure such as dangling chain ends. The stress-strain curve for simple shear tests according to the kinetic theory of rubber elasticity is

$$\sigma_s = \frac{\rho RT}{\overline{M}_c}\left(\frac{L}{L_O} - \frac{L_O}{L}\right) = G \tan \theta \qquad (6)$$

where the shear stress σ_s is based upon the dimensions of the deformed specimen in this case, and θ is the shearing angle as defined in Figure 2 of Chapter 1. From equations 5 and 6, the moduli are:

$$G = \frac{\rho RT}{\overline{M}_c} \qquad (7)$$

$$E = \frac{3\rho RT}{\overline{M}_c} \qquad . \qquad (8)$$

The stress-strain curve for a biaxial tensile test, in which the material is simultaneously stretched equal amounts in two directions, as predicted by the kinetic theory of rubber elasticit

$$\sigma = \frac{E}{3}\left[\left(\frac{L}{L_O}\right)^2 - \left(\frac{L_O}{L}\right)^4\right]. \qquad (9)$$

This equation predicts that the stress in each of two directions required to stretch a rubber by a given amount is greater for a biaxial test than for the usual uniaxial tensile test. This is expected since the only dimension that is free to contract in a biaxial test is the thickness dimension.

The kinetic theory of rubber correctly predicts that the modulus increases as the degree of crosslinking increases, that is, as $\overline{M}_c$ decreases. However, at large deformations the theory does not correctly predict the shape of the stress-strain curve. Figure 12 compares the stress-strain curve of a typical cross-linked rubber with the curve predicted by the kinetic theory.

The elongation to break of a rubber decreases as the degree of crosslinking increases. The tensile strength goes through a

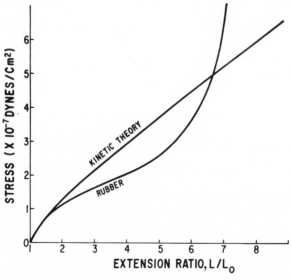

Fig. 12

The stress-strain curve of a typical vulcanized natural rubber compared to the stress-strain curve predicted by the kinetic theory of rubber elasticity.

pronounced maximum at a low degree of crosslinking and then
rapidly decreases as the crosslinking increases (24,58-62).
Both of these effects are illustrated in Figure 13 (58). The
undesirable effects found with increasing crosslinking are at
least partly due to a heterogeneity in M_c or the spacing between
crosslinks which puts most of the stress on a relatively few of
the network chains. These highly stressed chains break first,
and their loads are then distributed to other chains, forcing

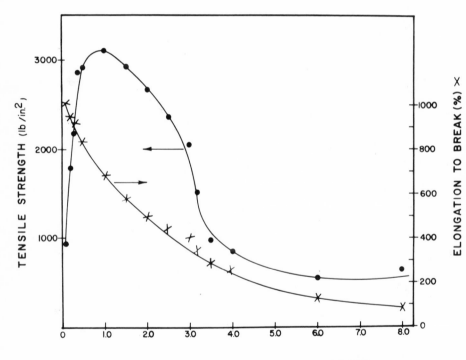

CONCENTRATION OF CROSS-LINKING AGENT

Fig. 13

Stress-strain properties of rubber as a function of the
percent of crosslinking agent. [Reprinted from Nielsen,
J. Macromol. Sci., C3, 69 (1969) from the data of Flory,
et al., J. Polymer Sci., 4, 435 (1949).]

them to either break or slip so as to relieve the stress on them.
Case (63,64) has made theoretical calculations which show that
a regularly spaced crosslinked network should have a higher
elongation to break than a network in which the spacing between
crosslinks varies in a random manner. This prediction has been
borne out by experiments on special rubbers in which the
uniformity of the spacing between crosslinks could be
controlled (65). Also, networks containing trifunctional
crosslinking points should have a greater ε_B than networks
containing tetrafunctional crosslinks. Trifunctional crosslinks
impose less drastic restrictions on chain motions than tetrafunctional crosslinks. A number of approximate theories have
been developed to explain the ultimate properties of vulcanized
rubbers (59,66-68). The extension ratio L/L_o at break, λ_B,
should be proportional to the square root of the reciprocal of
the density of effective crosslinks ν_e, (59,66) that is,

$$\lambda_B \propto 1/\nu_e^{1/2} \tag{10}$$

The effective number of crosslinked chains per unit volume ν_e
is related approximately to the molecular weight between
crosslinks $\overline{M}_c$ by

$$\nu_e \doteq \frac{\rho N_o}{\overline{M}_c} \tag{11}$$

where N_o is Avogadro's number. Equation 10 holds for some
experimental results but not for others (24,69). Smith and
Chu (24) find that the exponent on ν_e is not 0.50 but 0.40.
The tensile strength σ_B according to some theories should be

proportional to $\nu_e^{2/3}$ or ν_e for low degrees of crosslinking
before the maximum is reached in σ_B (59,67,68). Experimentally,
however, some data indicate that σ_B is proportional to $\nu_e^{0.5}$ or
$\nu_e^{0.6}$ rather than to $\nu_e^{2/3}$ or ν_e (24,70). The wide variations
found in experimental data are probably due to differences in
network structures which cannot be described by a single
average parameter such as $\overline{M}_c$ or ν_e.

Crosslinking has little effect on rigid high molecular
weight materials; entanglements and interpenetration of the
molecules are as effective as crosslinks in producing strength.
However, many thermosetting resins are so low in molecular
weight that the materials have essentially no strength unless
crosslinked. Although the modulus of rigid polymers is determined
largely by the strength of Van der Waals' intermolecular bonds,
through-going covalent chains are needed to tie the structure
together for strength.

There is an interesting correlation of the energy to break
U_B of an elastomer (or the area under its stress-strain curve)
and the hysteresis to break H_B (71,72). The hysteresis to
break is the energy dissipated by damping for an amplitude of
strain just below that required to break the elastomer. The
empirical correlation is given by the equation

$$U_B = KH_B^{2/3} \tag{12}$$

The constant K varies slightly from polymer to polymer, and it
may be related to the cohesive energy density of the rubber.

I. Effect of Crystallinity

Unoriented crystallites at temperatures below T_g tend to

make polymers brittle with low strengths. This brittleness may
result from strains imposed on the amorphous phase by the
crystallites, by the presence of voids produced during the
crystallization process, or from stress concentrations produced
by the crystallites. There may be still another important
factor which produces brittleness. Crystalline polymers are
made up of lamellae containing folded chains. The lamellae are
held together by "tie molecules" which go from one crystalline
layer to another (73-77). Chain ends and molecular imperfections
tend to collect in the amorphous portion between crystallite
lamellae, so very few "tie molecules" may exist, and a brittle
material of low strength results. Strength comes primarily from
the "tie molecules."

For elastomeric or very ductile materials, the presence
of a crystalline phase produces quite different stress-strain
behavior. In going from no crystallinity to a high degree of
crystallinity, the stress-strain curve changes from that of an
uncrosslinked rubber to one that is similar to a crosslinked
rubber and on to that of a rigid material showing a yield point.
At very high degrees of crystallinity, especially if large
spherulites are present, the polymer has the stress-strain
curve of a brittle material in many cases (53, 78-84). Figure 14
illustrates these effects over a rather limited range of
crystallinities for polypropylene (78). An increase in
crystallinity brings about increases in modulus and yield
strength but decreases in elongation to yield and elongation
to break (80).

It is difficult to separate the effects of degree of
crystallinity from those of morphology since it often is found

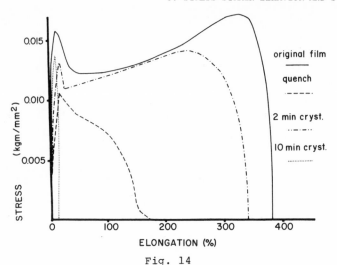

Fig. 14

The stress-strain properties of isotactic polypropylene
after different thermal histories: - the original film may
have been oriented. --- Quench-cooled from the melt (no
spherulites). ·-·- 2 minutes crystallization at 125°C
(partial spherulization). .... 10 minutes crystallization
at 125°C (completely spherulitic). [Reprinted from Barish,
J. Appl. Polymer Sci., 6, 617 (1962).]

---

that a more pronounced spherulitic structure, which can be

brought about by either slow cooling or annealing, accompanies

an increase in crystallinity (79). Large spherulites often

break along their radii (73). At other times, fracture takes

place at the boundaries between spherulites where there are few

"tie molecules" but a high concentration of impurities and low

molecular weight polymer (79). With small or imperfect spheru-

lites there is an increased ductility if T_g is below the test

temperature, and there is an increased probability of cold-

drawing during which the morphology of the spherulite is destroyed.

Cold-drawing changes the folded chain structure into a fibrillar

structure in which the unfolded chains become highly aligned in

the direction of stretch. The detailed mechanism of cold-drawing
of crystalline polymers has been discussed by Peterlin (75-77),
Horio (74), Keith and Padden (73), and others. However, even
before the actual cold-drawing process starts, Stein (85-87)
has shown that there is a complex combination of partial
orientations of the amorphous and crystalline components.
Zaukelies (88) has shown that in ductile crystalline polymers,
such as nylon, the crystallites may deform by motion along slip
planes in a manner similar to ductile metals.

Closely related to the crystallinity and the spherulitic
structure of a polymer is its thermal history. Heat treatments,
such as slow cooling from above the melting point or annealing
below the melting point (especially near the crystalline alpha
transition temperature), tend to increase spherulite size and
brittleness. The addition of fine particles as nucleating agents
for the nucleation of crystallites also affects the spherulitic
structure of a polymer (81,89-92). For instance, sodium benzoate
in polypropylene reduces the size of spherulites (81). The
morphology and properties of a crystalline polymer are largely
determined by the initial rate of cooling or by a high
temperature annealing treatment. However, an aging or a slow
annealing process also may occur over long periods of time at
room temperature or below (81,93). This slow change, which
may continue at room temperature for many days, is believed to
be a secondary recrystallization process in which there is a
reorganization of part of the crystallites (94-96).

J.   Effects of Plasticization and Copolymerization
For amorphous polymers, the effects of plasticization and

copolymerization are primarily those to be expected from the
shift in the glass transition temperature T_g. The temperature
difference $(T-T_g)$ between the test temperature and T_g is the
important variable which superimposes most data to approximately
a common curve (6,25). However, in addition to the shift in T_g,
liquids and plasticizers produce other effects which appear to
be related to whether or not the liquid is a good solvent for
the polymer (97-99). Polymer molecules tend to be more tightly
coiled in a poor solvent than in a good solvent.

Plasticizers may increase the brittleness of a polymer if
it has a secondary glass transition which is eliminated or
reduced in intensity by the liquid (100-104). Polycarbonate and
polyvinyl chloride are examples where the addition of a small
amount of plasticizer can change the polymer from a ductile
material to a brittle one.

The situation is more complex with crystalline polymers,
and copolymerization may produce effects which are entirely
different from plasticization. Plasticizers lower T_g, slightly
decrease the degree of crystallinity, and dilute the amorphous
phase. Thus, the modulus and the yield or breaking stress tend
to decrease while the elongation to break may increase for a
plasticized polymer. Copolymerization, on the other hand,
greatly reduces the degree of crystallinity, decreases spherulitic
morphology, and shifts T_g either up or down in temperature. The
effect of each of these factors on the stress-strain behavior
of a material has already been discussed. The combined effects
of these variables is illustrated by the data in Table 1 for
ethylene-vinyl acetate copolymers (105). As the crystallinity
and spherulitic structure are destroyed by increasing amounts

Table 1

Stress-Strain Properties of Ethylene-Vinyl Acetate Copolymers

Property	Weight Percent Vinyl Acetate				
	9	15.4	26.3	30.9	45
Yield Stress (psi)	870	670	420	290	–
Tensile Strength (psi)	2700	2980	2640	1900	667
Elongation to Yield (%)	27	28	46	37	–
Elongation to Break (%)	800	970	1200	1390	196

of vinyl acetate, σ_y decreases and ε_y increases until the material becomes so rubbery that there is no longer a yield point. The elongation to break increases with vinyl acetate content until all the crystallinity is gone; then at vinyl acetate contents of 45 percent and above, a very weak uncrosslinked rubber is found. The tensile strength changes only slowly as long as there is any crystallinity to effectively crosslink the polymer, then σ_B dramatically decreases.

K. Molecular Orientation

The strength and ductility of polymers can be greatly modified by molecular orientation of the polymer chains. The orientation can be produced by either hot stretching of a molten polymer followed by rapidly cooling of the melt, or by cold-drawing, or by cold-rolling. The tensile strength of rigid polymers increases (sometimes dramatically) in the direction parallel to the uniaxial orientation, but the strength decreases in the direction perpendicular to the orientation (106-125).

The yield stress and Young's modulus show the same trends as the tensile strength, but the increase parallel to the orientation and the decrease in the perpendicular direction are often not as great as in the case of the tensile strength.

Figure 15 illustrates typical behavior of oriented brittle polymers. Parallel to the orientation direction, the polymer may become ductile and have a yield point and high elongation, but in the perpendicular direction the polymer becomes more brittle with low strength and elongation. Figure 16 illustrates the stress-strain behavior of many very ductile, especially

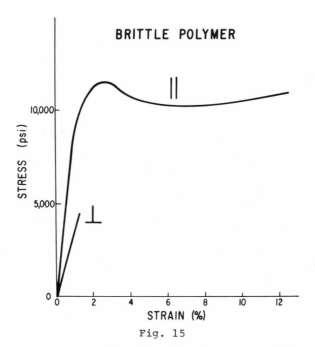

Fig. 15

The stress-strain behavior of typical polymers which are brittle in the unoriented state. ‖ = tensile stress parallel to direction of orientation. ⊥ = stress perpendicular to the direction of the uniaxial orientation.

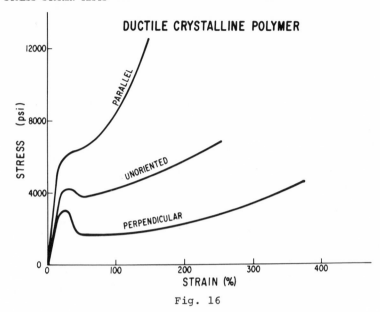

DUCTILE CRYSTALLINE POLYMER

Fig. 16

The tensile stress-strain behavior of ductile polymers:
Unoriented, measured parallel to the direction of uniaxial
orientation, and measured perpendicular to the direction
of the orientation.

crystalline, polymers. Oriented polymer tested in the parallel

direction has the higher yield strength, but its elongation to

break may be less than that of oriented polymer tested in the

perpendicular or transverse direction. The reason for this

unusually high transverse elongation is that on stretching the

previously oriented material in the perpendicular direction, the

molecules first deorient and then reorient in the direction of

the applied force. Brittle materials break before the

reorientation process gets started. Figure 17 shows how the

yield stress changes for polyvinyl chloride with the degree of

orientation or cold-drawing in the parallel and perpendicular

directions as measured by the draw ratio (114). The drawing

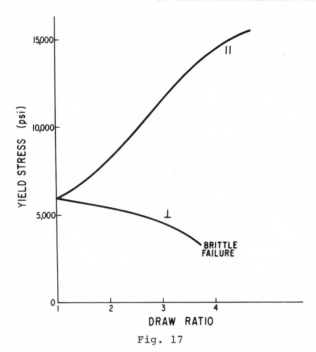

Fig. 17

The yield stress as a function of orientation (draw ratio) for rigid polyvinyl chloride. Tensile stress was either parallel or perpendicular to the direction of the orientation. [Modified from Rider and Hargreaves, J. Polymer Sci., A2, 7, 829 (1969).]

was done at 71°C (near T_g) for the data shown in Figure 17. In other results, which are not shown, the drawing was done above T_g (90°C). Considerably more molecular orientation was achieved at the lower temperature for a given draw ratio, so the differences between the curves for tests parallel and perpendicular to the orientation were less at 90°C than at 71°C.

Polymers have high strengths and moduli in the direction parallel to the orientation because the applied loads are carried largely by the strong covalent bonds of the polymer chains. The properties are poor (at least for brittle polymers)

in the direction perpendicular to the orientation because the
loads are carried primarily by the weak Van der Waals' bonds.
Also, if there are small cracks or other imperfections in the
polymer, they become oriented parallel to the orientation
direction.   These oriented cracks are strong stress concentrators
for loads applied perpendicular to the orientation direction.
The effects of orientation are shown in Table 2 by the data of
Jackson and Ballman (109) on polystyrene.   Since their specimens
were made by injection molding, the orientation was not perfectly
uniaxial but also contained some biaxial orientation.   For this
reason, the effects would be even more pronounced if the

Table 2

Mechanical Properties of Oriented Polystyrene

Birefringence $\Delta n \times 10^4$	Tensile Strength		Elongation to Break		Izod Impact Strength	
	$\parallel$	$\perp$	$\parallel$	$\perp$	$\parallel$	$\perp$
1.1	3940	3440	2.4	1.8	.24	.22
4.3	5340	4240	3.1	2.1	.32	.21
9.1	6320	4110	3.9	2.6	.36	.20
16.3	7550	4140	4.2	1.9	.65	.21
25.4	7640	3710	5.0	1.8	1.36	.18
30.9	7590	2630	6.8	1.3	–	–
41.4	8660	3440	5.2	2.1	1.54	.23
51.8	10170	4550	4.4	2.5	1.58	.18
53.7	8440	1290	7.0	0.7	–	–

Tensile strengths in psi

Elongation to break in %

specimens were more perfectly uniaxially oriented. In addition,
the orientation (birefringence) is not uniform in injection
molded specimens and varies through the thickness of the
specimen (126, 127).

Orientation also affects the shear properties of polymers
(107, 122, 128). The shear moduli remain nearly constant, but
G_{LT} may increase somewhat with orientation while G_{TT} tends to
decrease somewhat. (See Chapter 2 for notation.) The shear
strength of an oriented rod decreases if the molecules are
aligned along the axis of the rod. If the polymer is brittle,
the torsion on the rod will break it up into many long filaments.

Uniaxial orientation increases the yield strength and the
tensile strength in the direction of orientation. However, the
compressive yield strength in the direction of orientation
decreases as the orientation increases (129, 130). This is the
opposite of what is found for unoriented polymers where the
compressive yield strength is greater than the tensile yield
strength. Polymer chains can carry high tensile loads, but the
chains tend to buckle easily under compressive loads.

Perfectly biaxially oriented materials have the same
properties in any direction in the plane of orientation, and the
properties are better than those of the unoriented material.
(See Figure 2, Chapter 2.) This characteristic is important
in many practical applications where a load may be put on the
material from any direction. Biaxial orientation also improves
cold-forming operations (131,132). Biaxial orientation
eliminates many of the undesirable properties of uniaxially
oriented materials and keeps to a large extent the desirable
properties (108,133-137). Biaxial orientation increases the

modulus and the tensile strength. Up to moderate degrees of
biaxial orientation, the elongation to break also tends to
increase (especially for brittle polymers), but at very high
degrees of orientation the elongation to break may decrease.
A comparison of the stress-strain behavior of uniaxial and
biaxial orientation for a brittle polymer is illustrated in
Figure 18.

Biaxial orientation prevents or greatly reduces the crazing

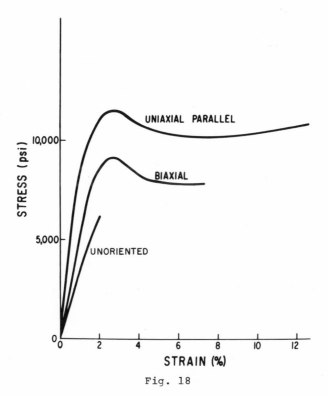

Fig. 18

Schematic comparison of the stress-strain behavior of a
brittle polymer: Unoriented, biaxially oriented, and
uniaxially oriented and tested parallel to the direction
of orientation.

of brittle polymers (133,135,136,138,139). Although both the
stress and the strain required to induce crazing are increased
by biaxial orientation, it appears that the strain is the more
basic variable (136,140). The critical strain at which crazing
starts for polystyrene can be increased by biaxial orientation by
a factor of 2 or 3 times in air or by as much as 5 or 6 times in
a liquid environment such as corn oil (136).

L. Polyblends, Block, and Graft Polymers

Two-phase polymeric systems such as polyblends and block
polymers are important for their stress-strain behavior in at
least two major areas of applications: 1. A rubbery phase is
added to a brittle polymer to increase the toughness and elongation
to break of the brittle polymer. 2. A rigid phase (often as
part of a block polymer) is added to a rubber to increase its
strength and decrease its tendency to flow or undergo permanent
deformation under a load (141-144). Figure 19 illustrates the
usual changes in stress-strain curves on adding increasing
amounts of the rubber phase to a brittle polymer such as
polystyrene. The same general trends are found with polyblends,
block polymers, and graft polymers in the temperature interval
between the glass transition temperatures of the two components.
Small amounts of rubber produce a rigid material which has a
yield point and shows necking or cold-drawing. The yielding
phenomenon is largely the result of crazing or breaking up of
the rigid continuous phase (140,145-147). Larger amounts of
rubber produce an indistinct yield point with uniform elongation.
The high elongation now is generally the result of the rubbery
phase being a continuous phase. Crazing may still occur, but

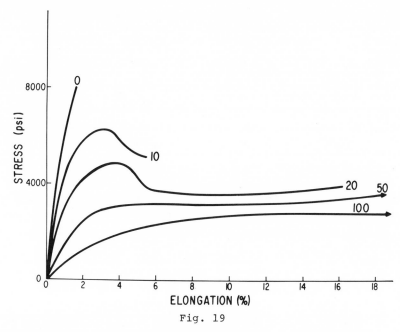

Fig. 19

Typical stress-strain behavior of polyblends of a rubber
in a brittle polymer. Numbers refer to the approximate
percent of rubber in the polyblends.

---

more likely there occurs a cavitation phenomenon with the

production of voids resulting from dewetting at the rubber-rigid

polymer interface.

　　There are also other types of polyblends such as mixtures

of two rubbers (141,148-150), mixtures in which the components

are more or less miscible to form one phase systems (151-154),

and mixtures of rubbers and crystalline polymers whose T_g is

below room temperature (148). Such polyblends generally behave

as rubbers or as crystalline polymers with a reduced degree of

crystallinity.

Most commercial high-impact polymers, including ABS
polymers, are a complex polyblend of a rigid polymer with a
rubbery graft polymer (155-160). The grafted chains on the
rubber are similar to the matrix, and these grafted chains
promote good adhesion between the phases. Good adhesion is
one of the requirements for a tough polymer with high impact
strength (161-164).

The properties of block polymers have been reviewed by
Estes, Cooper, and Tobolsky (165) and by Aggarwal (166). There
are a number of other papers which discuss the stress-strain
properties of block polymers (143,144,167-169). Graft polymers
have been reviewed by Battaerd and Tregear (170).

Di-block polymers (A-AAABBB-B) have different stress-strain
properties than tri-block polymers (A-AAAB-BBB-BAAA-A). The
tri-block polymers have higher tensile strengths than di-block
polymers if the rubbery B polymer is in excess of the rigid A
polymer so that the rubber forms the continuous phase. The reason
for this is illustrated in Figure 20. The rigid A polymer will
be aggregated in both cases, and both types of block polymers
have the characteristics of a rubber containing a rigid filler.
However, the rubber phase appears to be crosslinked in tri-
block polymers because both ends of each rubber chain are
attached to a rigid dispersed phase. In the di-block elastomer
the rubber chains are attached to a rigid phase at only one end,
and, therefore, are not crosslinked by the aggregates of A polymer
so that flow readily occurs in the rubbery phase.

II. Brittle Fracture and Stress Concentrators

A. Stress Concentrators

Cracks and other stress concentrators play a vital role in

TRI-BLOCK ELASTOMERS ABA

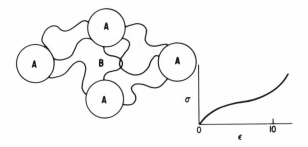

DI-BLOCK ELASTOMERS AB

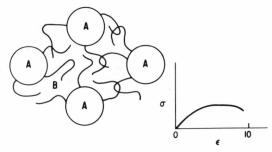

Fig. 20

Schematic of AB di-block and ABA tri-block polymers.
Typical stress-strain curves are shown as inserts.

---

the strength of brittle materials (171). At the tip of a
crack or a notch in a sheet, the stress is concentrated according
to the equation

$$\sigma_m \doteq \sigma_o \left[1 + 2 (a/r)^{1/2} \right] \tag{13}$$

The applied tensile stress is σ_o, σ_m is the maximum stress at
the crack tip, which has a radius of curvature r, and a is the
length of the crack or depth of the notch (172). Polymers may
contain naturally occurring flaws or inherent cracks with a length
of the order of 10^{-3} to 10^{-4} cm, and with widths approaching

molecular diameters, so very high concentrations of stress can occur at the tips of the cracks.

Inclusions and holes, as well as cracks, are stress concentrators. For instance, a circular hole in a sheet produces a stress concentration given by (173):

$$\sigma_t = \sigma_o (1-2\cos 2\theta). \tag{14}$$

The tangential stress at the edge of the hole is σ_t, and θ is the angle from the direction of the applied tensile stress. At the poles of the hole ($\theta = 0$), the tangential stress is compressive, i.e., negative. In the direction perpendicular to the stress, the stress is tensile and has a value of $3\sigma_o$ at the edge of the hole.

Spherical inclusions in a material act as stress concentrators (174,175). The greatest stress concentration occurs at the equator of the sphere (90° to the applied stress) when the sphere is an empty cavity; the tensile stress is then concentrated by a factor of about two. If the modulus of the inclusion is much greater than that of the continuous matrix, the tensile stress is reduced and may actually become compressive at the equator of the sphere if there is good adhesion between the sphere and the matrix. In this case of a very rigid inclusion, the stress is concentrated at the poles of the sphere ($\theta = 0$) so that the sphere tends to separate from the matrix by a process called dewetting.

B. Fracture Theory

Griffith (176) developed a theory for the strength of brittle materials in which it was assumed that cracks were the determining factor in the strength of such materials. To

increase the length of a crack, energy must be available to at
least equal the surface energy of the two new surfaces produced
by the growth of the crack. An applied load produces elastic
energy in a material. If a crack is to increase its length,
the rate of decrease of elastic energy in the volume of material
surrounding the crack must at least equal the rate at which
surface energy is created by the growth of the crack. The
tensile strength σ_B of a sheet or plate is then

$$\sigma_B \doteq (2\gamma E/\pi a)^{1/2}. \tag{15}$$

The surface energy per unit area of crack surface is γ, E is the
Young's modulus of the material, and a is the length of the crack.
For polymers, and many other materials, the strength is much
greater than what equation 15 predicts. It is found that γ is
of the order of 10^5 to 10^6 ergs/cm^2 for polymers instead of a
few hundred ergs/cm^2 as expected for a pure surface energy (177-181).
The reason for the high value of γ is that there is plastic flow
and cold-drawing of polymer during the crazing and growth of
cracks in polymers; the surface energy is a very small amount of
the total energy involved. Therefore, in reformulating the
theory to take into account the plastic flow, γ becomes the
plastic work or fracture energy (182). Chen (183) has shown
that an equation of the same form as the Griffith's equation
holds when the specimen contains multiple cracks. Williams (184,
185) has proposed that a modified Griffith's equation such as

$$\sigma_B \doteq k(E\gamma/a)^{1/2} \tag{16}$$

be used by design engineers in solving practical problems of the
strength of objects. The geometric constant k is generally

approximately 1.0. This constant can be determined for objects
of any shape from classical mechanics with the aid of computers.
However, reliable tables for the values of the fracture energy
γ of many polymers will be required before equation 16 can be
adopted for practical design work.

The experimental technique known as fracture mechanics is
a way of measuring fracture toughness, the fracture energy γ,
or its equivalent (186-188). The fracture toughness of a
material measures the ability of that material to resist the
extension of a pre-existing crack by a specified type of stress.
This technique of fracture mechanics is an attempt to relate
the behavior of real, brittle materials, which contain flaws,
to various kinds of applied loads. The tensile, or other tests
such as a cleavage test, are made on specimens containing
artificial cracks of known length. From the load at which the
crack starts to rapidly propogate, the fracture surface energy
can be calculated for a specimen of specified geometry by fairly
complex equations. In this technique, fracture toughness is
defined in terms of either of two factors: a critical stress
intensity factor K_c or a critical strain energy release rate G_c.
These factors are related by the following equations:

$$K_c^2 = EG_c \qquad \text{(For thin sheets)} \qquad (17)$$

or

$$K_c^2 = EG_c(1 - \nu^2) \quad \text{(For thick sheets)} \qquad (18)$$

where E is Young's modulus, and ν is Poisson's ratio. The
fracture surface energy γ of the Griffith's equation is related
to the critical strain energy release rate G_c by

$$G_c = 2\gamma. \qquad (19)$$

The relationship of fracture toughness to impact strength
is not clear. In some cases impact strength increases as the
fracture toughness increases, but in other cases the impact
strength seems to decrease as the fracture toughness increases.

A simple relationship holds for many materials between
Young's modulus and the tensile strength or yield strength (189-
191):

$$\sigma_B \doteq \frac{E}{30} \qquad (20)$$

and

$$\frac{1}{60} \leq \frac{\sigma_y}{E} \leq \frac{1}{30} \quad . \qquad (21)$$

These approximations hold for many polymers under all kinds of
conditions, including changes in temperature, pressure, degree
of orientation, and degree of crystallinity (191).

III. Theories of Yielding and Cold-Drawing

Yielding and cold-drawing are very important since essentially
all very tough polymers and those with high impact strengths show
these phenomena. Yielding implies a yield point in the stress-
strain curve. The yield point can be either a distinct maximum
or a region of strong curvature approaching zero slope in the
stress-strain curve. Cold-drawing manifests itself as a necking
of the polymer during stretching. Necking starts at a localized
point in the specimen, and the cross section becomes much less
than that of the remaining portion of the specimen while the
force remains nearly constant during stretching. Cold-drawing
after the yield point means that there must be a strain hardening
process, otherwise, the material would break without drawing at

the reduced cross section where necking took place. The strain
hardening generally results from molecular orientation which
increases the modulus, and tensile strength. However, the
strain hardening of crystalline polymers might come partly from
strain-induced recrystallization (192). The necked down section
increases in length as stretching continues until all the
specimen becomes cold-drawn. Cold-drawing of a given section
stops at a critical elongation known as the natural draw ratio
of the material. The draw ratio is a function of temperature,
orientation, and other variables. On further stretching of the
cold-drawn polymer, the stress generally rapidly increases and
failure soon occurs. During cold-drawing, the polymer chains
become highly oriented in the direction of stretching.

The natural draw ratio, that is, the ratio of the length of
a cold-drawn region to the length of the same material before
it was stretched, may either increase or decrease with temperature;
it increases with molecular weight and speed of testing (14,120,
193). If the material was partially oriented before cold-drawing,
the natural draw ratio decreases. It appears that the sum of
the orientation before cold-drawing and the orientation brought
about by the cold-drawing process is approximately a constant.
In crystalline polymers, cold-drawing disrupts the crystallite
morphology from that of a folded chain structure in spherulites
to a fibrillar extended chain morphology in which the chains in
the crystallites are highly oriented in the stretching direction.
Peterlin (77) believes the cold-drawing of ductile crystalline
polymers consists of three stages: 1. Plastic deformation of the
spherulites with rotation of stacks of lamellae, crystal twinning,
and chain slippage. 2. Discontinuous transformation of the

spherulitic structure into a fibrous structure by micro-necking.
3. Plastic deformation of the fibrous structure with chain
slippage and chain fracture.

Many theories of yielding and cold-drawing have been
proposed, but the subject still is being actively debated. One
of the first proposals was that as energy was put into the polymer
during the stretching process, localized hot spots developed
which raised the temperature of these spots to the glass
transition temperature (or to the melting point for crystalline
polymers)(192,194-196). Thus, cold-drawing was assumed to be
the spot by spot stretching of a rubbery material near T_g. This
theory is now generally believed to be unacceptable except
possibly at cryogenic temperatures for polymers which have
prominent very low temperature secondary glass transition
temperatures (197). The very low heat capacity of polymers
makes it possible for small amounts of heat energy to produce
large enough increases in temperature to possibly put the
material above its secondary glass transition temperature.

Other theories are based upon a dilation of the polymer
when a stress is applied. If this increase in volume is an
increase in free volume, then T_g is lowered to the stretching
temperature, so that the cold-drawing process becomes similar
to the stretching of an elastomer (6,15,198-201). The dilation
may be accompanied by the formation of microvoids or craze cracks,
and some theories suggest that yielding is due largely to the
formation of voids and craze cracks (15,40,202-204). Although
craze cracks appear very similar to true cracks, they actually
contain about 50 percent oriented polymer (205-207). Craze
cracks consist of a row of voids about 25 to 200 Å in size

separated by oriented polymer. These voids can be detected by
small angle x-ray scattering (208-211). Crazing appears to be
especially important in the yielding of polyblends and high
impact plastics (1,140,146,147,164,212).

Still other theories of cold-drawing use a concept similar
to Eyring's (213) theory of viscosity in which the applied stress
makes the potential wells for segmental motions unsymmetrical.
This makes it easier for motion to occur in the direction of the
force (214-217). Finally, there are similar theories which
emphasize the importance of free radicals formed from the
breaking of over-stressed polymer chains at the start of the
necking or fracture process (218-221). In these theories the
broken chains quickly relax. The stress-biased probability of
chain rupture P_l is

$$P_l = w_o \exp\{-(\Delta H - \Lambda\sigma_c)/kT\} \tag{22}$$

where w_o is a collision parameter, ΔH is the energy of activation,
Λ is the activation volume, σ_c is the stress on a polymer chain
(not the stress on the specimen), and k is Boltzmann's constant.
This probability equation is stressed-biased so that the taut
chains break first; the stress is then redistributed among the
remaining chains (220). This relaxation of the stress at the
points of stress concentration may favor cold-drawing. Another
possibility is that the free radicals formed by the breaking of
one chain may catalyze the fracture of other chains around it
by a chain reaction mechanism so that a void develops at the
region where the new chain ends contract as the stress on them
is removed (221). This small void may nucleate a craze crack
which leads to either yielding or failure.

Possibly all the above theories have some merit. Yielding
and cold-drawing may take place by several possible mechanisms,
and the relative importance of different mechanisms may vary
from one polymer to another. On a molecular scale, something
like the following may take place in a glassy polymer: Polymers
are not homogeneous on a molecular scale, but there are weak
and strong regions. As illustrated in the top part of Figure 21,
the weak regions and imperfections can consist of aggregates of
chain ends, regions where loops in several chains are in close
proximity but do not entangle with one another, and regions in
which a cluster of several chain segments are oriented
perpendicular to the direction of the stress. Strong regions
include chain entanglements and regions where a cluster of
chain segments is oriented parallel to the stress. Although
several chains oriented parallel to the stress act as strong
regions, a single stretched out chain surrounded by chains
with slack acts as a weak point in the structure. A single
taut chain is easily broken by a stress in its axial direction
since it carries all the load around it, and a void may develop
in the region of the chain break as indicated above (220,221).
When a load is applied to a polymer, the weak regions are first
to break or pull apart to form many submicroscopic cracks and
voids as illustrated in the middle section of Figure 21. These
initial voids, or the voids formed as they enlarge, can be
detected by small angle x-ray scattering when they reach a
size of about 20 to several hundred Angstrom units (208-210).
Under the influence of the applied stress, the voids continue
to grow or coalesce to form larger voids until visible craze
cracks are formed, as illustrated in the bottom section of

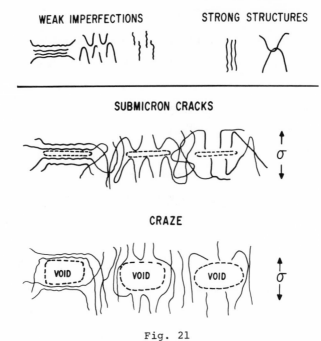

Fig. 21

Top: Regions of weakness and strength on a molecular scale
in a polymer which appear to be important in the development
of craze cracks. Bottom: Sequential steps in the development
of voids, oriented polymer, and craze cracks as the result
of a tensile stress applied in the vertical direction.

Figure 21. In addition to the voids, a craze crack consists of

oriented and molecularly cold-drawn material which is not easily

fractured because these regions originally contained some of the

strong structures discussed above. These oriented regions

between the voids in a craze crack tend to prevent coalescence

of the voids which would result in a true crack and catastrophic

failure. In the process of forming the highly oriented polymer

in the crazes, some chains will find so much stress on them

that they will break if slippage cannot occur. These broken

chains form free radicals which may be detected by electron
spin resonance (ESR) measurements (222-225). Why do craze
cracks in brittle glassy polymers such as polystyrene appear
to be so straight rather than zigzagged along their length?
At least two factors must be involved: First, the submicroscopic
cracks initially formed in the weak regions will be pointed in
the direction perpendicular to the stress. The pointed ends of
these submicroscopic cracks are strong stress concentrators
which encourage further growth in the same direction. Secondly,
if two craze cracks find themselves in a colinear position with
respect to one another, the stress fields favor further growth
so that the two cracks coalesce into a single longer craze
crack (226). On the other hand, two craze cracks which are not
colinear will tend to grow until the tips of the cracks pass
each other and overlap; the stress fields around their tips
then interact to hinder further growth (1,183). Thus, on the
basis of the above concepts, the yielding and cold-drawing of
polymers consists of a complex combination of chain fracture,
void formation, and crazing along with molecular orientation
and chain slippage. Crazing and void formation dominate in
the more brittle polymers while chain slippage and oriented
fibrillar effects dominate in the more ductile polymers. Some
secondary glass transitions aid the slippage and orientation
process by giving some short chain segments or groups more
freedom of motion so that stresses are more easily relaxed in
the regions of stress concentration.

Somewhat similar phenomena are involved in the high-impact
polyblended materials in which a rubbery polymer is dispersed

in a brittle polymer. Small amounts of a dispersed rubber
phase are capable of converting a brittle polymer into a
material which has a yield point and high elongation to break.
Many theories have been proposed on the mechanisms giving rise
to the toughness and high impact behavior of such two-phase
systems. These theories have been reviewed by Bragaw (147).
Strella and Newman (227,228) suggest that the rubber particles
in polyblends put a dilational triaxial stress on the matrix.
This triaxial stress lowers the T_g of the matrix to the test
temperature. Thus, the matrix around the rubber particles
behaves as a rubber when a polyblend is stressed according to
this theory. In free-volume theories of the glass transition
temperature, the lowering of T_g by a tensile load which
produces a dilation $\Delta V/V_o$ is (229):

$$\alpha \Delta T_g = \frac{\Delta V}{V_o} = (1 - 2\nu)\varepsilon. \qquad (23)$$

The lowering of T_g is ΔT_g, α is the volume coefficient of
thermal expansion, ΔV is the volume change associated with the
tensile elongation ε, V_o is the initial volume of the unloaded
polymer, and ν is Poisson's ratio. Other workers have
emphasized the role of craze cracks in making polyblends tough
ductile materials (1, 145, 146, 164, 212). Rubber particles act
as stress concentrators so that a tremendous number of craze
cracks first start near the equator of the particles approximately
perpendicular to the stress (174,230,231). The craze cracks grow
until they run into another rubber particle. The crack may then
stop since the radius of the particle is greater than the radius
of curvature of the crack tip, so the intensity of the stress

concentration is decreased. Because of the large number of
rubber particles, millions of craze cracks are initiated in
polyblends rather than just a few cracks which could quickly
grow to catastrophic failure if not hindered by the stress
fields of other cracks (1,183). Large quantities of energy are
thus dissipated in the generation of new crack surfaces in
polyblends. The rubber particles thus act as artificial weak
regions in the polymer rather than the naturally occurring ones
shown in Figure 21. Craze cracks in polyblends tend to zigzag
from rubber particle to rubber particle rather than going in
the apparent straight line observed with craze cracks in single-
phase polymers.

Litt and coworkers (199,200), Rusch and Beck (201), and
DiBenedetto and coworkers (6,15) all have somewhat similar
quantitative theories for the elongation at yield ε_y of glassy
polymers based upon free volume concepts. These last researchers
assume that as long as the stress-strain curve is linear, no
free volume is generated which is effective in either lowering
T_g or in generating voids. The ε_y is made up of two parts — a
linear elastic part ($\varepsilon_e = \sigma_y/E$) and a viscous or plastic part.
Both components of ε_y approach zero as the temperature is raised to
near T_g. The elongation at yield by this theory is:

$$\varepsilon_y = \frac{\sigma_y}{E} + \left(\alpha_g - \alpha_c\right)\left(\frac{\overline{v}_c}{\overline{v}_a}\right)\left(\frac{T_g - T}{1 - 2\nu}\right) . \qquad (24)$$

In this equation, σ_y is the yield strength, E is Young's modulus,
α_g is the volume coefficient of thermal expansion of the
amorphous glass, α_c is the coefficient of thermal expansion if
the glass were really a crystal, $\overline{v}_a$ and $\overline{v}_c$ are the specific

volumes of the amorphous glass and the crystal, respectively,
ν is Poisson's ratio, T_g is the glass transition temperature,
and T is the test temperature. This equation shows the
importance of T_g in determining the yield behavior of glassy
polymers.

IV.   Impact Strength and Tearing

A.   Nature of Impact Tests

Impact tests are high speed fracture tests which measure
the energy to break a specimen. In the Izod and Charpy impact
tests a pendulum with a hammer-like weight strikes a specimen
(a notched or unnotched bar), and the energy required to break
the specimen is determined from the loss in kinetic energy of
the weight (232-235). In the falling ball or falling dart
impact tests the amount of energy required to break a sheet or
plate of the material is determined from the weight of the ball
and the height from which it was dropped (236-238). Still
another type of impact test measures the area under the curve
obtained in a high speed tensile stress-strain test (239-241).

The agreement among the various impact tests is poor,
and different tests often rank a series of polymers in different
order. In addition, a given type of impact test does not give
a value which is a material constant. The geometry of the
specimen is important, since the impact strength depends upon
sample size even if an attempt is made to normalize the values
to a constant specimen size (235, 242, 243). Thin specimens
tend to give higher impact strengths than thick ones. The
disagreement between different kinds of tests indicates that

impact tests are controlled by at least two or more basic physical properties. Two factors which enter into impact behavior are: 1. The energy needed to initiate a crack. 2. The energy required to propogate a crack.

The units used to express impact strength can be confusing. In high speed tensile tests, and similar tests, on unnotched specimens the impact strength is defined in terms of the area under the stress-strain curve or as energy to break, with units such as foot-pounds/(inch)^2 or kilojoules/(meter)^2. 1 ft-lb/in^2 = 2.10 kJ/m^2. For notched Izod and Charpy tests, impact strength is defined in terms of energy per length of notch. Conversion factors are: 1 ft-lb/in notch = 2.5 ft-lb/in^2 = 5.25 kJ/m^2.

Table 3 lists the typical range of notched Izod impact strengths for some common plastics (1,244).

B. Effect of Notches

The impact strength of a notched specimen is less than that of an unnotched one (172,233,235,245). The main reason for this is that notches are stress concentrators. The stress concentration is greatest for sharp notches with small radii of curvature of their tips. (See Equation 13.) However, there are other reasons why a notch reduces impact strength and why notches are more detrimental in some polymers than others. In an unnotched specimen the deformation tends to take place throughout the length of the specimen. In a notched specimen, most of the deformation takes place in the neighborhood of the tip of the notch, so that material in the notch experiences an extremely high apparent rate of deformation compared to that in a similar unnotched specimen (1,245). At high rates of deforma-

Table 3

Notched Izod Impact Strength of Rigid Plastics at 24°C

Plastic	Impact Strength (ft lbs/in notch)
Polystyrene	0.25 - 0.40
High impact polystyrenes	0.5 - 8.00
ABS polymers	1.0 - 10.0
Polyvinyl chloride (rigid)	0.4 - 3.0
Polyvinyl chloride (polyblends)	3.0 - 20.0
Polymethyl methacrylate	0.4 - 0.5
Cellulose acetate	1.0 - 5.6
Cellulose nitrate	5.0 - 7.0
Ethyl cellulose	3.5 - 6.0
Nylon 66	1.0 - 3.0
Nylon 6	1.0 - 3.0
Polyoxymethylene	2 - 3
Polyethylene (low density)	> 16
Polyethylene (high density)	0.5 - 20.0
Polypropylene	0.5 - 2
Polycarbonate (Bis Phenol-A)	12 - 18
Polyvinyl formal	1 - 20
Phenol-formaldehyde (gen. purpose)	0.25 - .35
Phenol-formaldehyde (cloth-filled)	1 - 3
Phenol-formaldehyde (glass fiber-filled)	10 - 30
Polytetrafluorethylene	2.0 - 4.0
Nylon 6-12	1.0 - 1.4
Nylon 11	1.8
Polyphenylene oxide	5.0
Polyphenylene oxide (25% glass fibers)	1.4 - 1.5
Polysulfone	1.3 - 5
Polyester (glass fiber-filled)	2 - 20
Epoxy resins	.2 - 5.0
Epoxy resin (glass fiber-filled)	10 - 30
Polyimide	0.9

tion a material may change from a ductile to a brittle material
with lower impact strength. Thus, the difference between a
notched and an unnotched specimen can be greater for ductile
than for brittle materials (246). Another factor affecting
the sensitivity of a material to notches comes from fracture
being a process which involves both the initiation of a crack
and its propogation. In a notched specimen, an apparent crack
is already initiated, so the amount of energy absorbed is
dependent primarily upon the energy to propogate a crack. The
energy to initiate a crack is emphasized in unnotched specimens,
and this energy is added on to the energy required to propogate
the crack (235). The effect of the sharpness of the tip of the
notch on the impact strength of several polymers is illustrated
in Figure 22 (235). In this figure, nylon and polyvinyl chloride
(PVC) are very notch sensitive compared to an acrylic polymer
and a high impact ABS material. The effect of notching a
specimen is shown again in Figure 23 for the impact strength
of polypropylene as a function of temperature. The great
increase in impact strength on raising the temperature above
0°C for the unnotched specimen is due to the T_g of the polymer
(-10°C). The upturn is not apparent for the specimens with a
blunt notch (IS2) until about 20°C; part of this shift is due
to the apparent increase in T_g with the increase in rate of
deformation as a result of the notch. With a sharp notch
(IS 1/4), the increase in impact strength above T_g is hardly
noticeable.

From the above discussion, it is obvious that notches,
cuts, and scratches may have a tremendous effect on the toughness

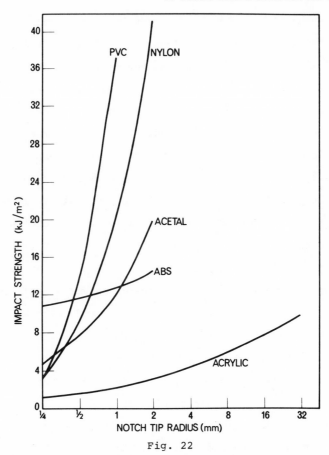

Fig. 22

Impact strength as a function of the radius of the tip of
the notch for different polymers. [Reprinted from Vincent,
Impact Tests and Service Performance of Thermoplastics,
The Plastics Inst., London, 1971.]

and impact strength of a material. To get any realistic

appraisal of the behavior of a polymer in the form of a

practical object, impact tests should be made on notched

specimens, preferably at several radii of curvature of the

notch (172,235).

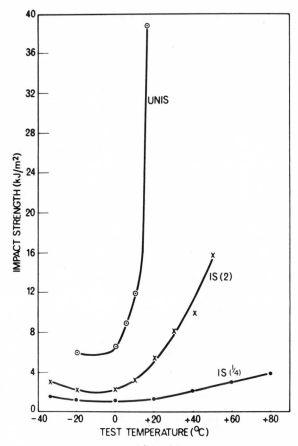

Fig. 23

Effect of temperature on the impact strength of polypropylene. UNIS = unnotched specimens. IS(2) = specimens
with a notch with a 2 mm radius of curvature. IS(1/4) =
specimens with a notch with a radius of curvature of 1/4 mm.
[Reprinted from Vincent, Impact Tests and Service Performance
of Thermoplastics, The Plastics Inst., London, 1971.]

C. Effect of Temperature

Impact strength increases as the temperature increases

(51,172,235,247-252). For amorphous polymers the impact

strength increases dramatically as the temperature is raised
to the neighborhood of T_g or higher. Most crystalline polymers
also have greater impact strength above T_g than below it. At
temperatures around T_g or above, molecular motions are great
enough to relieve stress concentrations, much energy can be
dissipated into heat by the high mechanical damping, and
yielding with high elongations to break becomes possible. The
effects of temperature are shown in Figures 23 (235) and 24 (249).

However, some polymers have very high impact strengths even
below T_g. These high impact materials have prominent low
temperature damping peaks due to either secondary glass
transitions or to a second rubbery phase as in high impact
polyblends (1,161,162,249,253-256). Not all secondary glass
transitions are effective in increasing impact strength. Some
secondary glass transitions which are associated with motion of
groups or segments in the backbone of the polymer chains are
more effective than motions due to side groups (255). Thus, in
some cases there is a correlation between the low temperature
dynamic mechanical properties and impact strength (247-249, 253,
254, 256-260). When the correlation holds, the impact strength
increases as the height of the damping peak increases or as the
area under the damping peak increases.

D.   Effects of Orientation

The effects of molecular orientation on impact strength
can be predicted from the stress-strain behavior. Orientation
generally increases impact strength if the impacting force is
parallel to the orientation, and the impact properties are
poorer if the force is applied perpendicular to the orientation
(109,235,261-263). In practical situations, in which the impact

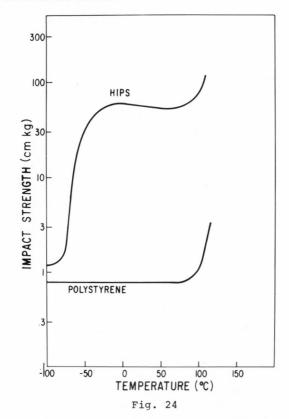

Fig. 24

The impact strength as a function of temperature for
polystyrene and high impact strength polystyrene (HIPS).
[Modified from Jones, J. Polymer Sci., C16, 3845 (1968).]

loads may come from any direction or may be biaxial, an object
always breaks in the weakest direction. The high impact
strengths parallel to the orientation can seldom be used to
advantage in practical service conditions. Thus, injection
molded test specimens, which always contain some orientation,
may give very misleading impact strengths (109, 235, 261-263).
The effects of injection molding conditions on orientation and
on impact strength are illustrated in Figure 25 (235). The

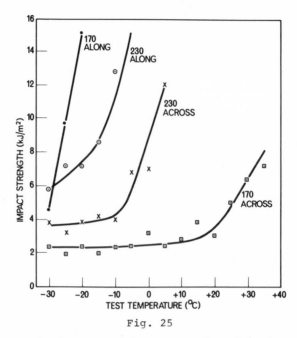

Fig. 25

Impact strength of an ABS polymer as a function of
temperature for oriented specimens. Specimens were molded
at 170°C (high orientation) and at 230°C (lower orientation).
Along = stress applied parallel to the uniaxial orientation.
Across = stress applied perpendicular to the orientation.
[Reprinted from Vincent, Impact Tests and Service Performance
of Thermoplastics, The Plastics Inst., London, 1971.]

---

higher temperature (230°C) in the cylinder of the injection

molding machine allows the orientation to relax more than at the

lower temperature (170°C). There is a very great difference in

impact strength parallel to the orientation (along the flow

direction) and perpendicular to the orientation (across the

flow direction), especially for the more highly oriented

specimens molded at 170°C. Similar effects are shown in Table 2

where impact strength and stress-strain properties are compared

as a function of birefringence (or orientation) for injection molded specimens (109). Falling ball impact tests, which apply

biaxial stresses, tend to correlate better with practical

experience than Izod or Charpy tests do on oriented specimens

(261, 263, 264).

E. Other Factors Affecting Impact Strength

The impact strength tends to increase somewhat with

molecular weight up to an asymptotic value where the impact

strength becomes nearly independent of molecular weight (39, 51,

53). The effect of molecular weight seems to be most pronounced

with crystalline polymers, such as polypropylene, above their T_g.

Crystallinity generally decreases the impact strength of

polymers which have a T_g well above the test temperature. As

the spherulitic structure of such materials increases as a

result of slow cooling from the melt or by annealing below the

melting point, the impact strength decreases. Impact strength

has no meaning for elastomers, which have a T_g below the test

temperature. However, the impact behavior of such materials

can be measured if a fairly high degree of crystallinity occurs

as in polyethylene and polypropylene. In the range of

crystallinities from roughly 40 to 65 percent, polymers with

glass transition temperatures well below room temperature are

extremely tough materials. At higher degrees of crystallinity,

the impact strength decreases, but it still may be high compared

to a brittle amorphous polymer (53, 238, 265). Again, super-

imposed on the degree of crystallinity is the effect of the

crystallite morphology. As the spherulites become larger and

more prominent, the impact strength decreases. An important

factor in determining the impact strength of crystalline

polymers is their abiliby to yield and have high elongations
to break.

Plasticizers lower T_g, and so they can greatly increase
the impact strength of a polymer if T_g is near the test
temperature. However, with such polymers as polyvinyl chloride,
polycarbonate, and polysulfone, addition of small amounts of
some plasticizers makes these polymers brittle (104,266,267).
The conversion of these ductile materials into brittle ones is
a result of the suppression of prominent secondary glass
transitions by the plasticizer as discussed in Chapter 4.

F. Impact Strength of Polyblends

Brittle polymers such as polystyrene can be converted
into high impact materials by the addition of a rubber. There
is a sacrifice of modulus of elasticity and of breaking strength,
but the increase in elongation to break and the ability to
dissipate large amounts of energy more than compensates for
the reduced strength and stiffness. Three conditions are
essential to produce a polyblend with high impact strength (1,
161-164): 1. The glass transition temperature of the elastomeric component should be well below the test temperature. To
have good impact strength at room temperature, the rubber
should have a T_g at least 20 to 40°C lower to compensate for
the high rate of deformation in an impact test. 2. The
elastomeric material must form a second phase dispersed in the
rigid polymer. 3. There should be good adhesion between the
two phases. Good adhesion can be achieved by grafting polymer,
which is similar to or the same as the rigid phase, onto the
rubbery particles. Adhesion may also be improved by increasing

the similarity in solubility behavior of the two components by
using a copolymer for one or both of the polymers. The
similarity in solubility behavior of the two polymers must not
be increased to the extent that they become soluble in one
another. Grafting of the proper polymer onto the rubber
particles is an especially effective way of increasing the
adhesion between the phases. Such materials have much better
impact strength than polyblends made by mechanical mixing of
two polymers (251,258,268,269). Even with good adhesion, there
may be dewetting of the rubber particles from the matrix (160).
The dewetting absorbs energy and adds to the impact strength.
Large particles dewet before small particles.

The mechanisms responsible for the high impact strength
are essentially the same as those giving rise to yielding and
cold-drawing discussed earlier in this chapter. The rubber
particles act as stress concentrators in producing many craze
cracks. The very large surface area produced during the crazing
and dewetting process along with the cold-drawing of the polymer
filaments between the voids is capable of absorbing a great deal
of energy. In addition, the triaxial compressive stress in the
matrix immediately adjacent to the rubber particles appears to
lead to more cold-drawing than if the particles were acting only
as stress concentrators.

The impact strength increases with the size of the rubber
particles up to some limiting value (147,270,271). The morphology
of the rubber phase affects impact strength (260). The rubber
particles often are spherical in shape with spherical inclusions
of the rigid phase (259,272). At a concentration of about 20
percent of the rubbery phase, the dispersed particles tend to

agglomerate or to form elongated rather than spherical particles. At this point an inversion of the phases starts, accompanied by a more rapid decrease in modulus and a large increase in impact strength as the concentration of rubber increases. Both phases tend to be continuous in the concentration range where the two phases are present in roughly the same amount. (Phase inversion will be discussed in more detail in Chapter 7.)

There is often a good correlation between the impact strength and the dynamic mechanical properties of polyblends (249,251,257,259,260,272). Impact strength generally increases as the size of the damping peak due to the rubber phase increases (257,259,260). The correlation is best within a family of similar materials since rubber phase morphology, specimen preparation, adhesion, and other factors may affect the correlation to some extent. The biggest factor determining the size of the damping peak, and the corresponding drop in the modulus, is the concentration of the rubbery phase. It is not the amount of rubber present that is important, but the total amount of rubbery phase (rubber plus occluded rigid particles) that determines the size of the damping peak.

G. Tearing

The energy to tear a rubbery material is somewhat analogous to the impact strength of rigid polymers. Tearing tests are generally tensile tests made on sheets which contain a cut or a notch (273-275). The tensile test specimen may be a strip of rubber with a razor cut on an edge, or the specimen may be similar in shape to a pair of trousers in which the legs are pulled apart. The force to propogate the cut is measured as in a stress-strain test.

With crosslinked rubbers, the energy to tear the rubber is generally very high. In the tearing process, chains must be broken. The surfaces of tear cracks are rough on a molecular scale since the tear follows a path of least resistance to minimize the number of chains that are broken. The first chains to be broken are those in a taut configuration; as the tearing proceeds, other chains become taut and break.

The tearing process can be analyzed by an energy balance similar to that used by Griffith for brittle materials (276-279). The tearing energy U_t, which is the amount of work required to extend a tear to the extent that a unit amount of new surface is generated, is given by

$$U_t = - \frac{1}{D} \left(\frac{\partial W}{\partial C} \right)_\ell . \qquad (25)$$

In this equation, D is the thickness of the sheet, C is the length of the tear, and W is the total strain energy in the test piece; the subscript ℓ indicates that the degree of extension (jaw separation) is held constant during the tearing process. A cut in rubber will not grow below a critical strain or below a critical amount of stored energy. This critical strain defines a fatigue limit for rubber (280,281). In addition to the relation between tearing energy U_t and fatigue life, U_t is also related to the dynamic mechanical properties of the rubber (279,282). The tearing energy increases as the damping E" increases. The tearing energy increases slowly as the speed of testing or tearing rate increases.

V. Summary

Stress-strain behavior, impact strength, and tearing all involve fracture. Fracture is a very complex phenomenon, which does not depend upon chemical and molecular structure as much as it depends upon imperfections, weak spots, voids, and cracks in the material. Some factors involved in the fracture of polymers are submicroscopic void formation, crazing, chain fracture and the generation of free radicals, and cold-drawing in which there is chain slippage and molecular orientation. Some of these factors are more important in brittle fracture than they are in ductile fracture. Tools which are important in studies of the factors in the fracture process are :
1. Small angle x-ray scattering to measure void and craze formation. 2. Electron spin resonance (ESR) measurements for the study of the number and kind of free radicals formed during the breaking of polymer chains. 3. Microscopy techniques including optical, electron, and scanning electron microscopy for viewing crazes, cracks, and fracture surfaces as well as for determinations of the morphology in crystalline and two-phase polymers.

In stress-strain tests, the factors which increase the modulus, the yield stress, and the tensile strength generally decrease the elongation to break and the ductility. For ductile or relatively tough polymers, the yield strength can be increased by increasing the speed of testing, increasing the degree of crystallinity, or decreasing the temperature.

High impact strength and toughness are generally character-ized by yielding accompanied by large elongation to break and large areas under the stress-strain curve. However, a polymer which has a yield point at a slow speed of testing may fracture in a brittle manner at high speeds. Also, many polymers which are ductile under normal testing conditions may appear to be brittle if the test specimen contains a notch or a crack.

Molecular orientation can have a very great effect on stress-strain and impact behavior. Parallel to the molecular alignment, the polymer can be very strong, but in the direction perpendicular to the orientation, the polymer is much weaker. Unfortunately, in most service conditions, the behavior of an object is determined by its lowest strength, that is, by the properties perpendicular to the direction of uniaxial orientation. However, many of the undesirable characteristics of uniaxial orientation can be overcome by biaxially orienting the material.

Brittle polymers can be converted into tough high impact materials by the addition of a second phase which is a rubber. Although the theory is only partially developed, empirically it is well known what conditions must be fulfilled in order to produce a material with high impact strength.

VI.   Problems

1. An elastomer with an M_c of 3000 obeys the kinetic theory of rubber elasticity up to an extension ratio L/L_o of 2. Plot the stress-strain curve if the density of the polymer is 0.9.

2. Prove that the area under a stress-strain curve is proportional to the work done in deforming the material.

3. A polystyrene gave the following tensile load-deformation data. Calculate and plot the stress-strain curve if the specimen had a gage length of 2 inches, a width of 0.5 in.,

and a thickness of 1/8 in. What is Young's modulus, σ_B and ε_B?

Load (lbs)	Change in Length $(L-L_o)$ (inches)
125	0.010
250	0.020
352	0.030
385	0.036 (fracture)

4. A tensile stress-strain curve is given by the points in the following table. Plot the curve and calculate Young's modulus E_o, yield stress σ_y, elongation at yield, and the total energy to fracture the material.

Strain ε	Stress (psi)	Strain ε	Stress (psi)
.005	250	.07	1660
.010	500	.08	1500
.020	950	.09	1400
.03	1250	.10	1385
.04	1470	.12	1380
.05	1565	.15	1380 (fracture)
.06	1690		

5. In problem 4 assume that the polymer necked down in one small section and broke before the entire specimen could cold-draw. If the necked-down section had a natural draw ratio of 3.0, what would be the true stress-strain curve based on the true cross-sectional area of the smallest cross section rather than upon the original cross-sectional

area? Assume that the neck was fully developed at the
point where the stress-strain curve reached a nearly constant
value of engineering stress.

6. In some cases the stress-strain curve can be approximated
up to the yield point by a simple power series:

$$\sigma = A\epsilon - B\epsilon^2 = E_o\epsilon\left(1 - \epsilon/2\epsilon_y\right)$$

where A and B are constants, and E_o is Young's modulus
determined from the initial slope of the stress-strain curve.
Show that the following relations hold:

$$\sigma_y = E_o\epsilon_y/2$$
$$E = E_o\left(1 - \sigma/\sigma_y\right)^{1/2}$$

where E is the modulus at any point on the stress-strain
curve as defined by $E = d\sigma/d\epsilon$.

7. A polymer has an initial Poisson's ratio of 0.35. At high
loads the polymer crazes badly. How would you expect
Poisson's ratio to change after crazing starts?

8. A commercial film is biaxially oriented, but the film has
been stretched more in the "machine" (longitudinal) direction
than in the transverse direction. How would you tell which
is the machine direction?

9. Derive the equation for the stress-strain behavior of a
Maxwell element:

$$\sigma = K\eta[1 - \exp(-E\epsilon/K\eta)] \text{ where } K = d\epsilon/dt.$$

10. A tensile specimen has a gage length of 2 inches, a width
     of 0.50 inches, and a thickness of 0.125 inches. The
     stress-strain curve is essentially linear up to the point
     of fracture. The specimen broke when the load was 500
     pounds and the extensometer showed 0.032 inches increase
     in length. What is Young's modulus in psi and in N/m^2,
     the elongation to break in percent, and the tensile stress
     in psi?

11. A polymer has a modulus of 10^9 dynes/cm^2, a yield point of
     5 percent, a yield stress of 3000 psi, a tensile stress of
     4000 psi at failure, and an elongation to break of 50
     percent. If the stress-strain curve is linear up to 1
     percent, sketch the approximate stress-strain curve.

12. For the polymer in Problem 11, sketch the approximate curve
     for the load (force) versus change in length of the specimen.
     The original specimen had a gage length of 5 in., a width
     of 1 in., and a thickness of 0.10 in. Assuming a Poisson's
     ratio of 0.50, what are the final dimensions of the specimen
     if the stretching was uniform?

13. Plot the room temperature stress-strain curve predicted by
     the kinetic theory of rubber elasticity for a polymer which
     has a molecular weight of 300,000 before crosslinking and a
     molecular weight between crosslinks of 5000 after cross-
     linking. The density is 1.0, and the elongation to break
     is 500 percent.

14. For the same rubber as in Problem 13, plot the shear stress-
     strain curve and the biaxial stress-strain curve as predicted
     by the kinetic theory of rubber elasticity.

15. The creep of 2 polymers obeys the Nutting equation:

$$\varepsilon = K\sigma t^n$$

where K and n are constants. If K is the same for the 2
polymers while n = 0.15 for one and n = 0.30 for the other,
for which polymer do you expect the stress-strain properties
to change most rapidly as the speed of testing is changed?
Why?

16. A polymer has a stress-strain curve given by

$$\sigma = 4.5 \times 10^5 (1 - \varepsilon/0.10)\varepsilon$$

up to the yield point, where it breaks. What is the energy
to break for this material? Would you expect this material
to have a high impact strength? In the above equation,
the stress is in psi, and ε_y = 0.05.

17. During a compression test on a ductile polymer, the specimen
in the shape of a short cylinder becomes barrel-shaped,
that is, the specimen bulges in the middle. Why? What can
be done to minimize this effect?

18. Impact strength in many cases is related to the area under
the stress-strain curve of a high speed tensile test. A
stress-strain curve is measured on an oriented polymer with
the stress parallel to the direction of molecular
orientation. Why is such a test meaningless to compare
with a drop dart or falling ball type of impact test?

19. Two test specimens have the same Young's modulus in
tension. However, one of the specimens is homogeneous
while the other one has a skin which is stiffer than the
material at the center of the specimen. How will the
flexural modulus of the two specimens differ?

VII. References

1.   L. E. Nielsen, Mechanical Properties of Polymers,
     Van Nostrand Reinhold, New York, 1962.

2.   C. C. Hsiao and J. A. Sauer, ASTM Bull., No. 172, 29
     (Feb. 1951).

3.   W. H. Dukes, Unresolved Problems in Brittle Material Design,
     U. S. Govt. Rept., AD 654119 (1966).

4.   P. I. Vincent, Plastics, 27, 117 (Feb. 1962).

5.   T. S. Carswell and H. K. Nason, Modern Plast., 21, 121
     (June 1944)

6.   A. T. DiBenedetto and K. L. Trachte, J. Appl. Polymer Sci.,
     14, 2249 (1970).

7.   K. Ito, Trans. Soc. Rheol., 15, 389 (1971).

8.   R. F. Lark, Cryogenic Properties of Polymers, T. Serafini
     and J. Koenig, Ed., Marcel Dekker, New York, 1968,
     Chapter 1, p.1

9.   R. E. Eckert and T. T. Serafini, Cryogenic Properties of
     Polymers, T. Serafini and J. Koenig, Ed., Marcel Dekker,
     New York, 1968, p.73

10. J. Skelton, W. D. Freeston, Jr., and M. M. Schoppee,
     J. Appl. Polymer Sci., 14, 2797 (1970).

11. O. Ishai, J. Appl. Polymer Sci., 11, 963 (1967).

12. A. G. H. Dietz and F. J. McGarry, ASTM Spec. Tech. Publ.,
     No. 185, Amer. Soc. Testing, Mater., Philadelphia, Pa.,
     1956, p. 30.

13. J. K. Knowles and A. G. H. Dietz, Trans. ASME, 77, 177
     (1955).

14. J. M. Andrews and I. M. Ward, J. Mater. Sci., 5, 411 (1970).

15. L. Nicholais and A. T. DiBenedetto, J. Appl. Polymer Sci.,
     15, 1585 (1971).

16. C. Crowet and G. A. Homes, Appl. Mater. Res., 3, 1 (1964).

17. A. E. Moehlenpah, O. Ishai, and A. T. DiBenedetto,
     J. Appl. Polymer Sci., 13, 1231 (1969).

18. P. I. Vincent, Plastics, 27, 115 (Jan. 1962).

19. F. Bueche, J. Appl. Phys., 26, 1133 (1955).

20. H. W. Greensmith, J. Appl. Polymer Sci., 3, 175 (1960).

21. T. L. Smith, J. Polymer Sci., 32, 99 (1958).

22. T. L. Smith, J. Polymer Sci., A1, 3597 (1963).

23. T. L. Smith, Proc. Royal Soc., 282A, 102 (1964).

24. T. L. Smith and W. H. Chu, J. Polymer Sci., A2, 10, 133 (1972).

25. J. J. Lohr, Trans Soc. Rheol., 9, 65 (1965).

26. J. C. Halpin, J. Appl. Phys., 35, 3133 (1964).

27. K. D. Pae and D. R. Mears, J. Polymer Sci., B6, 269 (1968).

28. K. D. Pae, D. R. Mears, and J. A. Sauer, J. Polymer Sci., B6, 773 (1968).

29. D. R. Mears and K. D. Pae, J. Polymer Sci., B7, 349 (1969).

30. D. R. Mears, K. D. Pae, and J. A. Sauer, J. Appl. Phys., 40, 4229 (1969).

31. J. A. Sauer, D. R. Mears, and K. D. Pae, Europ. Polymer J., 6, 1015 (1970).

32. S. K. Bhateja and K. D. Pae, J. Polymer Sci., B10, 531 (1972).

33. D. Sardar, S. V. Radcliffe, and E. Baer, Polymer Eng. Sci., 8, 290 (1968).

34. R. W. Warfield, Makromol. Chem., 116, 78 (1968).

35. S. B. Ainbinder, M. G. Laka, and I. Yu. Maiors, Polymer Mech., 1, 50 (1966), Engl. transl.

36. W. I. Vroom and R. F. Westover, SPE J., 25, #8, 58 (1969).

37. S. Rabinowitz, I. M. Ward, and J. S. C. Parry, J. Mater. Sci., 5, 29 (1970).

38. A. W. Christiansen, E. Baer, and S. V. Radcliffe, Phil. Mag., 24, 451 (1971).

39. E. H. Merz, L. E. Nielsen, and R. Buchdahl, Ind. Eng. Chem., 43, 1396 (1951).

40. A. N. Gent, J. Polymer Sci., A2, 10, 571 (1972).

41. A. M. Sookne and M. Harris, J. Research Nat. Bur. Stds., 34, 467 (1945).

42. A. M. Sookne and M. Harris, Ind. Eng. Chem., 37, 478 (1945).

43. H. W. McCormick, F. M. Brower, and L. Kin, J. Polymer Sci., 39, 87 (1959).

44. A. F. Margolies, SPE J., 27, #6, 44 (1971).

45. P. J. Flory, J. Amer. Chem. Soc., 67, 2048 (1945).

46. P. J. Flory, Ind. Eng. Chem., 38, 417 (1946).

47. J. A. Yanko, J. Polymer Sci., 3, 576 (1948).

48. E. J. Lawton, J. S. Balwit, and A. M. Bueche, Ind. Eng. Chem.,
     46, 1703 (1946).

49. R. Toggenburger, S. Newman, and Q. A. Trementozzi, J. Appl.
     Polymer Sci., 11, 103 (1967).

50. R. F. Boyer, J. Polymer Sci., 9, 289 (1952).

51. J. M. Goppel, Plastics Progress, P. Morgan, Ed., Iliffe,
     London, 1960, p. 1.

52. D. P. Wyman, L. J. Elyash, and W. J. Frazer, J. Polymer Sci.,
     A3, 681 (1965).

53. J. van Schooten, H. van Hoorn, and J. Boerma, Polymer, 2,
     161 (1961).

54. L. H. Tung and S. Buckser, J. Phys. Chem., 62, 1530 (1958).

55. P. W. O. Wijga, Physical Properties of Polymers, Soc. Chem.
     Ind., Monograph #5, Macmillan, New York, 1959, p. 35.

56. P. J. Flory, Principles of Polymer Chemistry, Cornell
     University, Ithaca, N. Y., 1953, Chap. 11.

57. L. R. G. Treloar, The Physics of Rubber Elasticity,
     Clarendon Press, Oxford, 1956.

58. P. J. Flory, N. Rabjohn, and M. C. Schaffer, J. Polymer Sci.,
     4, 435 (1949).

59. G. R. Taylor and S. R. Darin, J. Polymer Sci., 17, 511 (1955).

60. F. B. Hill, C. A. Young, J. A. Nelson, and R. G. Arnold,
     Ind. Eng. Chem., 48, 927 (1956).

61. T. L. Smith and A. B. Magnusson, J. Polymer Sci., 42, 391
     (1960).

62. T. J. Dudek and F. Bueche, J. Appl. Polymer Sci., 8, 555
     (1964).

63. L. C. Case, Makromol.Chem., 37, 243 (1960).

64. L. C. Case and R. V. Wargin, Makromol. Chem., 77, 172 (1964);
     Rubber Chem. Techn., 39, 1489 (1966).

65. D. M. French, M. S. Chang, and A. S. Tompa, J. Appl. Polymer
     Sci., 16, 1615 (1972).

66. F. Bueche and J. C. Halpin, J. Appl. Phys., 35, 36 (1964).

67. F. Bueche, J. Polymer Sci., 24, 189 (1957).

68. F. Bueche and T. J. Dudek, Rubber Chem. Techn., 36, 1 (1963).

69. R. F. Landel and R. F. Fedors, Proc. 4th Internat. Congr.
     Rheol., Vol. 2, E. H. Lee, Ed., Wiley, New York, 1965, p. 543.

70. T. L. Smith and A. B. Magnusson, _J. Appl. Polymer Sci._, 5, 218 (1961).

71. J. A. C. Harwood and A. R. Payne, _J. Appl. Polymer Sci._, 12, 889 (1968).

72. A. R. Payne and R. E. Whittaker, _J. Appl. Polymer Sci._, 15, 1941 (1971).

73. H. D. Keith and F. J. Padden, Jr., _J. Polymer Sci._, 41, 525 (1959).

74. M. Horio, _Proc. 4th Internat. Congr. Rheol._, Vol. 1, E. Lee, Ed., Interscience, New York, 1965, p. 29.

75. A. Peterlin, _Internat. J. Fracture Mech._, 7, 496 (1971).

76. A. Peterlin, _Textile Res. J._, 42, 20 (1972).

77. A. Peterlin, _J. Mater. Sci._, 6, 490 (1971).

78. L. Barish, _J. Appl. Polymer Sci._, 6, 617 (1962).

79. C. F. Hammer, T. A. Koch, and J. F. Whitney, _J. Appl. Polymer Sci._, 1, 169 (1959).

80. H. W. Starkweather, Jr., G. E. Moore, J. E. Hansen, T. M. Roder, and R. E. Brooks, _J. Polymer Sci._, 21, 189 (1956).

81. L. S. Remaly and J. M. Schultz, _J. Appl. Polymer Sci._, 14, 1871 (1970).

82. R. W. Ford, _J. Appl. Polymer Sci._, 9, 2879 (1965).

83. W. M. D. Bryant, _J. Polymer Sci._, 2, 547 (1947).

84. H. W. Starkweather, Jr., and R. E. Brooks, _J. Appl. Polymer Sci._, 1, 236 (1959).

85. R. S. Stein, _Polymer Eng. Sci._, 9, 320 (1969).

86. H. Kawai, T. Itoh, D. A. Keedy, and R. S. Stein, _J. Polymer Sci._, B2, 1075 (1964).

87. P. Erhardt, K. Sasaguri, and R. S. Stein, _J. Polymer Sci._, C5, 179 (1964).

88. D. A. Zaukelies, _J. Appl. Phys._, 33, 2797 (1962).

89. M. Inoue, _J. Polymer Sci._, A1, 2013 (1963).

90. C. J. Kuhre, M. Wales, and M. E. Doyle, _SPE J._, 20, 1113, (1964).

91. T. A. Koretskaya, T. I. Sogolova, and V. A. Kargin, _Polymer Sci. USSR_ (Engl. transl.), 8, 1044 (1966).

92. H. N. Beck, _J. Appl. Polymer Sci._, 11, 673 (1967).

93. L. E. Nielsen, _Trans. Soc. Rheol._, 13, 141 (1969).

94. C. G. Cannon and F. P. Chappel, Brit. J. Appl. Phys., 10, 68 (1959).

95. F. P. Price, J. Polymer Sci., A3, 3079 (1965).

96. W. O. Statton and P. H. Geil, J. Appl. Polymer Sci., 3, 357 (1960).

97. E. H. Merz, L. E. Nielsen, and R. Buchdahl, J. Polymer Sci., 4, 605 (1949).

98. D. K. Rider, J. K. Sumner, and R. J. Meyers, Ind. Eng. Chem., 41, 709 (1949).

99. J. Malac, E. Simunkova, and J. Zelinger, J. Polymer Sci., A1 7, 1893 (1969).

100. E. B. Atkinson and R. F. Eagling, Physical Properties of Polymers, Soc. Chem. Ind. Monograph No. 5, Macmillan, New York, 1959, p. 197.

101. P. Ghersa, Modern Plast., 36, 135 (Oct. 1958).

102. W. J. Jackson, Jr. and J. R. Caldwell, Adv. Chem. Series, 48, 185 (1965).

103. W. J. Jackson, Jr. and J. R. Caldwell, J. Appl. Polymer Sci., 11, 211, 227 (1967).

104. L. M. Robeson and J. A. Faucher, J. Polymer Sci., B7, 35 (1969).

105. I. O. Salyer and A. S. Kenyon, J. Polymer Sci., A1, 9, 3083 (1971).

106. L. E. Nielsen and R. Buchdahl, J. Appl. Phys., 21, 488 (1950).

107. R. G. Cheatham and A. G. H. Dietz, Modern Plast., 29, 113 (Sept. 1951).

108. J. Bailey, India Rubber World, 118, 225 (1948).

109. G. B. Jackson and R. L. Ballman, SPE J. 16, #10, 1147 (1960).

110. D. R. Morey and E. V. Martin, Textile Res. J., 21, 607 (1951).

111. B. Maxwell, J. Appl. Polymer Sci., 5, S11 (1961).

112. A. A. Anderson and G. L. Moffit, Modern Plast., 35, 139 (Apr. 1958).

113. N. I. Shishkin, M. F. Milagin and A. D. Gabaraeva, Polymer Mech. (Engl. transl.), 3, 688 (1967).

114. J. G. Rider and E. Hargreaves, J. Polymer Sci., A2, 7, 829 (1969).

115. A. Keller and J. G. Rider, J. Mater. Sci., 1, 389 (1966).

116. Y. Tsunekawa, M. Oyane, and K. Kojima, J. Polymer Sci., 50
     35 (1961).

117. M. Inoue, M. Jishage, and T.Shibayama, Chem. High Polymer
     Japan, 19, 523 (1962).

118. J. W. Curtis, J. Phys., D3, 1413 (1970).

119. C. J. Heffelfinger and P. G. Schmidt, J. Appl. Polymer Sci.,
     9, 2661 (1965).

120. S. W. Allison and I. M. Ward, Brit. J. Appl. Phys., 18,
     1151 (1967).

121. M. Parrish and N. Brown, Plastic Deformation of Polymers,
     A. Peterlin, Ed., Marcel Dekker, New York, 1971, p. 189.

122. N. Brown, R. A. Duckett, and I. M. Ward, Phil. Mag., 18,
     483 (1968).

123. I. M. Ward, J. Polymer Sci., C32, 175 (1971).

124. D. M. Gezovich and P. H. Geil, J. Mater. Sci., 6, 531 (1971).

125. L. Holliday and J. W. White, Pure Appl. Chem., 26, #3-4,
     545 (1971).

126. W. H. Markwood, Jr. and H. M. Spurlin, J. Colloid Sci.,
     7, 244 (1952).

127. R. L. Ballman and H. L. Toor, Modern Plast., 38, 113
     (Oct. 1960).

128. J. Hennig, J. Polymer Sci., C16, 2751 (1967).

129. R. A. Duckett, I. M. Ward, and A. M. Zihlif, J. Mater Sci.,
     7, 480 (1972).

130. F. F. Rawson and J. G. Rider, J. Polymer Sci., C33, 87
     (1971).

131. H. L. Li, P. J. Koch, D. C. Prevorsek, and H. J. Oswald,
     J. Macromol. Sci., B4, 687 (1970).

132. M. Warshavsky and N. Tokita, SPE J., 26, #8, 55 (1970).

133. B. M. Axilrod, M. A. Sherman, V. Cohen, and I. Wolock,
     Modern Plast., 30, 117 (Dec. 1952).

134. C. P. Fortner, Rubber World, 129, 493 (1954).

135. I. Wolock, B. M. Axilrod, and M. A. Sherman, Modern Plast.,
     31, 128 (Sept. 1953).

136. L. S. Thomas and K. J. Cleereman, SPE J., 28, #4, 61 and
     #6, 39 (1972).

137. J. Miklowitz, J. Colloid Sci., 2, 217 (1947).

138. D. A. Hurst, SPE J., 12, 18 (May 1956).

139. I. Wolock and D. George, SPE J., 12, 20 (Feb. 1956).

140. C. B. Bucknall and D. Clayton, J. Mater. Sci., 7, 202 (1972).

141. A. M. Borders, R. D. Juve, and L. D. Hess, Ind. Eng. Chem.
      38, 955 (1946).

142. K. Satake, J. Appl. Polymer Sci., 14, 1007 (1970).

143. G. Holden, E. T. Bishop, and N. R. Legge, J. Polymer Sci.,
      C26, 37 (1969).

144. J-M. Charrier and R. J. P. Ranchoux, Polymer Eng. Sci.,
      11, 381 (1971).

145. S. Rabinowitz and P. Beardmore, Critical Rev. Macromol. Sci.,
      1, #1, 1 (1972).

146. C. B. Bucknall and R. R. Smith, Polymer, 6, 437 (1965).

147. C. G. Bragaw, Adv. Polymer Series, 99, 86 (1971).

148. R. G. Newberg, D. W. Young, and H. C. Evans, Modern Plast.,
      26, 119 (Dec. 1948).

149. D. W. Young, D. J. Buckley, R. G. Newberg, and L. B. Turner,
      Ind. Eng. Chem., 41, 401 (1949).

150. K. Fujimoto and N. Yoshimura, Rubber Chem. Techn., 41,
      1109 (1968).

151. R. A. Emmett, Ind. Eng. Chem., 36, 730 (1944).

152. D. W. Young, R. G. Newberg, and R. M. Howlett, Ind. Eng.
      Chem., 39, 1446 (1947).

153. W. Albert, Kunststoffe, 53, 86 (1963).

154. T. J. Sharp and J. A. Ross, Rubber Chem. Techn., 35, 726
      (1962).

155. D. J. Angier and E. M. Fettes, Rubber Chem. Techn. 38,
      1164 (1965).

156. K. Fletcher, R. N. Haward, and J. Mann, Chem. Ind., No. 45
      1854 (1965).

157. C. B. Arends, J. Appl. Polymer Sci., 10, 1099 (1966).

158. W. J. Frazer, Chem. Ind., No. 33, 1399 (1966).

159. K. C. Rusch and R. H. Beck, Jr., J. Polymer Sci., C30,
      447 (1970).

160. H. Keskkula, Appl. Polymer Sympos., 15, 51 (1970).

161. R. Buchdahl and L. E. Nielsen, J. Appl. Phys., 21, 482
      (1950).

162. R. Buchdahl and L. E. Nielsen, <u>J. Polymer Sci.</u>, 15, 1
      (1955).

163. E. H. Merz, G. C. Claver, and M. Baer, <u>J. Polymer Sci.</u>,
      22, 325 (1956).

164. J. A. Schmitt and H. Keskkula, <u>J. Appl. Polymer Sci.</u>, 3,
      132 (1960).

165. G. M. Estes, S. L. Cooper, and A. V. Tobolsky, <u>J. Macromol.
      Sci.</u>, C4, 313 (1970).

166. S. L. Aggarwal, Ed., <u>Block Polymers</u>, Plenum Press, New York,
      1970.

167. S. Ye. Bresler, L. M. Pyrkov, S. Ya. Frenkel, L. A. Lauis,
      and S. I. Klenin, <u>Polymer Sci. USSR</u>, (Engl. transl.), 4
      89 (1963).

168. M. Morton, J. E. McGrath, and P. C. Juliano, <u>J. Polymer Sci.</u>,
      C26, 99 (1969).

169. J. F. Beecher, L. Marker, R. D. Bradford, and S. L. Aggarwal,
      <u>J. Polymer Sci.</u>, C26, 117 (1969).

170. H. A. J. Battaerd and G. W. Tregear, <u>Graft Polymers</u>,
      Interscience, New York, 1967.

171. S. F. Pugh, <u>Brit. J. Appl. Phys.</u>, 18, 129 (1967).

172. R. A. Horsley, <u>Appl. Polymer Sympos.</u>, 17, 117 (1971).

173. S. Timoshenko and J. N. Goodier, <u>Theory of Elasticity</u>,
      2nd Ed., McGraw-Hill, New York, 1951, p. 80.

174. J. N. Goodier, <u>J. Appl. Mech.</u> (<u>Trans. ASME</u>), 55, A39 (1933).

175. J. Rehner, Jr., <u>J. Appl. Phys.</u>, 14, 638 (1943).

176. A. A. Griffith, <u>Philos. Trans. Royal Soc.</u>, A221, 163 (1920).

177. J. J. Benbow and F. C. Roesler, <u>Proc. Phys. Soc.</u>, 70B, 201
      (1957).

178. J. P. Berry, <u>SPE Trans.</u>, 1, 109 (1961).

179. J. P. Berry, <u>J. Polymer Sci.</u>, 50, 107 and 313 (1961).

180. J. P. Berry, <u>J. Polymer Sci.</u>, A1, 993 (1963).

181. B. Rosen, <u>Fracture Processes in Polymeric Solids</u>, Interscience,
      New York, 1964.

182. E. Orowan, <u>Rept. Phys. Soc. Progress In Physics</u>, 12, 185
      (1958).

183. P. E. Chen, <u>Proc. 5th Internat. Congr. Rheol.</u>, Vol. 1,
      S. Onogi, Ed., Univ. Tokyo, Tokyo, 1969, p. 531.

184. M. L. Williams, Internat. J. Fracture Mech., 1, 292 (1965).

185. M. L. Williams and F. N. Kelley, Proc. 5th Internat. Congr. Rheol., Vol. 3, S. Onogi, Ed., Univ. Tokyo, Tokyo, 1970, p. 185.

186. G. R. Irwin, J. Appl. Mech., 61, A49 (1939).

187. S. Mostovoy and E. J. Ripling, J. Appl. Polymer Sci., 10, 1351 (1966).

188. E. J. Ripling, S. Mostovoy, and H. T. Corten, J. Adhesion, 3, 107 (1971).

189. A. H. Cottrell, Dislocations and Plastic Flow in Crystals, Oxford Univ., Oxford, 1956.

190. R. Buchdahl, J. Polymer Sci., 28, 239 (1958).

191. N. Brown, Mater. Sci. Eng., 8, 65 (1971).

192. I. M. Ward, Mechanical Properties of Solid Polymers, Interscience, New York, 1971.

193. I. Marshall and A.B.Thompson, Proc. Royal Soc., A221, 541 (1954).

194. K. Jaeckel, Kolloid Zeit., 137, 130 (1954).

195. F. H. Mueller, Kolloid Zeit., 126, 65 (1952).

196. G. Binder and F. H. Mueller, Kolloid Zeit., 177, 129 (1961).

197. J. Skelton, W. D. Freeston, Jr., and M. M. Schoppee, J. Appl. Polymer Sci., 14, 2797 (1970).

198. P. I. Vincent, Polymer, 1, 7 (1960).

199. M. H. Litt and A. V. Tobolsky, J. Macromol. Sci., B1, 433 (1967).

200. M. H. Litt, P. J. Koch, and A. V. Tobolsky, J. Macromol. Sci. B1, 587 (1967).

201. K. C. Rusch and R. H. Beck, Jr., J. Macromol Sci., B3, 365 (1969).

202. A. N. Gent, J. Mater. Sci., 5, 925 (1970).

203. R. N. Haward, B. M. Murphy, and E. F. T. White, J. Polymer Sci., A2, 9, 801 (1971).

204. R. Natarajan and P. E. Reed, J. Polymer Sci., A2, 10, 585 (1972).

205. R. P. Kambour, Polymer, 5, 143 (1964).

206. R. P. Kambour, J. Polymer Sci., A2, 4159 (1964).

207. R. P. Kambour and A. S. Holik, J. Polymer Sci., A2, 7,
     1393 (1969).

208. S. N. Zhurkov, V. S. Kuksenko, and A. I. Slutsker,
     Fracture, 1969, P. L. Pratt, Ed., Chapman Hall, London,
     1969, p. 531.

209. V. S. Kuksenko, A. I. Slutsker, M. A. Gezalov, and
     A. F. Ioffe, IUPAC, 1970, Abst. Leiden Meeting, 1970, p. 985.

210. W. O. Statton, J. Polymer Sci., 58, 205 (1962).

211. D. G. LeGrand, R. P. Kambour, and W. R. Haaf,
     J. Polymer Sci., A2, 10, 1565 (1972).

212. J. A. Schmitt, J. Appl. Polymer Sci., 12, 533 (1968).

213. H. Eyring, J. Chem. Phys., 4, 283 (1936).

214. J. S. Lazurkin, J. Polymer Sci., 30, 595 (1958).

215. R. E. Robertson, J. Appl. Polymer Sci., 7, 443 (1963).

216. R. E. Robertson, J. Chem. Phys., 44, 3950 (1966).

217. C. Bauwens-Crowet, J-C. Bauwens, and G. Homes, J. Mater. Sci.,
     7, 176 (1972).

218. Yu. B. Zaks, M. L. Lebedinskaya, and V. N. Chalidze,
     Polymer Sci. USSR, (Engl. Transl.), 12, 3025 (1970).

219. S. N. Zhurkov, Internat. J. Fracture Mech., 1, 311 (1965).

220. B. A. Lloyd, K. L. DeVries, and M. L. Williams,
     J. Polymer Sci., A2, 10, 1415 (1972).

221. S. N. Zhurkov, V. A. Zakrevskyi, V. E. Korsukov, and
     V. S. Kuksenko, J. Polymer Sci., A2, 10, 1509 (1972).

222. D. Campbell and A. Peterlin, J. Polymer Sci., B6, 481 (1968).

223. A. Peterlin, J. Polymer Sci., C32, 297 (1971).

224. K. L. DeVries, D. K. Roylance, and M. L. Williams,
     J. Polymer Sci., A1, 8, 237 (1970).

225. K. L. DeVries, D. K. Roylance, and M. L. Williams,
     Internat. J. Fracture Mech., 7, 197 (1971).

226. L. T. Berezhnitskiy and A. P. Datsyshin, Prikladnaya
     Mekhanika, 4, 112 (1968); Engl. transl. in U.S.Dept.
     Commerce Rept. AD 688072

227. S. Newman and S. Strella, J. Appl. Polymer Sci., 9, 2297
     (1965).

228. S. Strella, Appl. Polymer Sympos., 7, 165 (1968).

229. J. D. Ferry and R. A. Stratton, Kolloid Zeit., 171, 107 (1960).

230. R. H. Edwards, J. Appl. Mech., 18, A19 (1951).

231. M. A. Sadowsky and E. Sternberg, J. Appl. Mech., 14, A191 (1947).

232. ASTM D256, Annual ASTM Standards, Part 27, Amer. Soc. Testing Mater., Philadelphia.

233. D. R. Morey, Ind. Eng. Chem., 37, 255 (1945).

234. H. Burns, Encyclopedia of Polymer Science and Technology, Vol. 7, Interscience, New York, 1967, p. 584.

235. P. I. Vincent, Impact Tests and Service Performance of Thermoplastics, Plastics Inst., London, 1971.

236. ASTM D1709, Annual ASTM Standards, Part 26, Amer. Soc. Testing Mater., Philadelphia.

237. G. Lubin and R. R. Winans, ASTM Bull., No. 128, 13 (1944).

238. K. Fujioka, J. Appl. Polymer Sci., 13, 1421 (1969).

239. ASTM D1822 and D2289, Annual ASTM Standards, Part 27, Amer. Soc. Testing Mater., Philadelphia.

240. S. Strella, High Speed Testing, Vol. 1, A. G. H. Dietz and F. R. Eirich, Ed., Interscience, New York, 1960.

241. P. I. Vincent, Plastics, 27, 133 (May 1962).

242. L. A. Cohen, Testing of Polymers, Vol. 3, J. V. Schmitz and W. E. Brown, Ed., Interscience, New York, 1967, p. 15.

243. W. E. Wolstenholme, S. E. Pregun, and C. F. Stark, J. Appl. Polymer Sci., 8, 119 (1964).

244. Modern Plastics Encyclopedia, McGraw-Hill, New York, 1971.

245. P. I. Vincent, Plastics, 27, 116 (Apr. 1962).

246. D. Telfair and H. K. Nason, Modern Plast., 22, 145 (Apr. 1945).

247. L. Bohn and H. Oberst, Acustica, 9, 191 (1959).

248. H. Oberst, Kunststoffe, 52, 4 (1962).

249. T. T. Jones, J. Polymer Sci., C16, 3845 (1968).

250. C. B. Bucknall, J. Mater., 4, 214 (1969).

251. M. Matsuo, A. Ueda, and Y. Kondo, Polymer Eng. Sci., 10, 253 (1970).

252. H-W. Otto, Kunststoffe, 55, 170 (1965).

253. R. F. Boyer, Polymer Eng. Sci., 8, 161 (1968).

254. J. Bussink and J. Heijboer, Physics of Non-Crystalline Solids, J. A. Prins, Ed., Interscience, New York, 1965, p. 388.

255. J. Heijboer, J. Polymer Sci., C16, 3755 (1968).

256. Y. Wada and T. Kasahara, J. Appl. Polymer Sci., 11, 1661 (1967).

257. G. C. Karas and B. Warburton, Trans. Plast. Inst., 30, 198 (1962).

258. S. G. Turley, J. Polymer Sci., C1, 101 (1963).

259. E. R. Wagner and L. M. Robeson, Rubber Chem. Techn., 43, 1129 (1970).

260. H. Keskkula, S. G. Turley, and R. F. Boyer, J. Appl. Polymer Sci., 15, 351 (1971).

261. C. H. Adams, G. B. Jackson, and R. A. McCarthy, SPE J., 12 13 (Mar. 1956).

262. H. Hoegberg, ASTM, Spec. Tech. Publ., No. 247, Amer. Soc. Testing Mater., Philadelphia, 1958, p. 95.

263. H. Keskkula and J. W. Norton, Jr., J. Appl. Polymer Sci., 2, 289 (1959).

264. G. Hulse, Physical Properties of Polymers, Soc. Chem. Ind. Monograph No. 5, MacMillan, New York, 1959, p. 157.

265. S. M. Ohlberg, J. Roth, and R. A. V. Raff, J. Appl. Polymer Sci., 1, 114 (1959).

266. L. Bohn, Kunststoffe, 53, 826 (1963).

267. R. A. Horsley, Plastics Progress, 1957, P. Morgan, Ed., Iliffe, London, 1958, p. 77.

268. O. W. Lundstedt and E. M. Bevilacqua, J. Polymer Sci., 24, 297 (1957).

269. R. N. Haward and J. Mann, Proc. Royal Soc., 282A, 120 (1964).

270. B. W. Bender, J. Appl. Polymer Sci., 9, 2887 (1965).

271. M. Baer, J. Appl. Polymer Sci., 16, 1109, 1125 (1972).

272. G. Cigna, J. Appl. Polymer Sci., 14, 1781 (1970).

273. P. Kainradl and F. Handler, Rubber Chem. Techn., 33, 1438 (1960).

274. N. A. Brunt, Kolloid Zeit., 239, 561 (1970).

275. R. F. Landel and R. F. Fedors, Fracture Processes in

Polymeric Solids, B. Rosen, Ed., Interscience, New York, 1964, p. 361.

276. R. S. Rivlin and A. G. Thomas, J. Polymer Sci., 10, 291 (1952).

277. A. G. Thomas, J. Appl. Polymer Sci., 3, 168 (1960).

278. H. W. Greensmith, J. Appl. Polymer Sci., 3, 183 (1960).

279. H. W. Greensmith, L. Mullins, and A. G. Thomas, Trans. Soc. Rheol., 4, 179 (1960).

280. G. J. Lake and A. G. Thomas, Proc. Royal Soc., 300A, 108 (1967).

281. A. N. Gent, P. B. Lindley, and A. G. Thomas, J. Appl. Polymer Sci., 8, 455 (1964).

282. L. Mullins, Trans. Inst. Rubber Ind., 35, 213 (1960).

Chapter 6

Other Mechanical Properties

I. Heat Distortion Temperature

The heat distortion temperature (HDT), the softening
temperature, or the deflection temperature under load (DTUL)
denote the maximum temperature at which a polymer can be used
as a rigid material. The heat distortion temperature also may be
considered as the upper temperature limit at which the material
can support a load for any appreciable time. Thus, the HDT or
DTUL is a very practical and important property of a polymer.
For amorphous polymers the HDT is near the glass transition
temperature, while for highly crystalline polymers, the HDT is
closer to the melting point. Most HDTs or softening temperatures
are arbitrarily defined as a single point in some kind of a
deflection-temperature curve. Much useful information is thrown
away, however, if the entire curve is not retained. Only in
Russia, where they are called thermomechanical tests, is the
entire deflection-temperature curve generally used (1-6).

Most heat distortion or softening temperature tests fall into
one of three catagories: In the first a tensile load is applied
to the specimen and its length is measured in the same manner as
in a creep test except that the temperature is increased at a
constant rate. A typical test is the ASTM tensile heat distortion
temperature test for plastic sheeting (D1637)(7). In this test a

load of 50 psi is applied to a strip, and the temperature is

increased at a rate of 2°C/minute. The HDT temperature in this

case is defined as the temperature at which the elongation

becomes 2 percent. If the sheet is oriented, it may shrink

before it starts to elongate at a rapid rate. Typical curves

obtained with a HDT test of this sort are shown in Figure 1 (8).

In such figures, the slope of the first part of the curves is

proportional to the linear coefficient of thermal expansion

except at very high loads. The break in the curve occurs near

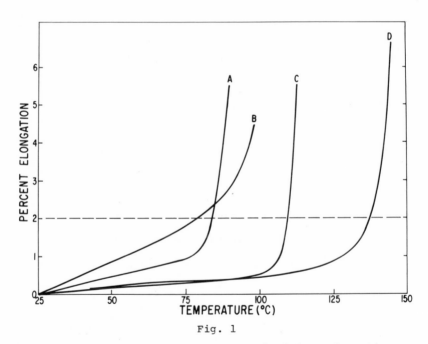

Fig. 1

Heat distortion temperatures as determined from elongation-
temperature curves. The rate of temperature rise was 2°C/min.
A. Rigid polyvinyl chloride (Load = 50 psi);   B. Low density
polyethylene (Load = 50 psi);   C. Styrene-acrylonitrile
copolymer (Load = 25 psi);   D. Plasticized cellulose acetate
(Load = 25 psi). HDT defined as temperature at which
elongation becomes 2%.

T_g for amorphous polymers, and the steep part of the curve results from viscous or viscoelastic flow which accompanies the drop in modulus (9-15).

Annealing polystyrene and other polymers raises the HDT, as shown in Figure 2 (15-17). The closer the annealing temperature is to T_g the less the time required to increase the HDT a given amount. This effect is due mostly to the reduction in free volume, but part of the effect also may be the result of relaxing of frozen-in stresses. Similar effects are found with crystalline polymers in which annealing increases the degree

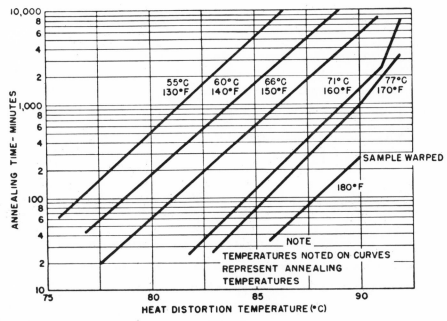

Fig. 2

The HDT as a function of annealing time and temperature for injection molded bars of polystyrene. [Reprinted from Cleereman, Karam, and Williams, ASTM Bull. No. 180, 37 (Feb. 1952).]

of crystallinity, changes the crystallite morphology, or relieves
built-in stresses in the amorphous phase. Likewise, in thermoset
resins, increasing the curing time often brings about increases
in the degree of crosslinking, T_g, and the heat distortion
temperature (18).

An increase in applied stress causes a decrease in HDT (14,16)
The major cause of this effect is the decrease in modulus with
temperature with the consequent greater deformation at the higher
temperature for a given load. By definition, the HDT occurs at
about a constant deformation. This deformation is proportional
to the load and inversely proportional to the modulus. In the
tensile HDT test, part of the deformation also results from
thermal expansion. Figure 3 schematically illustrates how the
HDT as a function of stress depends upon the modulus-temperature
curve (14). In Figure 3, T_1 and T_2 are the heat distortion
temperatures at applied stresses of σ_1 and σ_2, respectively. The
total deformation of the specimen is the same for all stresses at
the HDT. An approximate equation which implicitly relates the
HDT to the applied stress σ_0 is

$$\left(\varepsilon_{HDT} - \varepsilon_T\right) \doteq K = \sigma_0\left(\frac{1}{E} - \frac{1}{E°}\right) \tag{1}$$

where ε_{HDT} is the strain arbitrarily taken at the HDT (generally
1 or 2 percent), ε_T is the strain resulting from thermal expansion,
E is Young's modulus of the polymer at the HDT corresponding to
the stress σ_0, and $E°$ is the modulus at room temperature. The
last term involving $E°$ is generally very small for glassy polymers.
If the HDT is defined in terms of 1 percent elongation, $K \simeq 0.005$,
but if the elongation is 2 percent, $K \simeq 0.015$. The HDT is

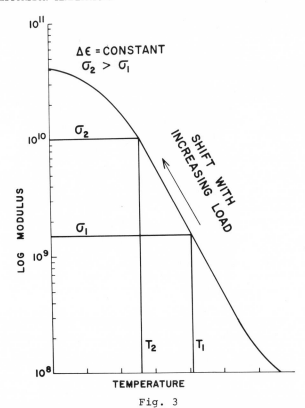

Fig. 3

Schematic modulus-temperature curve illustrating how the
heat distortion temperature decreases as the applied load
increases. T_1 is the HDT corresponding to a stress σ_1.
[Reprinted from Nielsen, Trans. Soc. Rheol., 9, 243 (1965).]

---

estimated from equation 1 by noting the temperature at which the

modulus of the polymer is E. Figure 4 shows HDT as a function of

load for several plastics (14).

A test similar to the above tensile HDT is the ASTM D648

deflection temperature under load test (7). In this test a bar

5 inches long, 1/2 inch thick, and 1/8 to 1/2 inch in width is

bent in flexure by supporting the beam at its ends and applying

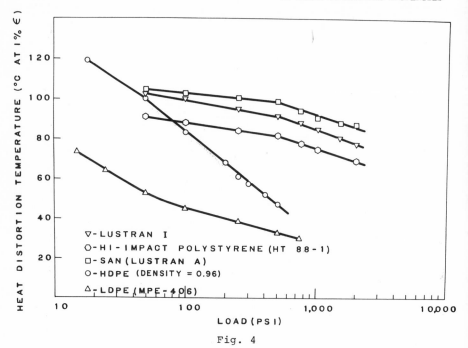

Fig. 4

Heat distortion temperature as a function of tensile load for several plastics. Lustran I is an ABS polymer. SAN is a styrene-acrylonitrile copolymer. HDPE and LDPE are high density and low density polyethylenes, respectively. Heating rate = 2°C/min. [Reprinted from Nielsen, Trans. Soc. Rheol., 9, 243 (1965).]

a load in the center. The heating rate is two degrees per minute. The HDT is defined as the temperature at which the deflection of the center reaches 0.010 inches under an applied load of either 66 or 264 psi. The load of 264 psi is generally used for rigid polymers such as polystyrene while the load of 66 psi is used for softer crystalline materials, such as polyethylenes, which have glass transition temperatures below room temperature.

A second type of HDT is defined from the shear modulus versus temperature curve such as already illustrated in previous

chapters. The shear modulus can be determined from a dynamic
test, but more generally either a Clash-Berg (19) or a Gehman (20)
torsion tester is used as described by ASTM D1043 or D1053 tests (7).
Many such shear modulus versus temperature curves have been
published (21-27). In these tests the modulus is calculated from
the angle of twist in the specimen 5 or 10 seconds after the
torque is applied. Various softening temperatures have been
defined in terms of the shear modulus-temperature curve. The
flex temperature T_F is defined as the temperature at which the
shear modulus is 45,000 psi. The T_4 temperature is defined as the
temperature at which the modulus is 10^4 psi; this temperature is
near the inflection temperature in the log G versus temperature
curve. The flex temperature can be correlated with the ASTM D648
HDT (27). The HDT at 264 psi corresponds closely to the
temperature at which the shear modulus is 10^5 psi, and the HDT at
66 psi occurs at about the temperature where the shear modulus
is 3×10^4 psi.

The third type of HDT or softening temperature test is a
penetration test (27, 27a). Typical of this type of test is the
Vicat softening temperature as described by the ASTM D1525
test (7). In this test a flat ended needle of 1 mm^2 circular
cross section is pressed into a thick sheet of the polymer with
a load of 1000g. The polymer is heated at a rate of either 50 or
120°C per hour. The Vicat softening temperature is the
temperature at which the needle has penetrated the polymer to a
depth of 1 mm. The penetration is associated primarily with the
decrease in modulus, or for low molecular weight amorphous
uncrosslinked materials, the penetration is due to viscous flow
above T_g. A material must be very soft for the Vicat needle to

penetrate a polymer to a depth of 1 mm. For this reason, the
Vicat softening temperature is higher than most of the other
HDT tests.

II. Fatigue

Up to this point, fracture or failure of a material has been
associated with stress-strain tests or with creep rupture. Fatigue
however, is material failure or degradation of mechanical
properties due to oscillatory deformations or stresses. Fatigue
life is defined as the number of cycles of oscillation N before a
specimen fractures at a given applied stress or strain. Since
fatigue life is a function of the maximum stress, fatigue curves
are generally given as the stress versus the number of cycles
to bring about failure at that stress.

There are many kinds of fatigue testers (28-30). These
include tensile or flexural tests at constant deformation or
constant stress, and rotating beam instruments. Some instruments
superimpose the oscillations on a static stress or deformation.
In the Prot (31-33) test, the stress is increased at a constant
rate rather than being held constant. The advantage of the Prot
test is that much testing time can be saved by having failure take
place in a shorter number of cycles. Constant deformation
testers have two disadvantages compared to constant stress
testers. First, if a large crack develops in the material, the
stress decreases in some types of testers so that the test can
continue for some time before complete failure occurs. Second,
a constant deformation puts a smaller stress on a low modulus
material than on a high modulus material; this gives an advantage
to the low modulus materials. Fold tests (34) are another type

of fatigue test which is important for sheets or for thin sections used as hinges in many molded objects. A material used as a hinge must be capable of being flexed many times.

As plastics replace metals and other materials in many critical structural applications, fatigue tests become more important since the maximum oscillatory load that a material can sustain is only a fraction of its tensile strength. Thus, the more conventional tests give little indication of the lifetime of an object subjected to vibrations or repeated deformations. Fatigue tests are especially important for the so-called engineering plastics and composite materials which are used in load-bearing structures subjected to varying loads.

Figure 5 shows a typical fatigue life curve. When the stress is high, the specimen breaks after a few cycles. The fatigue life, expressed as the number of cycles before failure occurs, increases as the maximum stress per cycle decreases. Below some value of maximum stress, called the fatigue or endurance limit, the fatigue curve levels off, and the material can be subjected to an infinite or very large number of cycles without failure. The material may be deformed many millions of times at stresses below the endurance limit. It is important to remember that each fatigue life curve holds only for a given type of fatigue test at a given temperature and at a fixed number of cycles per second. Fatigue life generally decreases as the frequency of the oscillations increases. The effect is small at low frequencies, but the decrease in fatigue life with an increase in frequency can be great if there is an increase in the temperature of the specimen due to its damping (35). Fatigue life decreases as the temperature increases. The fatigue life often

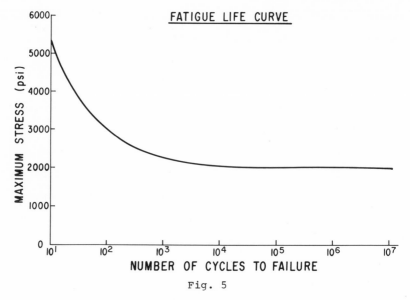

Fig. 5

Fatigue life, as defined by the number of cycles before
failure occurs, versus maximum stress applied during a
cycle.

———————————

is given by (28):

$$Log\ N = A + B/T \qquad\qquad (2)$$

where N is the fatigue life in number of cycles, A and B are

constants, and T is the absolute temperature. The fatigue life

of polymethylmethacrylate decreased 58 percent when the

temperature was raised from -30°F to 80°F (36). The decrease in

fatigue life was 25 percent for the same temperature increase

for a fabric laminated phenolic material. The temperature of

the specimen may be considerably higher than the ambient

temperature because of the damping. The energy dissipated per

second in the specimen is proportional to the loss modulus E",

the frequency, and the square of the maximum deformation or

stress. The fatigue limit for most polymers is only 20 to 40
percent of the static tensile strength. In one type of
reinforced plastic the fatigue limit as measured by a Prot test
correlated with about 40 percent of the tensile strength (32).

Fatigue failure is generally due to the progressive growth
of cracks (29, 37-42). Materials always contain flaws which
develop into submicroscopic cracks if the stress is above some
critical value. The microscopic cracks grow a small amount during
the peak load of each cycle. Eventually one or more of the
cracks grows until it is no longer microscopic in size; at this
point it may propagate rapidly and cause failure. This crack
growth or tearing process occurs in both rigid polymers and
rubbers. The fatigue properties appear to be related to the
tearing energy of the material (37,38). Some materials are
inherently more resistant to tearing than others; in these tear
resistant materials it is more difficult to propogate cracks.

A second important factor in determining fatigue life of
polymers is related to their mechanical damping and the resulting
heat build-up in the material (41-46). The strength of polymers
generally decreases with temperature, and crack growth becomes⁻
easier, so the fatigue life decreases as the temperature builds
up. Below T_g, E" and E"/E' increase with temperature. Thus,
a small temperature increase can make the situation worse so
that the temperature increases at an even faster rate until
failure occurs. If the material doesn't fail by crack growth,
it softens so much that it fails because of its low stiffness.
Below a critical rate of energy dissipation resulting from
damping, an equilibrium temperature is reached in which the heat
is lost by radiation and conduction as fast as it is produced

so that fatiguing does not occur or is not apparent. However, above the critical rate of heat production in the specimen, the temperature continues to rise until failure occurs.

Very little is known about the chemical and structural factors affecting fatigue life. Some of the factors affecting mechanical damping were discussed in Chapter 4. However, practically nothing is known about how the chemical and molecular structure of a polymer affect the ease of crack formation and propogation. The formation of cracks as related to imperfections and flaws in a material was discussed briefly in Chapter 5. Factors which increase the strength of a polymer also tend to increase fatigue life. Thus, increasing molecular weight increases fatigue life up to a limiting molecular weight (47-48). Fatigue life is increased by factors which decrease crazing such as orientation of the molecules parallel to the applied stress (49). Orientation appears to be important in the molding of polypropylene hinges which can take many flexures before failing. Since fatigue is largely due to the growth of cracks, notches or scratches on a specimen can cause a great reduction in fatigue life, especially for notch-sensitive materials. In fibers and crosslinked rubbers, fatigue may result from actual fracture of polymer chains and the generation of free radicals.

The literature on the fatigue life of common plastics is not extensive. Studies include fatigue of polystyrene polymers (32,33), polyvinyl chloride (41,50), polyethylene (29), polymethyl-methacrylate (29,33,38,41), nylons (29,40,41,46), rubbers (37,43), polytetrafluoroethylene (45), polycarbonate (41), and crosslinked epoxies (35,42). Much of the experimental work, along with the theory of fatigue, has been reviewed by Andrews (39) and Hearle (49)

III. Friction

The frictional behavior of polymers is important in many
practical situations involving abrasion, wear, and scratching of
polymers. It is desirable to have high friction of a tire against
a road surface or of a shoe sole against many surfaces, including
plastic floor tile. Low friction is wanted in plastic bearings
or for plastic coated skiis against snow. Friction also plays a
role in the first section of extruders where granulated polymers
must be moved into the section where the polymers become molten.

Friction is a measure of the force resisting the motion of
one surface against another surface. The coefficient of friction
μ is defined by

$$\mu = F/W \hspace{3cm} (3)$$

where F is the tangential force required to produce motion at
the interface between two surfaces when they are pressed together
by a normal load W. Friction can be divided into three classes –
static, dynamic, and rolling. These different classes of friction
generally have different values. The coefficients of friction
depend upon many factors such as temperature, velocity of sliding,
load, nature of the surfaces (smooth or rough), area of the
surfaces, presence or absence of lubricants, and the type of
measuring apparatus.

The frictional behavior of polymers has been reviewed by
Bowden and Tabor (51). The friction of rubbers has been reviewed
by Conant and Liska (52), and by Schallamach (53,54). The
frictional behavior of polymer bearings has been reviewed by
Glaeser (55) and by Pinchbeck (56).

Friction can be measured by a great variety of instruments

from a simple inclined plane to complex apparatus measuring the
force to drag a rounded stylus across a smooth surface or the
force required to roll a ball or wheel across a surface (57-65).
Unfortunately, because of the complexity of friction phenomena,
the data from one type of apparatus often do not agree with the
data obtained with another instrument.

Molecular adhesion is an important factor in friction. For
this reason, nonpolar polymers tend to have lower coefficients
of friction than polar polymers against metals. The relative
hardness of the two materials in contact is another factor in
friction. The total frictional force is made up of several factors
which include: 1. The shearing of junction points where the two
surfaces are in intimate contact. This force results from
adhesive forces and the interaction of asperities on the surfaces.
2. A ploughing process in which the harder material displaces the
softer material at points of contact to produce a scratch.
3. Mechanical damping or internal friction. The mechanical damping
is a major factor in rolling friction such as experienced by
automobile tires. If polymers were perfectly elastic with no
damping, a rigid ball or wheel should have no friction when
rolling over a smooth surface. As a ball or wheel rolls, it
depresses the polymer in front of it, but the polymer behind the
ball immediately snaps back and pushes the ball from the rear.
If the polymer has mechanical damping, part of the energy in
deforming the polymer is dissipated as heat, leaving less elastic
energy available for pushing on the back side of the rolling
object. Thus, rolling friction should correlate with damping,
and the variables which change the damping should affect the

coefficient of rolling friction in the same manner (58,60,65-74).
The equation relating the coefficient of rolling friction μ_r to
damping was derived by Flom (58,68). A corrected equation has
been proposed by Gent and Henry (73):

$$\mu_r = K\frac{E''}{E'}\left(\frac{W}{E'R^2}\right)^{1/3} \tag{4}$$

where W is the load on the ball of radius R, E' and E"/E' are the
dynamic mechanical properties, and K is a constant which varies
slightly with Poisson's ratio but has a value of about 0.48. A
similar equation has been derived for rolling wheels (65).

Because of the close relationship between the dynamic
mechanical properties and the coefficient of friction (at least
for the rolling coefficient part), the temperature and velocity
variation of friction should follow a time-temperature superposition principle. In some cases, it has been found that
friction data obtained at different temperatures and velocities
can be superimposed by the W-L-F equation (60,71,75). The
master curve for the coefficient of friction goes through a
maximum when plotted against reduced velocity. Schallamach (71)
and Grosch (60) report that the maximum correlates with the loss
modulus E" on a smooth surface, but the maximum correlates with
E"/E' on a rough surface. In general, the maximum in coefficient
of friction correlates, as expected, with T_g. Low temperature
friction maxima may correlate with secondary transitions in the
glassy state (72). Other friction peaks may not correlate with
glass transitions but are due to changes in molecular adhesion (60).

With crystalline polymers, the coefficient of friction is affected by spherulite size and by crystallite morphology (74,76). Friction increases with spherulite size in polypropylene, and the friction is greater at the center of a spherulite than at its boundary.

Figures 6 and 7 illustrate the typical changes in the coefficient of friction as a function of the variables velocity of sliding, temperature, and load. The coefficient of friction generally decreases slowly with load (51,59,63,77-79). However, the coefficient of friction may increase with load if the mechanism of friction changes, say from typical sliding to ploughing, or if the type of friction is rolling friction (58,65, 68,73,80).

If one of the surfaces is a smooth sheet and the other surface is a stylus, the coefficient of friction may depend

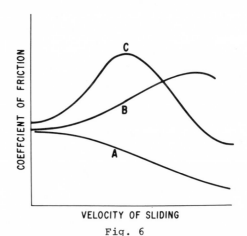

VELOCITY OF SLIDING

Fig. 6

Coefficient of friction as a function of velocity of sliding (logarithmic scale). A. Rubber, B. Glass transition region, C. Rigid or glassy polymer.

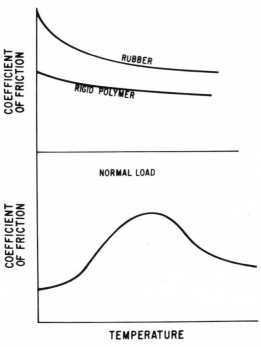

Fig. 7

Coefficient of friction as a function of normal load and as
a function of temperature.

———————————

upon which material is in the stylus (81). A hard stylus

tends to plough into the softer sheet and give a higher friction.

Other material factors also affect the friction. For instance,

the coefficient of friction tends to increase as the compliance

increases (79,82). The coefficient also increases with

plasticizer concentration in polyvinyl chloride (64). This

plasticizer effect may be due to the increase in compliance as

the concentration of plasticizer increases.

Table 1 lists the coefficient of friction for some common

polymers. The list is compiled from various sources using

Table 1

Coefficients of Friction of Polymers

Polymer	Metal Against Polymer	Polymer Against Metal
Polytetrafluoroethylene	.04 - .15	0.04
Polyethylene (low density)	.30 - 0.8	.1 - .6
Polyethylene (high density)	.2	
Polypropylene	.67	
Polystyrene	.33 - .5	
Polystyrene polyblend	.38	
Polymethyl methacrylate	.25 - .5	.4
Polyethylene terephthalate	.2 - .3	
Nylon 66	.15 - .4	low
Nylon 6	.39	
Polyvinyl chloride	.2 - .9	.4 - .6
Polyvinylidene chloride	.68 - 1.8	.8 - 2.0
Polyvinyl fluoride		.1 - .3
Polycarbonate	.25	
Phenol-formaldehyde	.6	
Rubber	.3 - 2.5	
Rubber (near T_g)	~ 4	
Cellulose acetate	.55	
Polyacrylonitrile	.40	

different techniques, so the values are often not directly
comparable. The low values for polytetrafluoroethylene and nylon
make these materials suitable for bearings.

IV. Abrasion, Wear, and Scratch Resistance

Gavan (83) defines wear as the unwanted progressive loss of
substance from the surface of a body brought about by a mechanical
action from the rubbing of one surface against another.
Abrasion, wear, and scratch resistance are all similar and are
closely related to friction. The ploughing component of frictional
force is especially important in abrasion and in the process of
scratching a surface. In abrasion and scratching processes,
the relative hardness of the two materials is important since the
harder material tends to plough grooves or make scratches in the
softer material. The ploughing component of the frictional force
is quite similar on a microscopic scale to tearing. When an
elastomer moves over a surface, as an automobile tire does,
large deformations can occur where the asperities of the hard
surface contact the elastomer. If these localized deformations
are great enough, the elastomer tears and small pieces are
broken off. Shallamach (53,84) has developed a theory of rubber
abrasion or wear based upon these concepts.

In the abrasion process, high temperatures may be produced
in localized areas where the asperities of one surface contact
the other material and produce large localized stresses and
strains. At these hot points, chemical reactions, such as
oxidation, can occur which speed up the rate of abrasion or
wear (83,85). Such a process can be considered as corrosion wear
in contrast to purely mechanical wear.

Most of the work on abrasion and wear has been done on
flooring, automobile tires, and other rubber goods. Many kinds
of test instruments have been developed for rubbers and other
materials (83, 86-88). Common abrasion machines include:

Taber abraser (ASTM D1044) (7), Armstrong abrader (89), Olsen
Wear-Ometer (ASTM D1242)(7,90), NBS abrader (ASTM D1630)(7),
DuPont-Grasselli abrader (ASTM D394)(7), and the Gardner wear
tester. Most of the abrasion instruments rotate the specimen
against a sandpaper or other abrasive surface. In some
instruments, such as the Armstrong abrader, a clean sandpaper
surface is always in contact with the polymer. In other
instruments the same abrasive surface is used continuously,
so the abrasive surface may wear away or gradually become filled
with polymer particles. Wear or abrasion is measured by the
loss in weight or thickness of the specimen or by change in
optical appearance. The various kinds of instruments very often
rank materials in entirely different order. An extreme example
is shown in Table 2 where the performance of a series of floor
coverings was evaluated by three different methods (83). In
another study, seven different flooring materials were tested
on 21 kinds of abrasion machines (91). The data from the

Table 2

Comparison of Three Abrasion Machines

Material	Loss (cm^3)		
	Olsen Wear-Ometer	Armstrong Abrader	Taber Abrader
Linoleum	0.89	1.29	0.51
Rubber tile	0.87	1.51	0.68
Vinyl asbestos tile	3.25	0.94	0.11
Cork tile	1.81	2.15	0.19

different machines did not agree with one another, and the
correlation with actual wear tests was poor. Thus, caution is
required in using the data from abrasion testers to predict
actual performance behavior.

Since abrasion involves the tearing away of small pieces of
material, the tensile strength of the polymer, its fatigue life,
its hardness, and its tear strength probably are important
factors in determining the wear characteristics of a polymer.
The factors involved in the tearing of rubbers have been
discussed by Gent, Lindley, and Thomas (92) and by Brunt (93).
High tensile strengths and high tearing energies should reduce
the rate of abrasion (86,94,95). Lewis (95) predicts that the
amount of abrasion is given by

$$\text{Abrasion loss} \doteq KWvt \qquad (5)$$

where K is a constant which depends upon the properties of the
polymer, W is the normal load per unit area that presses the
polymer to the abrasive surface, v is the velocity of sliding,
and t is the duration of the rubbing time. Juve and Veith (94)
and Zapp (96) give an equation of the following form for wear
or abrasion loss:

$$\text{Abrasion loss} \doteq \frac{KE'Ft}{U_t} = \frac{KE'\mu Wt}{U_t} . \qquad (6)$$

In this equation, U_t is the tearing energy or the area under the
stress-strain curve, F is the tangential friction force causing
the wear, μ is the coefficient of friction, W is the normal load
pressing the polymer to the abrasive surface, E' is the dynamic
Young's modulus, K is a constant, and t is the duration of the
test. Long fatigue life should inversely correlate with the
amount of abrasion since the polymer undergoes high localized

deformations during abrasion testing (86,92,97). The abrasion of
rough surfaces can be different from that of smooth surfaces (98).

Table 3 lists Marcucci's (99) abrasion data for a number of
plastics. Possibly another type of abrader would rank these
materials in a different order.

Another type of abrasion is the scratching of polymers. It
is desirable to have as high a scratch resistance as possible,
especially on transparent plastics, as scratches ruin the trans-
parency and optical appearance. Compared to glass, the scratch
resistance of most polymers is very poor. However, poor scratch
resistance does not necessarily imply poor abrasion or wear
behavior in terms of weight loss. Polyethylene, because of its
low hardness, is easily scratched, but it has very low abrasion
loss by some tests. The very hard melamine resins and some phenol-
formaldehyde resins have very good scratch resistance; therefore,
their laminates are often used in such applications as table and

Table 3

Relative Wear of Plastics

Plastic	Abrasion Loss (grams)
General purpose phenolic	0.057
Nylon 6	.015
Polytetrafluoroethylene	.159
Polystyrene polyblend	.64
High density polyethylene	.0016
Nylon 66	.025

counter tops. The softer polymers such as polyethylene have
poor scratch resistance. The Bierbaum scratch hardness of some
plastics are shown in Table 4 (100). High values indicate a
high resistance to scratching. Table 5 lists the scratch
resistance as measured by Bernhardt (101) by another method.   In
general, if the coefficient of friction of a polymer is high, its
scratch resistance is poor (101). The wear of plastics such as
nylon can be decreased by filling the plastic with a solid
lubricant such as molybdenum disulfide or graphite. The scratch
resistance of polymers and the instruments to measure it have been
reviewed by Gouza (87), Wiinikainen (88) and Bernhardt (101).

V. Hardness and Indentation Tests

Although most people believe they have an intuitive feeling

Table 4

Bierbaum Scratch Hardness

Polymer	Scratch Hardness
Vinylidene chloride	8.7
Cellulose nitrate	9.8
Polyvinyl chloride	10.1
Polystyrene	10.3
Nylon 66	11.1
Cellulose acetate	11.3
Unsaturated polyester	13.5
Polymethyl methacrylate	17.5
Phenolic (mineral filled)	21.2
Melamine resin	32.4

Table 5

Scratch Resistance of Polymers

Polymer	Scratch Resistance
Polyethylene	.0014
Polyvinyl chloride	.015
Celluloid	.015
Cellulose nitrate	.015
Nylon	.016
Polymethyl methacrylate	.046
Phenolic laminate	.063

for the hardness of materials, there are different kinds of
hardness which measure a number of complex properties.
Gouza (87) classifies hardness tests into three categories:
1. Hardness tests that measure the resistance of a material to
indentation by an indenter. Examples include Brinell hardness,
Vickers and Knoop indenters, Barcol hardness, and Shore
durometers (102). Some tests measure the indentation with the
load applied, and some measure the residual indentation after
the load is removed. 2. Hardness tests that measure the
resistance of a material to scratching by another material or by
a sharp point. Examples are the Bierbaum hardness or scratch
resistance test and the Moh hardness. 3. Hardness tests which
measure rebound efficiency or resilience. Examples of this
type of test are the various Rockwell hardness tests as described
by the standard ASTM test D785. Many of the hardness tests,
including the Rockwell tests, are a combination of classes 1 and 3.

Tests which measure the penetration of a material by a loaded indenter are really measuring a Young's modulus in the case of elastic materials. Hertz worked out the theory of the penetration of a loaded sphere into a softer elastic material. This theory has been reviewed by Timoshenko (103) and others (104). The depth of penetration h of the spherical indenter into the flat surface of the plastic or other material is:

$$h = \left[\frac{3}{4} \left(\frac{1 - \nu_1^2}{E_1} + \frac{1 - \nu_2^2}{E_2} \right) \right]^{2/3} F^{2/3} R^{-1/3} . \tag{7}$$

The Young's modulus of the sphere is E_1 and that of the flat specimen is E_2. Poisson's ratio of the sphere and the flat surface is ν_1 and ν_2, respectively. The total force or load on the sphere of radius R is F. If the modulus of the sphere is very much greater than that of the polymer or other material in the flat specimen, then the Young's modulus of the material making up the specimen is:

$$E_2 \doteq \frac{3 \left(1 - \nu_2^2 \right) F}{4 h^{3/2} R^{1/2}} . \tag{8}$$

When a sphere is pressed into a flat surface, the radius r of the circle of contact is

$$r = \left[\frac{3}{4} \left(\frac{1 - \nu_1^2}{E_1} + \frac{1 - \nu_2^2}{E_2} \right) \right]^{1/3} F^{1/3} R^{1/3} \tag{9}$$

The pressure P_m at the center of the contact area is

$$P_m = \frac{3F}{2 \pi r^2} . \tag{10}$$

This pressure, which is a maximum at the center of the contact area, is 1.5 times the average pressure over the entire area of contact. The maximum tensile stress σ_t, which is in the radial direction, occurs in the flat specimen at the edge of the circle of contact. This stress is:

$$\sigma_t = \frac{(1 - 2\nu_2)F}{2\pi r^2} \quad . \tag{11}$$

The Hertz equations assume that the thickness of the sheet is much greater than the diameter of the spherical indentor. The penetration is less for thin sheets and only becomes constant when the thickness of the sheet is at least five times the radius of the circle of contact (105). Other studies on the effect of the thickness of the plastic or rubber flat surface include those of Chapoy and Aklonis (106) and Taylor and Kragh (107). For soft sheets or layers on hard surfaces, Taylor and Kragh found the following empirical equation to hold for the shear modulus G:

$$G = \frac{0.36 \ Fg}{R^2} \left(\frac{D - h}{h}\right)^{3/2} \tag{12}$$

In this equation D is the thickness of the sheet or coating, g is the acceleration of gravity, and F is the load on the spherical indentor. The ASTM D1415 hardness test for rubbers is based upon the empirical equation of Scott (108):

$$F = 0.00017E_2R^{0.65} h^{1.35} \tag{13}$$

where F is the indenting force in kilograms, E_2 is in kg/cm^2, R is in cm, and h is in hundredths of millimeters. The exponents on R and h in this empirical equation are not quite the same as those predicted by the Hertz equation.

Equations have been developed for the calculation of elastic moduli from the penetration of indentors with shapes other than spheres such as flat-ended cylinders (109) and cones or wedges (110). The depth of penetration depends upon whether or not the sheet and indentor are lubricated so that slippage can occur at the interface (105,109).

ASTM hardness tests include D785 (Rockwell hardness), D1415 (International standard for rubber hardness), D2240 (Durometer hardness of elastomers), and E92 (Vickers hardness of metals) (7). The Rockwell alpha scale hardness test measures the depth of penetration with the load applied. However, the Rockwell R, L, M, and E scales measure the depth of penetration caused by a spherical indentor after most of the load has been removed. Thus, the amount of rebound or the recoverable deformation is important in these hardness tests. As a function of temperature, the Rockwell R, L, M, and E scales give a curve with a pronounced minimum near T_g (111,112). The hardness-temperature curves by these tests are very similar to a resilience (or inverse damping) curve as a function of temperature. In the Vickers microhardness test a microscope is used to measure the diagonals of the pits left by a diamond-shaped indentor (104,113).

Table 6 lists hardness data on several polymers as determined by several types of tests (100,113-115). The different tests do not rank all the polymers in the same order. The very rigid thermoset resins (phenolics and melamines) generally are the hardest by all the methods shown. The soft plastics such as polyethylene have the lowest hardness. Thus, there is a rough correlation of hardness with elastic modulus.

Table 6

Hardness of Plastics as Measured by Different Methods

Polymer	Vickers kp/mm^2	Rockwell			Bierbaum Scratch
		α	M	R	
Polystyrene	17.50	109	66	124	10.3
High impact polystyrene	13.20	–	20-80	50-100	–
Polymethyl methacrylate	20.59	102	72	125	17.5
Polyvinyl chloride	12.84	105	60	123	10.1
Polycarbonate	12.20	–	75	120	–
Low density polyethylene	1.57	-151	-25	10~	–
High density polyethylene	4.05	–	–	20~	–
Polytetrafluoro-ethylene	3.26	–	–		–
Polyacetal	17.60	–	94	120	–
Nylon 66	9.2	102	70	120	11.1
Polyethylene terephthalate	22.95	–	94	120	–
Phenolic resin	35.70	–	–	–	–
Phenolic (mineral-filled)	–	128	–	124	21.2
Phenolic (wood flour-filled)	–	120	116	–	–
Polyester resin	–	91	72	124	13.5
Cellulose nitrate	–	78	23	112	9.8
Cellulose acetate	8.92	68	25	115	11.3
Vinylidene chloride	–	38	–	92	8.3
Melamine resin	–	130	–	129	32.4
Polypropylene	8.0	–	–	95	–

Some ductile polymers, such as polycarbonate and ABS polymers, can be fabricated like metals by punching and cold-forming techniques. These fabrication techniques are analagous to hardness tests in that a very rigid indentor is pressed into a sheet of less rigid plastic. Punching and cold-forming of plastics have been discussed by several authors (116-120).

VI. Summary

Many of the tests described in this chapter do not yield constants which are characteristic of a material. The results, even for standard tests, depend upon the type of testing instrument and upon the conditions of the test. The tests measure a complex combination of a variety of phenomena. The practical value of such tests is to find correlations with end use or with field use in certain applications of a material. These correlations can generally be found by using the proper instrument under certain specified operating conditions. These tests often try to simulate field usage so as to have as closely as possible the same factors affecting the material in use and in the test. However, it is often a difficult problem to find which of the many variables are really the important ones in a given practical application. For instance, the important factors which determine the wear of a shoe sole may not be the same factors which determine the wear of a plastic bearing.

Most of the tests are too limited in scope to be generally useful, and they do not cover a wide enough spectrum of variables. For instance, a single temperature does not characterize the heat distortion behavior of a polymer. Not only is the complete deformation versus temperature curve needed at a single load, but the curves should be determined using several loads. With such a set of curves available, an engineer or designer can make much more reasonable estimates of the ability of a polymer to maintain its dimensionable stability under all kinds of service conditions. A single heat distortion temperature does not provide this type of information. A similar situation applies to many other tests.

VII. Problems

1. Why does the heat distortion temperature of crystalline polymers such as polyethylene tend to be more dependent upon the applied load than does the HDT of glassy polymers?

2. A polymer has a Young's modulus as a function of temperature as shown in the following table. What is the tensile heat distortion temperature with a load of 100 psi? What is the HDT with a load of 500 psi? The HDT is defined as that temperature at which the elongation becomes 2%.

Temperature (°C)	Young's modulus (dynes/cm^2)
80	3.0×10^{10}
85	2.6×10^{10}
90	2.1×10^{10}
95	1.4×10^{10}
100	5.4×10^{9}
105	8.0×10^{8}
110	1.2×10^{8}
115	1.9×10^{7}

3. From the data in problem 2, what are the flex temperature T_F and the T_4 temperature? Assume that Poisson's ratio is 0.5.

4. Why do scratches on the surface of a fatigue test specimen generally reduce its fatigue life?

5. The dynamic modulus may decrease and the damping increase during a fatigue test. Would you expect this to be a gradual change, or would most of the change take place just before the specimen breaks? Why?

6. For two rigid materials, rough surfaces may give a higher coefficient of friction than smooth surfaces. However, a smooth rubber block against a smooth, flat, rigid surface may have a higher coefficient of friction than if the surfaces were rough. Why the differences in the two cases?

7. A steel ball bounces higher when dropped onto a thick sheet of natural rubber than it does when dropped onto a sheet of butyl rubber. Which rubber has the higher coefficient of rolling friction? Why might the coefficient of sliding friction be reversed for the two materials?

8. Rubber is generally considered as a soft material. Why do some hardness tests rate rubber as a hard material?

9. In hardness tests involving the amount of indentation into a flat sheet by a spherical indentor, doubling the load on the sphere does not double the indentation. Why?

VIII. References

1. A. P. Rudakov and N. A. Semenov, Polymer Mech. (Engl. transl. from Russian), 1, #3, 112 (1965).

2. G. S. Semenov, N. G. Ryzhov, and A. I. Kravtsov,
    Polymer Sci. USSR, 9, 258 (1967).

3. B. Ya. Teitel'Baum, Polymer Sci. USSR, 10, 1129 (1968).

4. M. M. Shteding, V. M. Gorchahova, and S. S. Voyutskii,
    Polymer Sci. USSR, 10, 61 (1968).

5. V. V. Korshak, V. A. Sergeyev, M. P. Danilova, and
    V. G. Danilov, Polymer Sci. USSR, 11, 2996 (1969).

6. V. P. Regeta, G. N. Pýankov, M. A. Brashkin, and
    E. G. Yarmilko, Polymer Mech. (Engl. transl.), 4, 755 (1968).

7. ASTM Standards, Amer. Soc. Testing Materials, Philadelphia,
    Pa., 1970.

8. L. E. Nielsen, unpublished data, Monsanto Co.

9. M. T. Watson, G. M. Armstrong, and W. D. Kennedy, Modern
    Plast., 34, 169 (Nov. 1956).

10. J. W. Liska, Ind. Eng. Chem., 36, 40 (1944).

11. J. A. Sauer, F. A. Schwertz, and D. L. Worf, Modern Plast.,
    22, 153 (Mar. 1945).

12. S. Newman and W. P. Cox, J. Polymer Sci., 46, 29 (1960).

13. G. R. Riser, W. S. Port, and L. P. Witnauer, J. Polymer Sci.,
    36, 543 (1959).

14. L. E. Nielsen, Trans. Soc. Rheol., 9, 243 (1965).

15. J. A. Melchore and H. F. Mark, Modern Plast., 31, 141 (Nov. 1953).

16. K. J. Cleereman, H. J. Karam, and J. L. Williams, ASTM Bull.
    No. 180, 37 (Feb. 1952).

17. R. H. Boundy and R. F. Boyer, Styrene and its Polymers,
    Copolymers, and Derivatives, Reinhold, New York, 1952, p. 1224.

18. H. P. Wohnsiedler, I. H. Updegraff, and R. H. Hunt, Jr.,
    Ind. Eng. Chem., 48, 82 (1956)

19. R. F. Clash, Jr. and R. M. Berg, Ind. Eng. Chem., 34,
    1218 (1942).

20. S. D. Gehman, D. E. Woodford, and C. S. Wilkinson, Jr.,
    Ind. Eng. Chem., 39, 1108 (1947).

21. D. Katz and A. V. Tobolsky, J. Polymer Sci., A2, 1595 (1964).

22. A. V. Tobolsky, D. Katz, M. Takahashi, and R. Schaffhauser,
    J. Polymer Sci., A2, 2749 (1964).

23. R. F. Clash, Jr. and R. M. Berg, Modern Plast., 21, 119
    (July, 1949).

24. M. C. Reed and J. Harding, Ind. Eng. Chem., 41, 675 (1949).

25. R. R. Lawrence and E. B. McIntyre, Ind. Eng. Chem., 41,
    689 (1949).

26. A. F. Fitzhugh and R. N. Crozier, J. Polymer Sci., 8,
    225 (1952).

27. L. P. Witnauer and W. E. Palm, J. Appl. Polymer Sci., 2,
    371 (1959).

27a. C. E. Stephenson and A. H. Willbourn, ASTM, Spec. Techn.
    Publ., No. 247, Amer. Soc. Testing Mater., Philadelphia, Pa.
    1959, p. 169.

28. J. H. Dillon, Advances in Colloid Science, Vol. 3, H. Mark
    and E. J. W. Verwey, Ed., Interscience, New York, 1950, p. 219.

29. A. J. McEvily, Jr., R. C. Boettner, and T. L. Johnston,
    Fatigue, J. J. Burke, N. L. Reed, and V. Weiss, Ed., Syracuse
    University, Syracuse, New York, 1964, p. 95.

30. ASTM Standards, D671, Amer. Soc. Testing Materials, Philadelphia.

31. E. M. Prot, Revue de Metallurgie, REMEA, 45, No. 12, 481
    (1948).

32. H. S. Loveless, C. W. Deeley, and D. L. Swanson, SPE Trans.,
    2, 126 (1962).

33. L. S. Lazar, ASTM Bull., No. 220, 67 (1957).

34. ASTM Standards, D2176, Amer. Soc. Testing Materials, Philadelphia.

35. J. W. Dally and L. J. Broutman, J. Composite Mater., 1, 424
    (1967).

36. B. J. Lazan and A. Yorgiadis, ASTM Spec. Tech. Publ.,
    No. 59, Amer. Soc. Testing Materials, Philadelphia, 1944,
    p. 66.

37. G. J. Lake and P. B. Lindley, J. Appl. Polymer Sci., 8,
    707 (1964).

38. N. E. Waters, J. Mater. Sci., 1, 354 (1966).

39. E. H. Andrews, Testing of Polymers, Vol. 4, W. E. Brown, Ed.,
    Interscience, New York, 1969, p. 237.

40. D. Prevorsek and W. J. Lyons, J. Appl. Phys., 35, 3152 (1964).

41. D. A. Opp, D. W. Skinner, and R. J. Wiktorek, Polymer Eng.
    Sci., 9, 121 (1969).

42. M. Schrager, J. Polymer Sci., A2, 8, 1999 (1970).

43. A. B. D. Cassie, M. Jones, and W. J. S. Nauton, Rubber Chem.
    Techn., 10, 29 (1937).

44. M. N. Riddell, G. P. Koo, and J. L. O'Toole, Polymer Eng. Sci.,
    6, 363 (1966).

45. G. P. Koo, M. N. Riddell, and J. L. O'Toole, Polymer Eng. Sci., 7, 182 (1967).

46. V. Zilvar, Plast. Polymers, 39, 328 (1971).

47. A. M. Sookne and M. Harris, Ind. Eng. Chem., 37, 478 (1945).

48. E. Foden, D. R. Morrow, and J. A. Sauer, J. Appl. Polymer Sci., 16, 519 (1972).

49. J. W. S. Hearle, J. Mater. Sci., 2, 474 (1967).

50. R. H. Carey, ASTM Bull., No. 206, 52 (1955).

51. F. P. Bowden and D. Tabor, The Friction and Lubrication of Solids, Clarendon Press, Oxford, 1954.

52. F. S. Conant and J. W. Liska, Rubber Chem. Techn., 33, 1218 (1960).

53. A. Schallamach, Wear, 1, 384 (1957), or Rubber Chem. Techn., 31, 982 (1958).

54. A. Schallamach, Rubber Chem. Techn. (Rubber Rev.), 41, 209 (1968).

55. W. A. Glaeser, Wear, 6, 93 (1963).

56. P. H. Pinchbeck, Wear, 5, 85 (1962).

57. F. P. Bowden and L. Leben, Proc. Royal Soc., 169A, 371 (1939).

58. D. G. Flom, Anal. Chem., 32, 1550 (1960).

59. T. Fort, Jr., J. Phys. Chem., 66, 1136 (1962).

60. K. A. Grosch, Proc. Royal Soc., 274A, 21 (1963).

61. R. F. Westover and W. I. Vroom, SPE J., 19, 1093 (1963).

62. N. Adams, J. Appl. Polymer Sci., 7, 2075 (1963).

63. D. K. Owens, J. Appl. Polymer Sci., 8, 1465, 1477 (1964).

64. J. B. DeCoste, SPE J., 25, #10, 67 (1969).

65. G. W. Schael, J. H. Thelin, and B. L. Williams, J. Elastoplastics, 4, 10 (1972).

66. D. Atack and D. Tabor, Proc. Royal Soc., 246A, 539 (1958).

67. A. M. Bueche and D. G. Flom, Wear, 2, 168 (1959).

68. D. G. Flom, J. Appl. Phys., 31, 306 (1960); 32, 1426 (1961).

69. R. H. Norman, British J. Appl. Phys., 13, 358 (1962).

70. H. H. Vickers, J. Appl. Polymer Sci., 6, 316 (1962).

71. A. Schallamach, Wear, 6, 375 (1963).

72. G. M. Bartenev and A. I. Elkin, _J. Polymer Sci._, C16, 1673
     (1967).

73. A. N. Gent and R. L. Henry, _Trans. Soc. Rheol._, 13, 255
     (1969).

74. G. V. Vinogradov, G. M. Bartenev, A. I. Elkin, and
     V. K. Mikhaylov, _Wear_, 16, 213 (1970).

75. E. Southern and R. W. Walker, _Nature (Phys. Sci.)_, 237,
     142 (1972).

76. V. A. Bely, V. G. Savkin, and A. I. Sviridyonok, _Wear_, 18,
     11 (1971).

77. M. W. Pascoe and D. Tabor, _Proc. Royal Soc._, 235A, 210 (1956).

78. G. M. Bartenev and V. V. Lavrentev, _Rubber Chem. Techn._, 34
     1162 (1961), or _Wear_, 4, 154 (1961).

79. N. C. Hilyard, _British J. Appl. Phys._, 17, 927 (1966).

80. D. A. Barlow, _Wear_, 20, 151 (1972).

81. K. V. Shooter and P. H. Thomas, _Research_, 2, 533 (1949).

82. D. I. James, R. H. Norman, and A. R. Payne, _Physical
     Properties of Polymers_, Soc. Chem. Ind., Monograph No. 5,
     Macmillan, New York, 1959, p. 233.

83. F. M. Gavan, _Testing of Polymers_, Vol. 3, J. V. Schmitz and
     W. E. Brown, Ed., Interscience, New York, 1967, p. 139.

84. A. Schallamach, _Proc. Phys. Soc._, 67B, 883 (1954), or
     Rubber Chem. Techn., 28, 906 (1955).

85. M. O. W. Richardson, _Wear_, 17, 89 (1971).

86. J. K. Lancaster, _Wear_, 14, 223 (1969).

87. J. J. Gouza, _Testing of Polymers_, Vol. 2, J. V. Schmitz, Ed.,
     Interscience, New York, 1966, p. 225.

88. R. A. Wiinikainen, _Mater. Res. Stds._, 9, #12, 17 (1969).

89. F. M. Gavan, _ASTM Bull._, No. 238, 44 (May 1959).

90. A. W. Cizek, P. H. Kallas, and H. Nestlen, _ASTM Bull._,
     No. 132, 25 (Jan. 1945).

91. Anonymous, _Wear_, 4, 479 (1961).

92. A. N. Gent, P. B. Lindley, and A. G. Thomas, _J. Appl. Polymer
     Sci._, 8, 455 (1964).

93. N. A. Brunt, _Kolloid Zeit._, 239, 561 (1970).

94. A. E. Juve and A. G. Veith, _Rubber Chem. Techn._, 35, 1276
     (1962).

95. R. B. Lewis, Testing of Polymers, Vol. 3, J. V. Schmitz and
     W. E. Brown, Ed., Interscience, New York, 1967, p. 203.

96. R. L. Zapp, Rubber World, 133, 59 (1955), or Rubber Chem.
     Techn., 29, 333 (1956).

97. K. Satake, T. Sone, M. Hamada, and K. Hayakawa, Rubber
     Chem. Techn., 44, 1173 (1971).

98. D. Bulgin and M. H. Walters, Proc. Internat. Rubber Conf.,
     Brighton, Maclaren, London, 1967, p. 445.

99. M. A. Marcucci, SPE J., 14, 30 (Feb. 1958).

100. L. Boor, J. D. Ryan, M. E. Marks, and W. F. Bartoe,
     ASTM Bull. No.145, 68 (Mar. 1947).

101. E. C. Bernhardt, Modern Plast., 26, 123 (Oct. 1948).

102. D. I. Livingston, Testing of Polymers, Vol. 3, J. V. Schmitz
     and W. E. Brown, Ed., Interscience, New York, 1967, p. 111.

103. S. Timoshenko, Theory of Elasticity, McGraw-Hill, New York,
     1934.

104. D. Tabor, Proc. Royal Soc., 192A, 247 (1948).

105. N. E. Waters, British J. Appl. Phys., 16, 557 (1965).

106. L. L. Chapoy and J. J. Aklonis, Trans. Soc. Rheol., 12,
     445 (1968).

107. D. J. Taylor and A. M. Kragh, J. Phys., D3, 29 (1970).

108. J. R. Scott, Trans. Inst. Rubber Ind., 11, 224 (1935).

109. D. W. Jopling and E. Pitts, British J. Appl. Phys., 16, 541
     (1965).

110. K. L. Johnson, J. Mech. Phys. Solids, 18, 115 (1970).

111. G. S. Yeh and D. I. Livingston, Rubber Chem. Techn., 34,
     937 (1961).

112. K. Ito, Modern Plast., 35, 167 (Nov. 1957).

113. P. Eyerer and G. Lang, Kunststoffe, 62, 322 (1972).

114. B. Maxwell, Modern Plast., 32, 125 (May 1955).

115. Modern Plastics Encyclopedia, McGraw-Hill, New York, 1972.

116. G. Gruenwald, Modern Plast., 38, 137 (Sept. 1960).

117. D. I. Livingston, G. S. Yeh, P. Rohall, and S. D. Gehman,
     J. Appl. Polymer Sci., 5, 442 (1961).

118. V. E. Malpass, Appl. Polymer Sympos., No. 12, 19 (1969).

119.   S. Ueno, H. Yamazaki, T. Oue, K. Ito, and M. Tsutsui,
       Trans. Soc. Rheol., 10, 627 (1966).

120.   F. J. Furno, R. S. Webb, and N. P. Cook, Product Eng. 35,
       (Aug. 17, 1964).

Chapter 7

Particulate-Filled Polymers

I. Introduction to Composite Systems

Composite materials may be defined as materials made up of
two or more components and consisting of two or more phases.
Such materials must be heterogeneous at least on a microscopic
scale. Composite materials may be divided into three general
classes: 1. Particulate-filled materials consisting of a
continuous matrix phase and a discontinuous filler phase made up
of discrete particles. 2. Fiber-filled composites. 3. Skeletal
or interpenetrating network composites consisting of two continuous phases. Examples of this last class include filled open-
cell foams and sintered mats or meshes filled with some material.

Many commercial polymeric materials are composites, although
they are often not considered as such. Examples include polyblends and ABS materials, foams, filled polyvinyl chloride
formulations used in such applications as floor tile and wire
coatings, filled rubbers, thermosetting resins containing a great
variety of fillers, and glass fiber-filled plastics. There are
many reasons for using composite materials rather than the
simpler homogeneous polymers. Some of these reasons are:

1. Increased stiffness, strength, and dimensional stability.

2. Increased toughness or impact strength.

3. Increased heat distortion temperature.

4. Increased mechanical damping.

5. Reduced permeability to gases and liquids.

6. Modified electrical properties.

7. Reduced cost.

Not all of these desirable features are found in any single
composite. The advantages that composite materials have to offer
must be balanced against their undesirable properties, which
include complex rheological behavior and difficult fabrication
techniques as well as a reduction in some physical and mechanical
properties.

The properties of composite materials are determined by the
properties of the components, by the shape of the filler phase, by
the morphology of the system, and by the nature of the interface
between the phases. Thus, a great variety of properties can be
obtained with composites just by alteration of the morphological
or interface properties. An important property of the interface
which can greatly affect mechanical behavior is the strength of
the adhesive bond between the phases.

II. Rheology of Suspensions

The flow behavior of suspensions of rigid particles in
liquids is important in filled systems. There are at least two
reasons for this importance: 1. Many fabrication techniques for
composites involve the flow of suspensions of liquids or molten
polymers. 2. Most of the theories of the moduli of composites
have their origin in the theory of the viscosity of suspensions.

The theory of composite systems starts with Einstein's
equation for the viscosity of a suspension of rigid spherical

particles (1):

$$\eta = \eta_1 (1 + k_E \phi_2).$$ (1)

The viscosity of the suspension η is related to the viscosity
of the suspending liquid η_1, the Einstein coefficient k_E, and the
volume fraction of the filler ϕ_2. In composite materials, subscripts 1 and 2 refer to the matrix or continuous phase and the
filler or dispersed phase, respectively. Einstein's equation only
holds for rigid particles in very dilute concentrations. Over a
hundred equations have been proposed for the viscosity of
suspensions of spheres up to moderate or high concentrations (2).
Of all these equations, only two of the most useful ones will be
discussed.

An equation that describes the viscosity of many kinds of
suspensions over the entire concentration range is the Mooney
equation (3):

$$\ln(\eta/\eta_1) = \frac{k_E \phi_2}{1 - \phi_2/\phi_m}.$$ (2)

The constant k_E is known as the Einstein coefficient (or the
intrinsic viscosity) and has the value 2.50 for dispersed spheres.
The volume fraction of filler is ϕ_2 while ϕ_m is the maximum
volume fraction that the filler can have because of packing
difficulties from particle-particle contacts. The quantity ϕ_m
is known theoretically in some cases, but it is generally
obtained from sedimentation measurements or from the maximum
packing of the dry particles under vibratory motion.

$$\phi_m = \frac{\text{True volume of the filler}}{\text{Apparent volume occupied by the filler}}.$$ (3)

Theoretically, the maximum value of ϕ_m is 0.74 for spheres in hexagonal close packing, but in practice ϕ_m is more like 0.637 (random close packing of spheres) or 0.524 (cubic packing)(4). Table 1 gives values of ϕ_m for different packings of spheres and aligned rods. The maximum packing fraction ϕ_m varies with particle shape and state of agglomeration. Except in a few cases, it is difficult to predict the value of ϕ_m from theory, so an experimental method such as sedimentation volume is used. Agglomerates and nonspherical particles generally have smaller ϕ_m than spheres (5).

For particles other than dispersed spheres, the Einstein coefficient k_E can often be estimated with fair accuracy. If the

Table 1

Maximum Packing Fractions ϕ_m

Particles	Type of Packing	ϕ_m
Spheres	Hexagonal close packing	0.7405
"	Face centered cubic	0.7405
"	Body centered cubic	0.60
"	Simple cubic	0.5236
"	Random close packing	0.637
"	Random loose packing	0.601
Fibers	Parallel hexagonal packing	0.907
"	Parallel cubic packing	0.785
"	Parallel random packing	0.82
"	Random orientation	0.52(?)

particles are rigid spheres which agglomerate to give strong
clusters which are roughly spherical in shape, the Einstein
coefficient is given by (5):

$$k_E = \frac{2.5}{\phi_a} = \frac{2.5 \; (V_S + V_L)}{V_S} \tag{4}$$

where ϕ_a is the volume fraction of an agglomerate that is made up
of spheres, V_S is the actual volume of the spheres in a typical
agglomerate, while V_L is the volume of the matrix fluid that is
entrapped within and on the surface of the agglomerate. Thus,
agglomeration increases the Einstein coefficient and viscosity.
For large agglomerates with spherical particles in cubic
packing, the Einstein coefficient approaches 4.77 (5). Particles
which are elongated ellipsoids or are rod-like in shape also
increase the Einstein coefficient (6). Figure 1 gives the
expected value of k_E as a function of the axial ratio of the
ellipsoids or rods for the case of randomly oriented particles
such as would occur at very low rates of shear (6). High rates
of shear orient the rods and decrease the effective value of the
Einstein coefficient.

Figure 2 shows plots of the Mooney equation for dispersed
spheres, aggregates consisting of three spheres, and large
aggregates containing many spheres. Viscosity increases very
rapidly with concentration and also with the state of aggregation.

A second equation which fits many experimental data on
viscosity of all kinds of suspensions is (7):

$$\frac{\eta}{\eta_1} = \left(1 - \frac{\phi_2}{\phi_m} \right)^{-2.5} \tag{5}$$

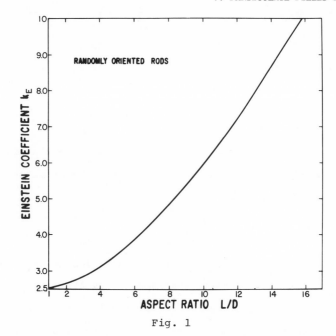

Fig. 1

The Einstein coefficient as a function of the length to
diameter ratio for rod-shaped particles.

This equation implies that the relative viscosity depends only
upon ϕ_m for particles of any size or shape. At very high
concentrations of filler, neither equation 2 nor equation 5
generally fits experimental data accurately because the suspensions
become non-Newtonian in behavior, and the viscosity changes as
the rate of shear changes. Such suspensions may have yield
values and may be either thixotropic or dilatant.

   The Cross equation often holds for non-Newtonian suspensions
if the apparent viscosity decreases as the rate of shear $\dot{\gamma}$
increases (8,9):

$$\eta = \eta_\infty + \frac{\eta_0 - \eta_\infty}{1 + \Omega\dot{\gamma}^m} \qquad (6)$$

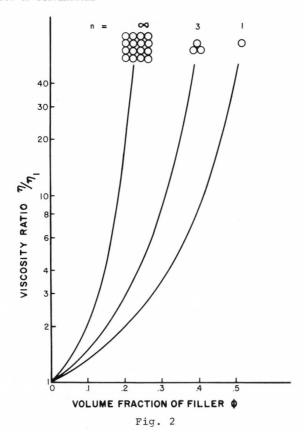

Fig. 2

The relative viscosity of suspensions of spheres as
predicted by the Mooney equation for: 1, dispersed spheres;
3, aggregates of 3 spheres, ∞, very large aggregates with
cubic packing of the spheres.

The constants Ω and m depend upon the system; typical values of m
are 1/2 or 2/3. The viscosity at zero rate of shear is η_0 while
η_∞ is the viscosity at very high rates of shear. For non-
Newtonian behavior the viscosity decreases with shear rate until
some lower limit is reached. It is generally assumed that the
shear rate dependence is due to some structural change in the

suspension, such as the breaking up of agglomerates, by the
shearing forces. Other shear-dependent theories have been
proposed by Krieger and Dougherty (10) and by Gillespie (11).

    Concentrated suspensions often show yield points in which
there is little, if any, shear deformation below a critical value
of the shear stress σ_s. In such cases, the Casson equation often
holds (12,13):

$$\sigma_s^{1/2} = k_0 + k_1 \dot{\gamma}^{1/2} \tag{7}$$

The yield stress is k_0^2, and k_1 is an empirical constant.

III.   Relation Between Viscosity and Shear Modulus

    The theoretical equations for viscosity and shear modulus
should be of the same form for a given instrument geometry (14-17)
The rate of shear in the viscosity equation is just replaced by
the shear strain in the modulus equation. Thus, for filled
systems in which the matrix phase is an elastomer having a
Poisson's ratio of 0.5, and the filler phase is rigid, there is
a simple relationship between relative viscosities and relative
shear moduli:

$$\frac{\eta}{\eta_1} = \frac{G}{G_1} . \tag{8}$$

In this equation G is the shear modulus of the filled material
while G_1 is the shear modulus of the unfilled matrix. Thus,
if one has a theory for the viscosity of a filled system, then
the same theory can be used to estimate the shear modulus.
Equation 8, however, is accurate only when Poisson's ratio of
the continuous phase is 0.5, and the rigidity of the filler is

very much greater than that of the matrix. Otherwise, the
modulus ratio is considerably less than the viscosity ratio.
A more accurate theoretical equation, which compensates for
Poisson's ratio of the matrix below 0.5, is (18):

$$\left(\frac{\eta}{\eta_1} - 1\right) = \frac{2.50(8 - 10\nu_1)}{15(1 - \nu_1)} \left(\frac{G}{G_1} - 1\right) \quad (9)$$

In this equation ν_1 is Poisson's ratio of the matrix, and it is
assumed that the filler particles are approximately spherical in
shape.

IV. Moduli of Filled Polymers

A. Regular Systems

The Mooney equation holds approximately for the shear
modulus of rubbers containing rigid fillers of any shape (19).
However, the Mooney equation predicts shear moduli which are
far too high when the matrix is a rigid material. Some of the
reasons for the modulus being lower than predicted are: Poisson's
ratio of the matrix is less than 0.5, there are thermal stresses
which reduce the effective modulus, and the modulus of the filler
is not infinitely greater than the modulus of the matrix. For
polymers containing nearly spherical particles of any modulus, the
Kerner equation (20) or the equivalent equation of Hashin and
Shtrikman (21) can be used to calculate the modulus of a composite
if there is some adhesion between the phases. The Kerner equation
can be greatly simplified in some cases. For fillers which are
much more rigid than the polymer matrix, the equation becomes,

up to moderate concentrations,:

$$\frac{G}{G_1} = 1 + \frac{15(1 - \nu_1)}{8 - 10\nu_1} \frac{\phi_2}{\phi_1} \, . \tag{10}$$

For foams and rubber-filled rigid polymers (such as high impact polystyrenes), the Kerner equation reduces to:

$$\frac{1}{G} = \frac{1}{G_1} \left[1 + \frac{15(1 - \nu_1)}{7 - 5\nu_1} \frac{\phi_2}{\phi_1} \right] \, . \tag{11}$$

Curve C of Figure 3 gives the prediction of the Kerner equation for the reduced shear modulus G/G_1 for a polymer with a Poisson's ratio of 0.35 filled with rigid spheres in which $G_2/G_1 = \infty$. Curve D of Figure 3 is the predicted reduced shear modulus of a foam or a rubber-filled rigid polymer.

Halpin and Tsai (22-24) have shown that the Kerner equation and many other equations for moduli can be put in a more general form. Lewis (19) and Nielsen (25) then showed how the equation can be generalized still further to:

$$\frac{M}{M_1} = \frac{1 + AB\phi_2}{1 - B\psi\phi_2} \tag{12}$$

where M is any modulus — shear, Young's, or bulk. The constant A takes into account such factors as geometry of the filler phase and Poisson's ratio of the matrix. The constant B takes into account the relative moduli of the filler and matrix phases; its value is 1.0 for very large M_2/M_1 ratios. The quantity B is defined as

$$B = \frac{M_2/M_1 - 1}{M_2/M_1 + A} \, . \tag{13}$$

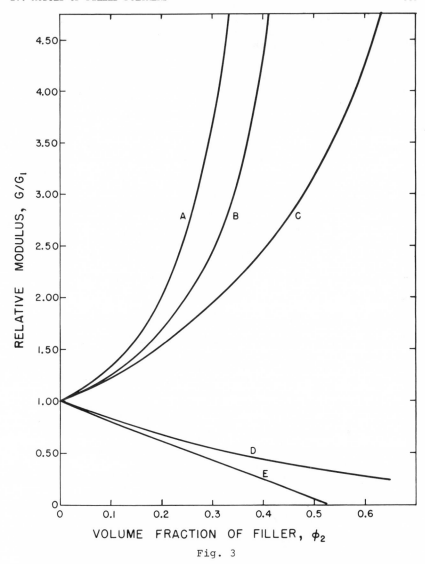

Fig. 3

Theoretical prediction of the relative modulus of various
types of composites: A. Mooney equation for spheres in a
matrix with Poisson's ratio of 0.5 and a maximum packing
fraction ϕ_m of 0.71; B. The modified Kerner or Halpin-Tsai
equations with $\phi_m = 0.64$; C. The original Kerner equation
for spheres; D. The original Kerner equation for foams;
E. The modified Kerner equation with $\phi_m = 0.64$ for foams.
In cases B through E, Poisson's ratio = 0.35, and one of
the phases is infinitely rigid compared to the other.

The factor ψ depends upon the maximum packing fraction ϕ_m of the filler. Two empirical functions which fulfill the necessary boundary conditions are:

$$\psi = 1 + \left(\frac{1 - \phi_m}{\phi_m^2} \right) \phi_2 \qquad (14)$$

and

$$\psi \phi_2 = 1 - \exp \left(\frac{- \phi_2}{1 - \phi_2/\phi_m} \right). \qquad (15)$$

The quantity $\psi \phi_2$ can be visualized as a reduced volume fraction. For $\phi_m = 1$, $\psi = 1$. The reduced concentration $\psi \phi_2$, as given by equation 14, is shown in Figure 4 as a function of the concentration ϕ_2 for the case where the maximum packing fraction ϕ_m is 0.50.

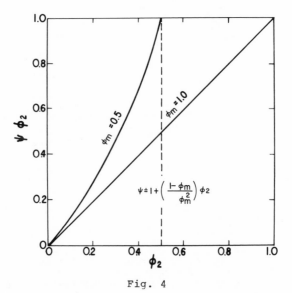

Fig. 4

Reduced concentration $\psi \phi_2$ as a function of ϕ_2 as predicted by equation 14 for $\phi_m = 0.50$ and $\phi_m = 1.0$.

The constant A is related to the generalized Einstein coefficient k_E by

$$A = k_E - 1. \tag{16}$$

Einstein (1) pointed out that $k_E = 2.5$ for a suspension of rigid spheres in a matrix with a Poisson's ratio of 0.5 when the type of deformation is shear. In general, for the case of the shear modulus with spherical fillers, the value of A for any Poisson's ratio of the matrix is

$$A = \frac{7 - 5\nu_1}{8 - 10\nu_1}. \tag{17}$$

Burgers (6) has tabulated values of k_E for randomly oriented ellipsoidal or rod-like particles as a function of the ratio of the length of the particles to their diameter. For such particles, the theoretical values of k_E are given in Figure 1 for matrices with a Poisson's ratio of 0.5. For long rods, the value of k_E (and, therefore, the shear modulus) is much greater than for composites containing spherical particles.

For composites filled with particles of nearly spherical shape, the shear modulus, according to the modified Kerner equation is given by:

$$\frac{G}{G_1} = \frac{1 + AB\phi_2}{1 - B\psi\phi_2} \tag{18}$$

where

$$A = \frac{7 - 5\nu_1}{8 - 10\nu_1} \text{ and } B = \frac{G_2/G_1 - 1}{G_2/G_1 + A}. \tag{19}$$

If the particles are not dispersed but are strong aggregates, the

factor A (and thus the Einstein coefficient) becomes larger, as
already discussed for the viscosity of suspensions of agglomerates.
The value of the Einstein coefficient will be less than that for
the viscosity case unless Poisson's ratio is 0.5. The extent of
reduction as defined by equations 9, 16 and 17 is expected to be
approximately as tabulated in Table 2 (18).
Also, as in the viscosity case, ϕ_m for aggregates will be less than
for dispersed spheres.

The theories indicate that the elastic moduli of a composite
material should be independent of the size of the filler particles.
However, experiments generally show an increase in modulus (or
viscosity of suspensions) as the particle size decreases (19,26).
There are several possible reasons for this discrepancy between
theory and experiment: 1. As size decreases, surface area of the
particles increases. If the polymer is changed in some manner
at the interface, as by adsorption, then the properties should

Table 2

Relative Einstein Coefficient for Different Poisson's
Ratios

Poisson's Ratio ν_1	$\dfrac{k_E \text{ at } \nu_1}{k_E \text{ at } \nu_1 = 0.5}$
0.50	1.00
0.40	0.90
0.35	0.867
0.30	0.84
0.20	0.80

change with particle size because of the change in surface area.
2. As particle size decreases, agglomeration of powders tends to
increase with a corresponding decrease in maximum packing volume.
This effect, as already discussed, increases moduli. 3. Most
composite specimens have a surface "skin" which is rich in polymer
as a result of being molded against a surface. This skin thickness is proportional to particle size. It will be shown in a
later section that this "skin" introduces an error which makes
moduli measured from flexural and torsional tests too small. The
error decreases as particle size decreases.

The distribution of particle sizes also has an effect on the
modulus of composites and the viscosity of suspensions (27-31).
Mixtures of different particle sizes can pack more densely than
monodispersed particles. Thus, a distribution of particle sizes
gives a larger ϕ_m, and therefore, lower modulus for a given
concentration. For bimodal mixtures, if the particles differ in
diameter by a factor of about 7 to 1, the small particles can
thread their way through the passages between the larger particles
so that very efficient packing can occur (28).

The Kerner and similar equations all assume that there is good
adhesion between the filler and matrix phases. Actually, good
adhesion is not important as long as the frictional forces between
the phases are not exceeded by the applied external stresses. In
most filled systems there is a mismatch in the thermal coefficients
of expansion so that cooling down from the fabrication temperature
imposes a squeezing force on the filler by the matrix. Thus, in
many cases, even if the adhesion is poor, the theoretical equations
are valid because there may not be any relative motion across the
filler-polymer interface. The extreme case of poor adhesion gives

results which are equivalent to a foam if the filler particles
are free to move around in their cavity. Sato and Furukawa (32)
have derived an equation for the intermediate case of relatively
poor adhesion in which an elastomer matrix pulls away from the
filler surface to give cavities at the poles of the spherical
filler particles. The modulus as a function of filler concentration for several cases is illustrated in Figure 3. The difference
between the cases of perfect adhesion and no adhesion can be very
dramatic. Weak agglomerates which break under the applied stress
show many of the characteristics of poor adhesion.

The modulus of a composite depends upon the ratio of the
moduli of the two phases, M_2/M_1, as defined by the factor B. The
greater the modulus ratio, the greater is the modulus of the
composite, especially at high concentrations of filler.

B. Inverted Systems and Phase Inversion

Phase inversion may occur in some systems so that the
more rigid phase becomes the continuous matrix phase. Such
systems are called inverted composites. Practical examples
include foams, polyblends, and block polymers. In some theoretical
studies the equations for the moduli are not exact but are upper
or lower bounds to the moduli. Although the upper and lower
bounds of some of the theoretical equations need not correspond to
the inverted and regular dispersed systems, respectively, in
practical cases they generally do. For the inverted case,
equation 12 becomes (33):

$$\frac{G_1}{G} = \frac{1 + A_i \, B_i \, \phi_2}{1 - B_i \, \psi \, \phi_2} \tag{20}$$

where for spherical particles

$$A_i = \frac{8 - 10\nu_1}{7 - 5\nu_1} \quad \text{and} \quad B_i = \frac{G_1/G_2 - 1}{G_1/G_2 + A_i} . \qquad (21)$$

The factor B_i also is valid for other particle shapes. Equations
14 and 15 still hold for inverted systems except that ϕ_m is
replaced by ϕ_m' — the maximum packing fraction of the low modulus
dispersed phase in the inverted system. In these equations the
subscript 1 still refers to the continuous phase, which is now
more rigid than the filler phase. An illustration of an inverted
system is the curve for a foam shown in Figure 3.

In some systems (such as polyblends and block polymers) an
inversion of the phases occurs at a volume fraction of about one
half. The exact composition at which phase inversion occurs can
be changed considerably by the intensity of mixing or by the
presence of solvents (34-36). Generally there is a range of
compositions where both phases are partly continuous and where
the modulus changes very rapidly with composition. This range of
overlapping continuous phases will occur between $(1 - \phi_m')$ of the
inverted system and ϕ_m of the regular dispersed system. The
equations give two values for the modulus in this range. It
appears that the experimental value in the region of two partly
continuous phases will be close to the average of the logarithms
of the two theoretical values of G according to the equation
(33, 37, 38):

$$\log M = \phi_U \log M_U + \phi_L \log M_L . \qquad (22)$$

In this equation M_U and M_L are the upper (inverted) and lower

(regular) bounds to the modulus, respectively, at a given concentration. The quantities ϕ_U and ϕ_L are limited to the overlap
region between $(1 - \phi_m')$ and ϕ_m. At some arbitrary concentration
ϕ_C in the overlap region, ϕ_U is that fraction of $[\phi_m - (1 - \phi_m')]$
between ϕ_C and $(1 - \phi_m')$. Likewise, ϕ_L is the fraction of the
overlap region that is between ϕ_C and ϕ_m (33,38). Figure 5
illustrates the definitions for some chosen overall composition ϕ_C.

$$\phi_U = \frac{\phi_C - (1 - \phi_m')}{\phi_m - (1 - \phi_m')} \quad ; \qquad\qquad \phi_L = \frac{\phi_m - \phi_C}{\phi_m - (1 - \phi_m')} \qquad (23)$$

In these equations ϕ_m' is the maximum packing fraction of the low
modulus component in the inverted system, and ϕ_m is the maximum
packing fraction of the more rigid component in the softer one.

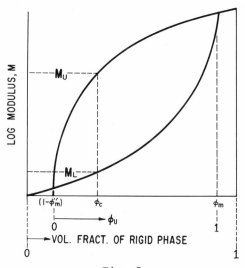

Fig. 5

Modulus and composition variables important in the region
of phase inversion. ϕ_C is an arbitrary volume fraction
of the more rigid component.

$\phi_U + \phi_L = 1$. For the special case where $\phi_m = \phi'_m = 1$, ϕ_L is the volume fraction of the rigid phase, and ϕ_U is the volume fraction of the low modulus material for any value of ϕ_C.

A number of cases, including inverted systems, is illustrated in Figure 6. Another illustration using experimental results on a styrene-butadiene-styrene block polymer is shown in Figure 7 (39). The calculated curve fits the experimental data very well, assuming that at high styrene content the polybutadiene is dispersed as spheres. Phase inversion occurs over the range of polystyrene volume fractions from 15 to 80 percent. The data also can be matched by using a combination of series and parallel models (40,41). However, such models cannot realistically take into account the morphology of the two-phase systems outside the region of phase inversion.

There is a high degree of symmetry between the equations for ordinary dispersed systems and the equations for inverted systems. The factor A in the equation for dispersed systems gives the same curve as $A_i = 1/A$ for the inverted system if the modulus ratio is expressed as G/G_1 in both cases. It is often more convenient to express both cases relative to the lower modulus material; then $A = \left(\dfrac{G_2}{G_1}\right)\dfrac{1}{A_i}$. This same relation holds for a 180° rotation of any curve about its center of symmetry at $\phi_2 = 0.5$ for either A or A_i. The symmetry is illustrated in Figure 8.

The factor A can vary between zero and infinity. For the case of $A = \infty$ (or $A_i = 0$), it can be shown that the generalized modulus equation becomes the "rule of mixtures":

$$G = G_1 \phi_1 + G_2 \phi_2. \tag{24}$$

This is the maximum possible modulus and is the result to be

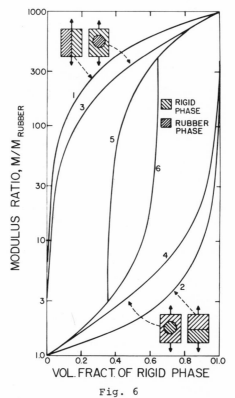

Fig. 6

Relative modulus of composites containing rubber and a rigid
polymer in which the rigid polymer has a modulus 1000 times
that of the rubber:

1. Rigid polymer and rubber in parallel.
2. Rigid polymer and rubber in series.
3. Rubber dispersed as spheres in rigid matrix, $\phi_m' = 1$.
4. Rigid polymer dispersed as spheres in rubber
   matrix, $\phi_m = 1$.
5. Rubber dispersed as spheres in rigid matrix, $\phi_m' = 0.64$.
6. Rigid polymer dispersed as spheres in rubber
   matrix, $\phi_m = 0.64$.
   Phase inversion in which both phases are continuous
   occurs in the range of volume fractions between
   5 and 6.

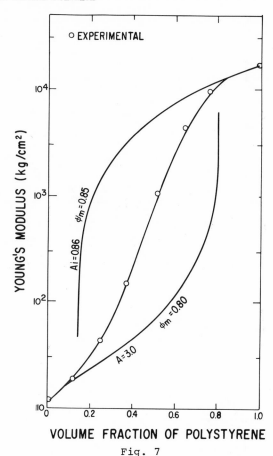

Fig. 7

Modulus of styrene-butadiene-styrene block polymers as a
function of composition. Phase inversion takes place over
the range of volume fractions of polystyrene between 0.15
and 0.80. The central solid curve is the fit of the
experimental data using $A = 3.0$, $\phi_m = 0.80$, $A_i = 0.86$
(polystyrene spheres), and $\phi_m' = 0.85$ along with the logarithmic rule of mixtures.

---

expected when the two materials making up the composite are

connected in parallel. An example is an aligned fibrous composite

with the force applied parallel to the fibers. When $A = 0$, the

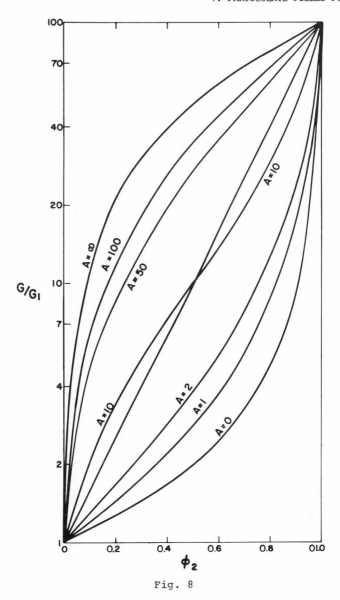

Fig. 8

Relative moduli of composites for various values of A and A_i
as a function of composition. G_2/G_1 = 100, and ϕ_m = 1.0.
The same curves are obtained if A is substituted by $100/A_i$
or if A is substituted for 100/A followed by a 180° rotation
about the central point.

lowest possible modulus is obtained, and the generalized equation
reduces to

$$\frac{1}{G} = \frac{\phi_1}{G_1} + \frac{\phi_2}{G_2} \quad . \tag{25}$$

This equation gives the results to be expected when two materials
are connected in series.

C. Errors in Composite Moduli

Many of the moduli data reported in the literature on
composite materials are too low because of a "skin effect."
Because of the restrictions imposed by the walls of molds, the
surface of most composites has an excess of polymer. Thus, in
torsion or flexural tests where the maximum stress is at the
surface, the properties of the surface are emphasized at the
expense of the interior, so the measured values of the moduli are
low (19). This error can be corrected by using thicker and
thicker specimens and extrapolating to infinite thickness, or by
using particles of smaller and smaller size and carrying out an
extrapolation to zero particle size. This skin effect can
produce errors as large as ten to twenty percent in some cases of
thin specimens. The error due to the skin can be approximately
corrected for in many cases (42). For specimens of rectangular
cross section,

$$\frac{M}{M_a} \doteq \frac{MD^3}{(M - M_1)(D - d)^3 + M_1 D^3} \tag{26}$$

where M is the true Young's modulus in flexural tests or the shear
modulus in torsion tests; M_a is the corresponding apparent modulus
actually calculated. The thickness of the specimen is D while the
diameter of the particles is d.

For foamed materials the skin gives apparent moduli which are greater than the true moduli in torsion or flexure. However, the above equation still can be used to correct for the error if the skin is about equal to the radius of the air bubbles in the foam.

There is another phenomenon which tends to make the modulus of a rigid composite too low. Below the glass transition temperature (or melting point) of a polymer one would expect the relative modulus G/G_1 to be nearly independent of temperature or at most to only decrease slightly as the temperature is lowered. Actually, the relative modulus often decreases quite noticeably as the temperature is lowered. This effect is due to the tensile stresses in the polymer resulting from the mismatch of the coefficients of thermal expansion of the polymer and filler. The high thermal stresses may be great enough to put the polymer in the nonlinear portion of its stress-strain curve where its modulus (i.e., slope of the stress-strain curve) is less than the value found in the absence of stresses (43). The thermally induced stresses σ^* are

$$\sigma^* = KE_{10}(\alpha_1 - \alpha_2)(T_O - T) \tag{27}$$

where K is a constant near unity, E_{10} is the modulus of the polymer in the unstressed state, α_1 is the coefficient of expansion of the polymer, and T_O is the temperature at which thermal stresses set in (generally at T_g). The concept is illustrated in Figure 9 where, because of the thermally induced stresses, the modulus of the polymer surrounding the filler particles is less than the modulus of unstressed polymer. As the

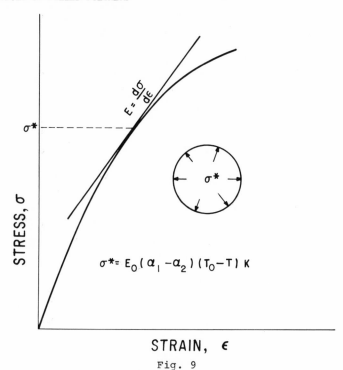

$$\sigma^* = E_0 (\alpha_1 - \alpha_2) (T_0 - T) K$$

STRAIN, ϵ

Fig. 9

Stress-strain curve of a matrix polymer, showing how the
Young's modulus (slope) decreases with stress. The modulus
of the polymer surrounding a rigid embedded particle is
less than the usual modulus because of the stress σ^* due
to thermal shrinkage stresses.

temperature is lowered, the thermally induced stresses increase,

so the relative modulus of the composite decreases as the tempera-

ture is lowered. In extreme cases the observed relative modulus

may only be about half the value expected from theory. A typical

example of the temperature dependence of relative modulus is shown

in Figure 10. The theory of Nielsen and Lewis (43) nearly

quantitatively explains the observed slopes of these curves.

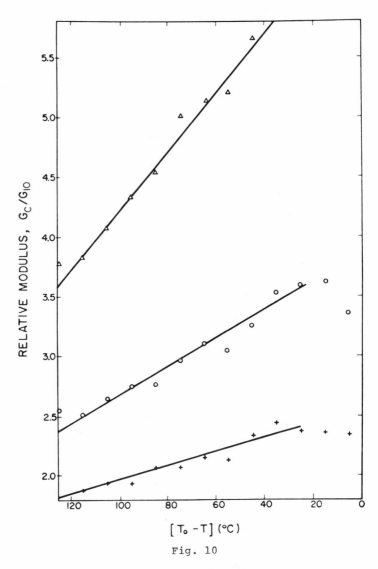

Fig. 10

The relative modulus of polyethylene filled with
wollastonite filler as a function of the difference
between the melting point T_O and the test temperature T.
T_O = 125°C. Volume fraction of filler are : +, 0.20;
0, 0.30; Δ, 0.40. [Reprinted from Nielsen and Lewis,
J. Polymer Sci., A2, 7, 1705 (1969).]

D. Experimental Examples

Many papers have been published on the experimental
moduli of particulate-filled polymers. A few of these papers
are listed in Table 3.

V. Strength and Stress-Strain Behavior

A. Rigid Fillers

From the preceding discussion, rigid particulate fillers
increase the modulus as measured from the initial slope of the
stress-strain curve, at least in the case of good adhesion.
Generally fillers cause a dramatic decrease in elongation to
break. Fillers also often decrease the tensile strength of a
material, but there are numerous exceptions, especially with such
fillers as carbon black in rubber. Typical stress-strain results
are shown in Figure 11 (68).

The decrease in elongation to break ε_B with rigid fillers
arises from the fact that the actual elongation experienced by
the polymer matrix is much greater than the measured elongation
of the specimen (69). This phenomenon is illustrated in Figure 12.
Although the specimen is part filler and part matrix, all the
elongation comes from the polymer if the filler is rigid. The
theory is complex and very incomplete at present, and the expected
results depend upon the exact fracture mechanism. However, simple
models give a qualitative and often a semi-quantitative understanding of experimental results. If there is good adhesion
between the phases, and if the fracture path tends to go from
particle to particle rather than giving a perfectly smooth
fracture surface, the following equation is expected to be

Table 3

Moduli of Particulate-Filled Polymers

Reference Number	Polymer	Filler
44	Polystyrene	Mica, asbestos, etc.
45	Styrene-acrylonitrile copolymer	Acetanilide, anthracene
46	Styrene-acrylonitrile copolymer	Glass beads
42	Polystyrene	Glass beads, salt
47	Polyethylene	Clay, silica, etc.
48	Polyethylene	Carbon black, silica
49	Polyethylene	Aluminum
50	Polypropylene	Asbestos
51	Elastomers	Vermiculite, etc.
52	Plasticized polyvinyl chloride	Glass beads
53	Plasticized polyvinyl chloride	Calcium carbonate, clay
54	Epoxy	Glass flakes
55	Epoxy and phenolic	Flakes
56	Epoxy	Glass beads and powder
57	Epoxy	Sand, air
19	Epoxy	Glass beads
58	Epoxy	Aluminum trihydrate
59	Epoxy and polyester	Glass beads
60	Polyurethane	Salt
61	Polyurethane	Salt
62	Urethane rubber	Aluminum powder
63	Polyisobutylene	Glass beads
64	Ethylene-propylene rubber	Carbon black
65	Natural rubber	Glass beads
66	Rubber	Carbon black
67	Polyethylenes	Kaolin, wollastonite

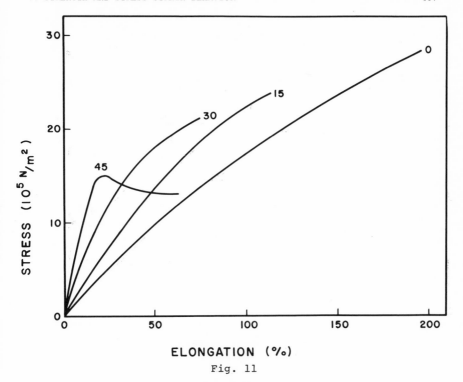

ELONGATION (%)

Fig. 11

Stress-strain curves of a polyurethane rubber filled with powdered rock salt. Numbers on the curves refer to the volume fraction of salt. [Modified from Nerderveen and Bree, U. S. Dept. Commerce Rept. AD 655634 (1967).]

approximately correct (52, 69):

$$\varepsilon_B \doteq \varepsilon_B^o \left(1 - \phi_2^{1/3}\right) \tag{28}$$

where ε_B^o is the elongation to break of the unfilled polymer. This equation is plotted in Figure 12. This curve shows the very dramatic decrease in elongation that can be brought about by only small amounts of filler. If there is poor adhesion, or if the

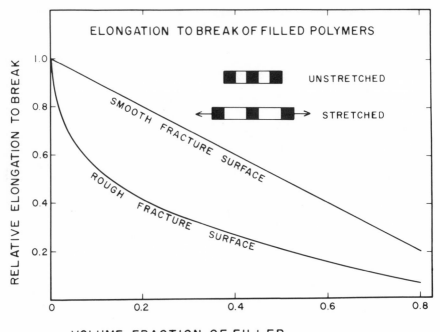

Fig. 12

Theoretical curves for the relative elongation to break of
filled polymers as a function of filler concentration when
there is good adhesion of the polymer to the filler.

---

fracture surface is smooth, the elongation to break may decrease

more gradually than equation 28 would indicate. Only in rare

instances where fillers introduce additional crazing, and perhaps

at the same time act as stoppers to crack growth, do polymers

filled with rigid fillers have elongations to break which are

equal to or greater than that of the unfilled polymer (70).

Fillers often induce yield points in the stress-strain curves

of rubbers and ductile polymers. The yielding phenomenon is

really due to a crazing effect or to a dewetting effect in which

the adhesion between the filler and matrix phases is destroyed
so that there is a dramatic decrease in the modulus of the material.
At the same time, voids are created and the specimen undergoes
dilation (52, 71-76). The development of a yield point at high
concentration of filler is clearly shown in Figure 11. The
dilation accompanying the strong deviations from Hookean behavior
of the stress-strain curve is shown in Figure 13 (71). The
yielding or dewetting behavior should depend upon the surface area
of the filler in the polymer, and thus should be a function of
$\phi_2^{2/3}$. The theory of Nicholais and Narkis (70) predicts the
following relation if enough micro-cavitation occurs before a
critical size of flaw develops which results in premature fracture:

$$\sigma_y = \sigma_{yo} \left[1 - \left(\phi_2 / \phi_m \right)^{2/3} \right]. \qquad (29)$$

In this equation σ_y and σ_{yo} are the yield stress of the composite
and unfilled polymer, respectively.

The detrimental effect of dewetting is illustrated in
Table 4 for a plasticized polyvinyl chloride filled with powdered
calcium carbonate (77). Dewetting, or the breaking of aggregates,
becomes more evident as the concentration of filler increases,
but undoubtedly, dewetting also occurs at lower filler concentrations at high elongations (74,78).

The stress-strain behavior of many filled polymers can be
changed by adhesion promoters and silane coupling agents which
change the adhesion and the nature of the filler-polymer interface (59, 79-82). Some of the silanes appear to react with both
the polymer and the hydroxyl groups of the filler surface, and

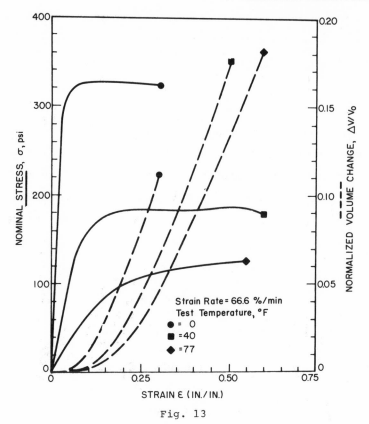

Fig. 13

Simultaneous stress-strain curves (solid lines) and
dilation (or increase in volume) curves (broken lines) of
a filled rubber. Volume fraction of filler = 0.73.
[Reprinted from Farris, J. Appl. Polymer Sci., 8, 25 (1964).]

---

thus, they increase adhesion. The treated fillers often give

composites with increased tensile strength. Especially after the

composite has been soaked in water, composites with treated filler

have better strengths than composites with untreated fillers.

Composites with untreated fillers may have fairly high tensile

strength when dry, but after the material is soaked in water, the

Table 4

Density and Stress-Strain Behavior of Plasticized Polyvinyl
Chloride Filled with Calcium Carbonate

Parts Filler per 100 Parts Plastic	Density	Tensile Strength (psi)	Elongation to break (%)	Young's Modulus (psi)
0	1.265	2825	365	1485
5	1.285	2780	380	1520
10	1.305	2960	335	1650
25	1.365	2830	375	1670
50*	1.46	2480	320	1605
100*	1.60	1765	260	1260
200*	1.82	1250	225	965

*Dewetting was clearly evident from appearance.

[Nielsen, J. Composite Mater., 1, 100 (1967), published by
Technomic Publishing, Inc.]

tensile strength decreases— probably as a result of poor adhesion
resulting from water adsorption at the interface. Some typical
data showing the effect of silanes are illustrated in Table 5 (83).

Although particle size has little, if any, effect on the
modulus of a composite in the absence of agglomeration, particle
size has a large effect on the tensile strength (47,53,66,74,
84-88). Tensile strength increases as particle size decreases.
Table 6 shows data on rock salt in urethane rubbers (74). The
reason for this phenomenon is not entirely clear, but the increase
in interfacial area per unit volume of filler as particle size
decreases must be an important factor. A second factor may also
be important. The stress fields near a particle are independent

Table 5

Effect of Silanes on Stress-Strain Behavior of Clay-Filled
Rubber*

Property	No Silane	Silane
Tensile Strength	2330	3500 psi
Elongation to break	700	230 %
Modulus	950	3480 psi

*80 parts clay in polychloroprene rubber.

[L. P. Ziemianski, C. A. Pagano, and M. W. Ranney, Rubber World, 163, #1, 53 (1970).]

Table 6

Effect of Particle Size of Rock Salt in Urethane Rubbers on
Stress-Strain Properties

Particle Size	Volume Fract. Filler (%)	Tensile Strength[a]	Ultimate Elong.
33–40μ	41	12.6	106%
50–60μ	41	12.1	104
90–105	42	11.4	73
210–300	42	4.8	42
300–480	42	3.8	36

(a) $10^5 N/m^2$ ($10^5 N/m^2 \doteq 14.5$ psi)

[F.R.Schwarzl, H.W.Bree, and C. J. Nederveen, Proc. 4th Int. Congr. Rheol., E. H. Lee, Ed., part 3, Interscience, New York, 1965, p. 2

of the size of the particle (89). However, the volume of polymer
that experiences a given value of stress concentration increases
with particle size, so the probability of finding a large flaw
within this volume also increases. If a large flaw exists within
an area of stress concentration, the tensile strength will be
reduced according to Griffith's theory (90). Also, large voids
are more detrimental than small ones to strength, so after dewetting
occurs, the larger the filler particle the larger the void.

Particle agglomeration tends to reduce the strength of a
material even though the agglomerate may be strong enough to
increase the initial modulus. Agglomerates are weak points in the
material and break fairly easily when a stress is applied to them.
A broken agglomerate then behaves as a strong stress concentrator.
In addition, since agglomerates are larger than the primary filler
particles, they produce weaker materials than composites containing
the dispersed particles, as explained in the previous paragraph.
These effects are well known in compounding carbon black in
rubbers (66,91,92). Carbon black has a strong tendency to
agglomerate. Thus, increased mixing or millrolling, which break
up the agglomerates, decrease the modulus of the rubber compound
but at the same time increase its tensile strength.

It is very difficult to mix fine powders into highly viscous
polymer melts and to get good dispersions. For this reason,
nearly all actual composites contain more or less entrapped air,
especially inside of particle agglomerates, and this entrapped air
decreases the density from the expected value. Small quantities
of entrapped air, as determined from the density of the composite,
have a great effect on the stress-strain behavior. The modulus

and the tensile strength decrease as the amount of entrapped air increases. Thus, a given composite can have a range of stress-strain properties depending upon the intensity and time of mixing and upon the kind of surface treatment given the filler particles for at least two reasons: 1. The mixing may break up agglomerates and change the degree of dispersion. 2. The mixing may change the amount of air entrapped in the composite.

Stress-strain tests can be made in compression as well as in tension. In tension, fillers often decrease the breaking strength. However, in compression, fillers generally produce increases in the strength of the polymer (93-96). Typical results have been reported by Strauch (95). For 40 percent glass beads in Nylon 66, the following data were obtained:

	Unfilled	Filled
Compressive Strength	4200 psi	36500 psi
Tensile Strength	11500 psi	14200 psi

Flakes produce unusually large increases in modulus, especially if the flakes are oriented predominantly in a plane (44,54,55,97,98). Typical flake materials are mica, aluminum boride, and glass flakes. Theoretically, flake composites could have very high strengths, but these high strengths are difficult to achieve experimentally. The reasons for the lower than expected strengths are: 1. It is difficult to perfectly align all the flakes and at the same time have optimum overlap of one flake over another. A few misaligned flakes or flakes stacked on top of each other act as stress concentrators and reduce the strength. 2. In many cases the matrix polymer was too brittle. To compensate for the mismatch in coefficients of thermal

expansion and to properly transmit most of the stress to the
flakes, a ductile matrix which has good adhesion to the filler is
required.

B. Polyblends, Block Polymers, and Foams

The stress-strain and fracture behavior of polyblends
containing rubber particles dispersed in a rigid matrix were
discussed in Chapter 5. The addition of a rubbery phase to a
rigid polymer often has the opposite effect of adding a rigid
filler. For instance, the impact strength and the elongation to
break may increase greatly while the modulus and tensile strength
are decreased by the rubber. Once enough rubber has been added
to a brittle matrix to produce a yield point, further increases
in rubber concentration cause the yield stress to decrease
gradually (99,100). The tensile strength also decreases (101).
The yield stress decreases with increasing temperature at a
constant concentration of rubber (102). This is to be expected
since an increase in temperature loosens the structure so that a
smaller stress is required to bring about yielding even for an
unfilled polymer.

The concentration of rubber is not enough to define completely the properties of polyblends and other similar two phase
systems; the morphology of the system also is important (38, 103,
104). The size and shape of the particles only partly define the
morphology. The rubber phase can be either the dispersed or the
continuous phase, the rubbery phase can contain occluded droplets
of rigid matrix, or both phases can be continuous if the polymers
form an interlocking network structure in the region of phase
inversion. The properties of a given system often can be changed

greatly by the extent and type of mixing, for example, on mill-rolls (101). Casting films from different solvents also can change dramatically the properties by changing the degree of phase separation or by inverting the phases (34,35,105-108). The nature of the interface also is important; grafting chains of the rigid polymer onto the rubber phase generally increases desirable properties by improving the adhesion between the phases (99,109,110). Commercial polyblends, such as high impact polystyrene, often have a complex morphology in which part of the rigid continuous phase is dispersed inside the rubber particles. In such cases, the total volume of the rubber phase plus the rigid occluded material inside the rubber is an important factor rather than just the volume of the rubber phase alone. Most polymer-polymer two-phase systems having common constituents have similar properties but with subtle differences. Thus, polyblends, graft polymers, block polymers, or mixtures of these materials all have similar properties (111).

In contrast to the ductile nature of rubber-filled rigid polymers, foams made from polymers tend to be brittle and to have low strengths when measured in tension. However, in compressive stress-strain tests, foams may behave similar to ductile polymers with apparent yield points, high elongations, and relatively high ultimate strengths. The apparent yield point is generally the result of the collapse of the cell structure rather than a true yielding of the polymer. Although several theories of the modulus of foams have been proposed (112-115), the Kerner equation or the modified Halpin-Tsai equations seem to agree with experiment about as well as any other (116). For low density foams, which are mostly gas, theory and experiment suggest that Young's modulus E

is given by

$$\frac{E}{E_1} \doteq \frac{\phi_1}{K} \tag{30}$$

where K is a constant between 2 and 6. Thus, the modulus is proportional to the density of the foam. Figure 14 shows typical compressive stress-strain curves of a foam for various densities (expressed in pounds per cubic foot (117). Foams are generally somewhat anisotropic because the effect of gravity and

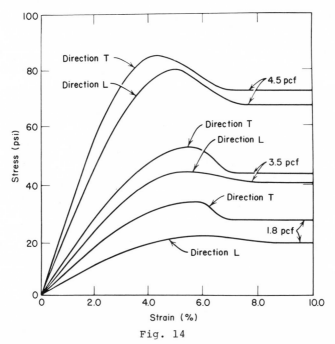

Fig. 14

Stress-strain curves of rigid polyurethane foam in compression. L = longitudinal direction, T = thickness direction. Density of foams are expressed in pounds per cubic foot (pcf). [Reprinted from Benning, Plastic Foams, Vol. 2, Interscience, New York, 1969, p. 200. Taken from a report by B. Hughes and R. L. Wajda, Battersea College of Technology, England.]

restraints during the foaming process is to elongate the foam
cells in the thickness (T) direction. It is more difficult to
collapse the cell structure in the thickness direction than in the
longitudinal L direction. Only part of the stress-strain curves
are shown in Figure 14. The curves extend to much higher elongations, and then the stress rapidly increases after complete
collapse has occurred because the cell walls are forced into
contact with one another.

In tension, foams have much lower strength than the unfoamed
polymer. If the polymer is a rubber, the elongation to break of
the foam is less than that of the starting rubber (118). The
tensile stress-strain properties are dependent upon the uniformity
of the cell size. A larger than average cell acts as a stress
concentrator where tearing will initiate. In many practical
applications, such as in furniture and car seats, the compressive
stress-strain behavior is the important mechanical property. Some
foams, such as those made from natural rubber or similar rubber,
have very little hysteresis. The compressive stress curve for an
increasing load is very nearly the same as for a decreasing load.
The compressive stress-strain curve of some polyurethane foams,
on the other hand, are less resilient and have a high hysteresis (11
For a given deformation, such foams have a much lower stress for
a decreasing load than for an increasing load.

VI.   Creep and Stress Relaxation

Rigid fillers tend to decrease both the elastic and viscous
components of creep as long as there is not serious dewetting of
the particles. Often the decrease in relative creep compliance of
a filled polymer is closely approximated by the reciprocal of the

relative elastic modulus of the same system as measured by stress-
strain or dynamic mechanical tests (67,120). That is,

$$\frac{\varepsilon(t)}{\varepsilon_1(t)} \doteq \frac{E_1}{E} . \qquad (31)$$

Thus, if this equation is valid, a great deal of time can be saved
in making creep tests by just measuring the moduli of the filled
and unfilled polymers and the creep of the unfilled polymer. This
equation implies that the filler does not change the properties of
the polymer itself in some manner. For instance, the filler does
not change the distribution of retardation times of the polymer.
Figure 15 illustrates a case where equation 31 does hold— polyethylene filled with kaolin (67). Equation 31 can be visualized
as a vertical shift of creep compliance curves by the factor
E_1/E (120).

At high elongations, at long times, and at high filler
concentrations, dewetting of the filler surfaces occurs. When
dewetting occurs, creep and creep rate dramatically increase, and
equation 31 no longer is valid (121-123). The catastrophic effect
of dewetting accompanied by vacuole formation is illustrated by the
upturn in the curves in Figure 16 (122). The effects due to
dewetting can be delayed and minimized by using smaller sized
particles and by treating the filler surface so as to increase
adhesion. Dewetting has another undesirable effect on creep
behavior too. Dewetting often decreases the elongation to break
in a creep test at the same time it decreases the creep rupture
strength or the load the material can bear without fracturing (122,
124).

The stress dependence of creep generally is proportional to

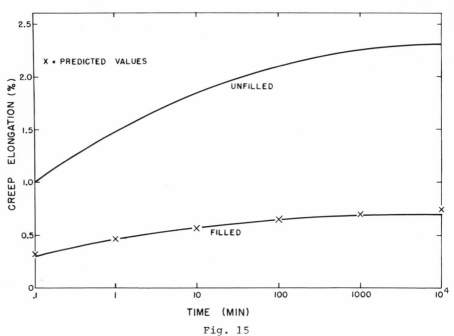

Fig. 15

Creep of polyethylene (ρ = 0.950)-unfilled and filled with kaolin, ϕ_2 = 0.20, T = 60°C, load = 400 psi. X = creep calculated from the dynamic modulus ratio G/G_1 = 3.15.

sinh (σ/σ_c) where σ is the applied stress and σ_c is a constant. For various types of particulate fillers in polyethylenes, Nielsen (67,125) found that σ_c was nearly independent of filler concentration and had the same value for unfilled and filled materials. However, Cessna (120) found that σ_c increased with filler concentration in polypropylene when the filler was glass fibers.

As expected from previous discussion, elastomeric fillers in a rigid polymer increase the compliance over that of the unfilled rigid polymer. As long as crazing or stress whitening does not occur, equation 31 should predict the behavior approximately.

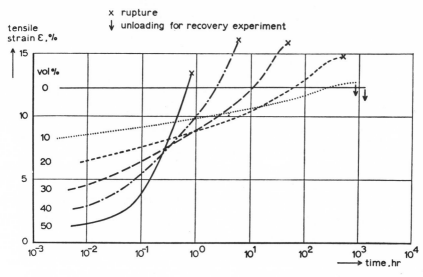

Fig. 16

Tensile creep of a polyurethane rubber filled with the
amounts of sodium chloride shown on left. Load = 3.0
kg/cm^2. T = 21°C. Particle size = 210 to 300 μm. X =
point of rupture. [Reprinted from Struik, Bree, and
Schwarzl, <u>Proc. Internat. Rubber Conf.</u>, Brighton, Maclaren
& Sons, London, 1967, p. 205. Reprinted by permission of
copyright owner, the Institution of the Rubber Industry,
London.]

After crazing occurs, the creep rate is expected to increase much
more than predicted by equation 31.

The stress relaxation behavior of filled polymers can be
anticipated from the creep behavior of such materials. The stress
relaxation modulus $E_r(t)$ is increased by rigid fillers and decreased
by elastomeric ones up to the point where dewetting or crazing
becomes pronounced. The rate of stress relaxation greatly increases
after the onset of dewetting for both rigid and elastomeric
fillers (126,127).

Rusch (128) studied the stress relaxation of polyblends which

appear to be essentially one phase systems rather than the more
general distinctly two-phase systems. The glass transition
region was more diffuse than for a pure homopolymer. The stress
relaxation of styrene-butadiene block polymers has been studied
by Shen and Kaelble (129). W-L-F (130) type of behavior was found
for temperatures around the glass transition of each of the
components, but the W-L-F equation did not hold for the
temperature-time shift factors at intermediate temperatures. In
contrast, Lim, Cohen, and Tschoegl (131) found that the W-L-F
shift factors only held in the region between the two glass
transition temperatures for similar block polymers.

VII. Dynamic Mechanical Properties

     The general effects of rigid fillers on dynamic mechanical
properties are clearly illustrated by the data of Schwarzl, et
al. (60) in Figures 17 and 18. Fillers have a larger effect in
raising the modulus above T_g than below it. The main reason for
this is the larger modulus ratio E_2/E_1 of the components when the
polymer is in the rubbery state compared to the rigid glassy state;
therefore the factor B of the Halpin-Tsai equations is larger
above T_g. Less important factors contributing to this effect are
the larger Poisson's ratio above T_g and the presence of induced
thermal stresses below T_g. These factors already have been
discussed in the section on moduli of composite materials.
Fillers also shift the break in the modulus curves to higher
temperatures (44,60). Also, at high filler concentrations, the
slope of the modulus curves decreases in the transition region.

     The effects of rigid fillers on the damping G''/G' are shown
in Figure 18. The most pronounced effect of fillers is the

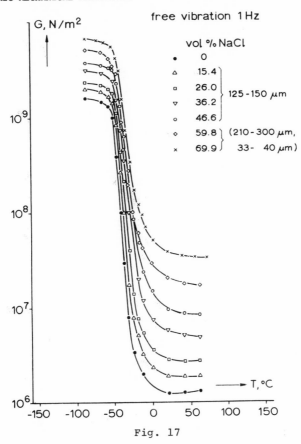

free vibration 1 Hz

Fig. 17

Shear modulus G at 1 Hz versus temperature for a polyurethane rubber filled with increasing amounts of sodium
chloride. [Reprinted from Schwarzl, et al., Rheol. Acta,
5, 270 (1966), Dr. Dietrich Steinkopff Verlag, Darmstadt.]

---

broadening of the transition region by high concentrations of

fillers. This broadening of the transition region is especially

great for flake fillers such as graphite and mica; this effect is

used in making some vibration damping and sound deadening

materials (132-134). Fillers often decrease the damping as

expressed by G"/G'; in which case the damping can generally be

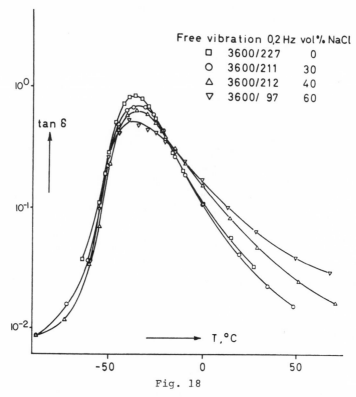

Fig. 18

Damping, tan δ = G"/G', at 0.2 Hz versus temperature for a
polyurethane rubber filled with increasing amounts of
sodium chloride. [Reprinted from Schwarzl, et al.,
Rheol. Acta, 5 270 (1966), Dr. Dietrich Steinkopff Verlag,
Darmstadt.]

approximated by (37,67):

$$G"/G' \doteq (G"/G')_1 \, \phi_1 + (G"/G')_2 \, \phi_2 \, . \qquad (32)$$

The damping of most rigid fillers is very low compared to that of
the polymer, so $(G"/G')_2$ is nearly zero and can be neglected.
However, there are numerous cases where fillers increase the
damping, probably by the introduction of new damping mechanisms

which are not present in the pure polymer. These new damping
mechanisms include: 1. Particle-particle friction where particles
touch one another as in weak agglomerates. 2. Particle-polymer
friction where there is essentially no adhesion at the interface.
3. Excess damping in the polymer near the interface because of
induced thermal stresses or changes in polymer conformation or
morphology. Figure 19 shows how treatment of the filler surface
can greatly increase the damping (135). The increased damping may
result from particle-polymer friction. An example where agglomeration may be the cause of excess damping and a drop-off in the
modulus from what would be expected is shown in Figure 20 (49).
At low concentrations of filler there is little, if any, agglomeration of particles in this case. At high concentrations, weak
agglomerates appear to be formed which are easily broken by
applied forces. As a result, the modulus is lowered, and particle-
particle friction gives rise to high damping.

Figure 18 shows the maxima in the damping curves to all occur
at the same temperature. This is a good indication that the filler
does not shift the glass transition temperature of the polymer in
this case. However, there are cases in which the filler shifts
the damping peak and T_g to higher temperatures (44,121,136-142).
The shift in T_g should be proportional to the surface area of the
filler, so the effect should increase with concentration and as
the size of the particles decreases since the effect should be due
to changes in the polymer which becomes adsorbed onto the filler.
Adsorption of polymer onto a surface restricts molecular motion,
changes the density of packing of polymer chains, and modifies the
conformation and orientation of chain segments in the neighborhood
of the surface. Although rigid fillers may either increase or

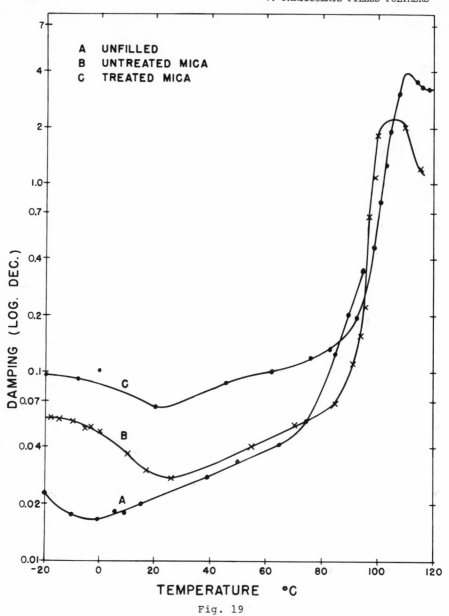

Fig. 19

Damping of a mica-filled phenoxy resin. Curve C is for
mica treated with dichlorodimethylsilane on the surface.

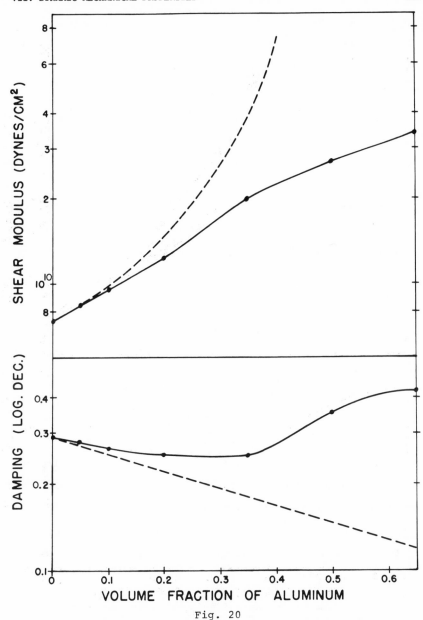

Fig. 20

Dynamic mechanical properties of polyethylene filled with
aluminum powder. Dotted lines are theoretical curves for
perfect adhesion with no agglomeration. [Modified from
Boehme, J. Appl. Polymer Sci., 12, 1097 (1968).]

decrease the damping as measured by G"/G', such fillers nearly
always increase the imaginary part of the modulus G". This is
because the increase in modulus G' more than compensates for any
decrease in G"/G' in the equation G" = (G"/G')G'.

Amplitude effects are much more prominent in composites than
with unfilled polymers (143-145). At low stress or strain
amplitudes, the dynamic mechanical properties are nearly independen
of the amplitude. However, at higher amplitudes, the modulus of
filled materials decreases and the damping increases. These
effects result from one or more of the following: 1. The adhesive
bond between the filler and polymer is broken. 2. The stress
concentrations around the filler particles result in many craze
cracks in the polymer. 3. Agglomerates of particles become broken.

Composites consisting of two polymeric phases such as polyblend
block, and graft polymers have two glass transitions characteristic
of the material in each phase. The modulus-temperature curves show
two sharp drops, and the damping curves show two peaks (34-36,106,
146-154). The relative heights of the two damping peaks is
determined by the concentration of the two components and by the
morphology of the system. Many of the commercial high impact
polystyrenes have a dispersed rubbery phase containing inclusions
of rigid polystyrene. The size of the damping peak for the
rubber phase is not determined by the amount of pure rubber but
by the amount of rubber plus the inclusions inside the rubber
particles (155-157).

Casting from different solvents can bring about changes in
morphology, including phase inversion. These changes in morphology
will bring about changes in the relative sizes of the two damping
peaks (34-36,106). This phenomenon is illustrated in Figure 39

of Chapter 4 (34). The more continuous a phase is, the higher is
its damping peak for a given composition. Good solvents for a
polymer tend to make it the continuous phase, while poor solvents
tend to make a polymer a more dispersed phase. It is even possible
to change the morphology so much by freeze drying some polyblends
that they appear to be single phase materials with only one damping
peak (35).

   In changing the composition of polyblends and block polymers
from one pure component to the other, a series of morphological
changes occur (38,39,41,152,158-161). On adding a little rubber
to a rigid polymer, the rubber becomes a dispersed phase. As the
concentration of rubber increases, both the rigid and rubbery
phases become continuous; this is the composition region where
inversion of the phases takes place. At still higher concentrations of rubber, the rigid phase becomes dispersed in the rubber.
Figure 7 shows how the modulus changes for a series of styrene-
butadiene-styrene block polymers (39). The experimental points
can be accurately predicted by the method discussed in the section
on moduli of systems undergoing phase inversion (38). The
modified Halpin-Tsai equations (shown as the upper and lower curves)
fit the experimental points with the following values: $A = 3.0$,
$A_i = 0.86$, $\phi_m = 0.80$, $\phi_m' = 0.85$, and Poisson's ratio is 0.5 for
the polybutadiene and 0.35 for polystyrene. This value of $A = 3.0$
would indicate that the polystyrene is elongated into short rods
or is made up of agglomerated spheres up to a volume fraction of
about 0.15. Between volume fractions of 0.15 and 0.80 of polystyrene, both phases form interlocking networks and are both
continuous phases. Above a polystyrene volume fraction of 0.8,
the rubber appears to be a dispersion of spherical particles in
the polystyrene.

VIII. Other Mechanical Properties

A. Impact Strength

Rigid fillers in a rigid polymer generally decrease the
impact strength of a polymer (93). There are a few exceptions
which are not clearly understood, but the impact strength is
largely determined by the dewetting and crazing phenomena. As
illustrated in Figure 21A a tensile stress produces a type of
stress concentration that results in dewetting and cavitation at

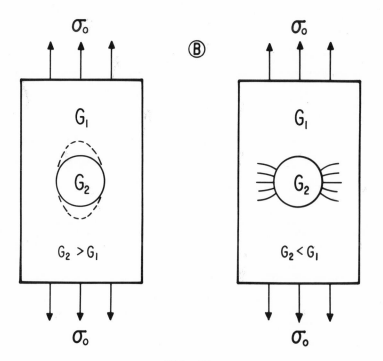

Fig. 21

(Left). Dewetting of a rigid filler particle in a matrix
of lower modulus. (Right). Crazing of a polymer around
a filler particle (or void) when the matrix has a higher
modulus than the filler particle.

the poles of a spherical particle (89, 162, 163). After dewetting
takes place, the nature of the stress concentration changes so as
to tend to produce cracks or crazing at the equator of the
particles as shown in Figure 21B.

On the other hand, rigid polymers filled with elastomeric
particles are capable of having very high impact strengths if good
adhesion exists between the phases. The impact strength of such
materials was discussed in Chapter 5.

B. Heat Distortion Temperature

Fillers generally increase the heat distortion temperature
of a material (164-168). This increase is mostly due to the
increase in modulus and the reduction of high temperature creep
rather than due to any large increase in the glass transition
temperature. The effect of modulus on heat distortion temperature
was discussed in Chapter 6. The increase in heat distortion
temperature can be large — often as much as 10° or 20°C or more.
Fillers often increase the heat distortion temperature of
crystalline and crosslinked polymers much more than they increase
it for glassy polymers. The increase in heat distortion
temperature for such materials is a result of the shape of their
modulus versus temperature curve and the increase in modulus on
the addition of filler. Figure 22 compares the deformation
behavior of polyethylene (density 0.95) with the same polymer
filled with 20 volume percent of kaolin (168). In this tensile
load type of test, the heat distortion temperature may be defined
arbitrarily as the temperature at which the deformation equals
1%. Table 7 lists the heat distortion temperature at two stress
levels. The filler raised the heat distortion temperature 24 to
27°C.

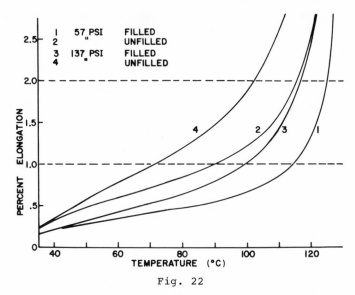

Fig. 22

Heat distortion temperature as measured by a tensile
elongation test in which the temperature is increased at
a rate of 2°C/minute. Polymer is polyethylene (ρ = 0.95),
either unfilled or filled with kaolin to a volume fraction
of 0.2.

Table 7

Heat Distortion Temperature of Polyethylene

Polymer	Load (psi)	Heat Distortion Temperature (°C)
Unfilled	57	90
Filled	57	114
Unfilled	137	72
Filled	137	99

C. Hardness and Wear

Rigid fillers are much harder than plastics as measured
by most tests, so it is not surprising that such fillers increase
the hardness of the composite over that of the polymer. Possibly
related to hardness is the abrasion and wear of composites.
Abrasion and wear are especially important in such applications as
plastic bearings (169,170), floor covering materials (53,171), and
automobile tires (172,173). Other factors in addition to hardness
which affect wear are coefficient of friction and the shape of the
filler particles. For instance, irregular shaped particles of
aluminum oxide in polytetrafluoroethylene increased the rate of
wear by a factor of several times over that found with spherical
particles in the same polymer (174). Both shapes of particles
increased the rate of wear over that of the unfilled polymer. It
was also noted that 10% irregular shaped particles doubled the
coefficient of friction compared to spherical particles.

In the above example, fillers increased the rate of wear.
However, in tires and in many kinds of floor tile, it has been
found that fillers greatly decrease the rate of wear. The wear of
filled polymers is strongly dependent upon the relative size of
the filler particles and the size of the abrasive. Wear is least
when the filler particles are large compared to the size of the
abrasive particles if the adhesion between filler and matrix is
good. Wear and abrasion are difficult tests to correlate with
actual use tests. In one cooperative test program seven different
floor covering materials were tested on 21 kinds of abrasion
machines (171). Most of the results from the different machines
did not agree with one another, and the correlation with practical

wear tests was generally poor. Usually, if there is a strong
adhesive bond between the filler and the polymer, fillers will
decrease the rate of wear of a polymer. On the other hand, these
filled polymers may take on many of the characteristics of sandpaper and may greatly increase the wear of whatever material they
come in contact with. For instance, polymers filled with
irregularly shaped particles of very hard fillers such as silica
can cause excessive wear to the parts of injection molding
machines.

Fillers can either enhance or degrade many properties. The
effects are difficult to predict because the final properties
depend so strongly on the type of testing machine, on the type of
fillers, and upon the nature of the interface and the strength of
the adhesion between the phases. As noted above, fillers may
either increase or decrease the rate of abrasion. Similar
conflicting evidence can be found for many other properties. For
instance, talc improves the impact fatigue life of polyvinyl
chloride-acrylonitrile rubber blends (175). On the other hand,
fillers in an epoxy resin lowers the resistance to compressive
fatigue (176). Fillers, which give good adhesion to the polymer,
including those treated by some silanes, improve the tear strength
of rubbers (165,177). However, if the fillers make the polymer too
brittle, or if the adhesion is poor, the tear resistance decreases
with increase of filler concentration.

D. Coefficients of Thermal Expansion

Polymers have much larger coefficients of expansion than
most rigid fillers. This mismatch in the coefficients of thermal
expansion of the components making up a composite produces several

important effects: 1. In cooling down from the fabrication or curing temperature, the polymer exerts a squeezing pressure on the filler. This tight fit of the filler against the polymer prevents frictional motion at the interface except for large forces even if the adhesion is poor. Thus, the modulus is nearly the same in most cases for both good and poor adhesion. 2. The polymer near the surface of a filler particle may be subjected to strong tensile forces in the tangential direction as a result of the mismatch of the coefficients of expansion. If the stress-strain curves of a rigid polymer is non-Hookean, the modulus of the composite can be less than what is expected, and the relative modulus G/G_1 will increase as the temperature is raised (43). 3. The squeezing of the filler particles may produce such high tensile stresses in the polymer that it may crack and reduce the strength of the composite. 4. The coefficient of expansion of a composite may be lowered from the high values characteristic of a pure polymer down to values characteristic of metals and other structural materials.

A number of equations have been proposed for calculating the coefficient of thermal expansion of a composite from material constants of the components (20,178-180). The different equations often predict quite different values for the coefficient of expansion of a given composite. Some experimental data agree with one equation while other data agree with a different equation (77). However, nearly all the equations predict coefficients of expansion which are less than what would be calculated from the simple "rule of mixtures" because of mechanical restraints of the matrix by the filler particles.

For nearly spherical particles dispersed in a matrix, Kerner (20)

derived the following equation for the coefficient of volume
expansion of a composite:

$$\alpha = \alpha_1 \phi_1 + \alpha_2 \phi_2 - (\alpha_1 - \alpha_2) \phi_1 \phi_2 \; \frac{\dfrac{1}{B_1} - \dfrac{1}{B_2}}{\dfrac{\phi_1}{B_2} + \dfrac{\phi_2}{B_1} + \dfrac{3}{4G_1}} \; . \qquad (33)$$

The volume coefficients of thermal expansion of the composite,
polymer, and filler are α, α_1, and α_2, respectively. The bulk
moduli of the components are B_1 and B_2. Equation 33 does not
deviate much from the "rule of mixtures" since spheres do not
impose mechanical restrictions on the matrix to the extent that
fibers do.

   If the filler particles are rod-like in shape, and are
randomly oriented in three directions, it is believed that the
Thomas (179) equation, or the logarithmic rule of mixtures, gives
a better estimate than the Kerner equation.

$$\log \alpha = \phi_1 \; \log \alpha_1 + \phi_2 \log \alpha_2 . \qquad (34)$$

Figure 23 compares the different equations for coefficients of
expansion for the case where the pertinent material constants are:

$$\alpha_1 = 10^{-4} \qquad\qquad\qquad \alpha_2 = 10^{-5}$$

$$K_1 = 5 \times 10^{10} \qquad\qquad K_2 = 1.67 \times 10^{11}$$

$$G_1 = 1.07 \times 10^{10} \qquad\quad G_2 = 1.25 \times 10^{11}$$

   All of the theories must be incorrect to the extent that the
coefficient of expansion is a smooth function of composition up to
the pure filler phase. Actually, there must be a break in the
curves where the filler particles are all in contact with one anoth

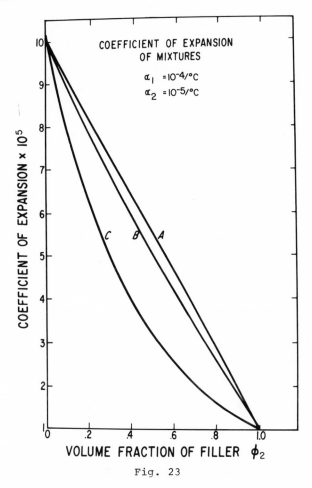

Fig. 23

Coefficient of thermal expansion. A = "rule of mixtures,"
B = Equation 33, C = Equation 34.

at the maximum packing fraction ϕ_m. In practice, this error due to
particle-particle contact may be small.

IX. Summary

The main effect of rigid fillers is to increase the elastic

modulus of a composite or the viscosity of a fluid suspension.
The important factors in determining the modulus are the concentration of the filler, shape of the particle (Einstein coefficient),
relative modulus of the components, and the manner in which the
particles pack. The nature of the interface and the degree of
adhesion generally are not very important factors in determining
the elastic modulus, but these factors are very important in
determining the strength and stress-strain behavior of composites.
Fillers tend to reduce drastically the elongation to break also.

The creep behavior often can be predicted from the relative
modulus of the composite and the creep behavior of the unfilled
polymer if dewetting has not occurred. After dewetting has occurred
the creep rate increases very rapidly. Some fillers, especially in
an agglomerated state, cause unusually high energy dissipation and
damping. Such composites may be used to dampen undesired vibrations and as sound deadening materials. Fillers increase the heat
distortion temperature. This effect is largely the result of the
increase in modulus rather than due to any large increase in T_g.

A second class of composites are the inverted systems such as
foams and high impact polymers. Inverted composites have moduli
which are less than those of the unfilled polymer. However, their
elongation to break, and often their impact strength, are greater
than that of the unfilled polymer.

X.   Problems

1.   The relative viscosity η/η_1 of a liquid epoxy suspension is 3.0
     at low rates of shear. The suspension is cured to give a rigid
     material with a Poisson's ratio of 0.4. What is the expected
     relative modulus G/G_1 if G_2/G_1 is very large?

2. A rubber containing 30 volume percent of a rigid spherical
    filler has a relative modulus G/G_1 of 2.42. The filler has a
    modulus 10,000 times that of the rubber. The rubber is cooled
    down to a temperature 100°C below its glass transition
    temperature where its Poisson's ratio becomes 0.35, and its
    modulus becomes 0.10 that of the filler. Assuming no thermal
    stresses, what is the relative modulus of the cooled composite?

3. A suspension containing 5 volume percent of a filler has a
    relative viscosity η/η_1 of 1.26. What can you say about the
    nature of the filler?

4. Prove that $E/E_1 \doteq G/G_1$.

5. Prove that the equation $M/M_1 = \dfrac{1 + AB\phi_2}{1 - B\phi_2}$ becomes the law of
    mixtures when A approaches infinity and that as A approaches
    zero, the equation becomes $\dfrac{1}{M} = \dfrac{\phi_1}{M_1} + \dfrac{\phi_2}{M_2}$.

6. If spherical particles could be packed in a perfect hexagonal
    close packed lattice or in a simple cubic lattice rather than
    in the more usual random packing, which of the two packings
    would give the higher modulus in a composite for the same volume
    concentration of filler?

7. A rectangular composite specimen 0.025 inches thick contains
    spheres 0.001 inch diameter. Young's modulus was measured in
    flexure to give a relative modulus E/E_1 of 2.5. What is the
    magnitude of the expected error in the modulus measurement?

8. For a crystalline polymer above its T_g, assume that any value
    of the modulus greater than 10^7 dynes/cm² is due to the filler
    action of the rigid crystallites. The modulus of the crystals
    is 10^{12} dynes/cm². Calculate the modulus as a function of the

degree of crystallinity assuming: (a) The crystals are the
dispersed phase. (b). The crystals are the continuous phase.
Are either of these assumptions realistic for a crystalline
polymer?

9. A polymer filled with a water-soluble salt ($\phi_2 = 0.3$) has a
relative modulus G/G_1 of 2.42.   The composite is then soaked
in water for a long time to extract all the salt, thus leaving
voids where the salt particles once were.   If the particles of
salt were nearly spherical in shape, what is the relative
modulus of the extracted polymer with spherical voids?   The
polymer has a Poisson's ratio of 0.5, and the salt has a
modulus 1000 times as great as that of the polymer.

10. A rigid polymer has an elongation to break of 2%.   The polymer
is filled with 10 volume percent of a rigid filler which forms
a good adhesive bond with the polymer.   The elongation to
break of the composite is 1%.   Is this what you would expect?

11. A series of polyblends of a rubber in polystyrene have the
following characteristics: At low concentrations of polystyrene, the dispersed particles of polystyrene have an
aspect ratio of 4 to 1.   The maximum packing fraction of
polystyrene in the rubber is $\phi_m = 0.7$.   At small concentrations of rubber in polystyrene, the rubber appears to be
dispersed spheres, and the packing fraction of rubber in
polystyrene is $\phi_m' = 0.7$.   Phase inversion occurs over the
range of volume fractions from 0.3 to 0.7.   The polystyrene
has a modulus 1000 times that of the rubber and a Poisson's
ratio of 0.35.   Plot the relative modulus G/G_{rubber} over the
entire composition range from zero to 100% polystyrene.

12. An unfilled polymer obeys the Nutting equation, $\varepsilon(t) = K\sigma\, t^n$ with the values of $K = 5 \times 10^{-6}$ and $n = 0.25$. The units of stress are psi, and time is in seconds. The same polymer with 20 volume percent kaolin as filler has a modulus twice that of the unfilled polymer. With a load of 2000 psi on a specimen of the filled polymer, plot a graph of its expected creep from 1 second to 10^4 seconds.

13. The damping of some filled polymers obeys the equation

$$\left(\frac{G''}{G'}\right)_F = \left(\frac{G''}{G'}\right)_U \phi_1$$ where the subscripts F and U refer to filled and unfilled materials, respectively. Derive this equation, clearly stating what assumptions must be made. Why does not the equation $G''_F = G''_U\,\phi_1$ hold?

14. A composite contains a volume fraction of 0.40 of a particulate filler. It has a modulus of 1.8 times that of the unfilled polymer. Give at least 2 possible reasons why $G/G_1 = 1.8$ instead of what might normally be expected.

15. A polymer contains a filler in the form of short oriented rods. Two creep tests are made: (a) The load is applied parallel to the rods. (b). The load is applied perpendicular to the rods. How does the creep differ in the two cases?

16. Plot G/G_1 versus ϕ_2 for a suspension of spheres in a matrix with a Poisson's ratio of 0.5 for: 1. $\phi_m = 1$, $G_2/G_1 = 10$, 2. $\phi_m = 1$, $G_2/G_1 = \infty$, 3. $\phi_m = 0.64$, $G_2/G_1 = 10$, 4. $\phi_m = 0.64$, $G_2/G_1 = \infty$.

17. Mica in polystyrene gives a relative modulus G/G_1 of 8.0 at $\phi_2 = 0.35$. What is the Einstein coefficient of the mica flakes if $\phi_m = 1$ and $G_2/G_1 = \infty$?

18. What is the shear modulus of the following system which is undergoing phase inversion? $G_1 = 10^7$ dynes/cm^2, $G_2 = 10^{10}$ dynes/cm^2, $\phi_m = \phi_m' = 0.64$. The overall composition is 50-50 volume percent. Assume Poisson's ratio is 0.5 for both components. Before phase inversion starts, the dispersed phases are spheres.

19. A suspension of uniform spheres in a composite has a $\phi_m = 0.63$. A suspension of a mixture of spheres of different sizes has a $\phi_m = 0.75$. At a concentration of 35 volume percent spheres, how much is the relative modulus decreased by using the mixture? Assume $G_2/G_1 = 100$.

20. Estimate the upper limit expected for the Einstein coefficient of cubical particles. (Assume the cubes immobilize enough of the surrounding matrix to make the cubes behave as spherical particles.)

21. A composite is made up of spheres in a rubber, which has a shear modulus of 10^7 dynes/cm^2. The spheres have a shear modulus of 10^{11} dynes/cm^2. The temperature is lowered to below T_g so that the modulus of the unfilled polymer becomes 10^{10} dynes/cm^2, and Poisson's ratio changes from 0.50 to 0.35. What is the relative modulus G/G_1 above and below T_g at a concentration of spheres of 30 volume percent? Assume a maximum packing fraction of 1.0.

XI. References

1. A. Einstein, Ann. Physik, 17, 549 (1905); 19, 289 (1906); 34, 591 (1911).

2. R. Rutgers, Rheol. Acta, 2, 305 (1962).

3.   M. Mooney, J. Colloid Sci., 6, 162 (1951).

4.   R. K. McGeary, J. Amer. Ceram. Soc., 44, 513 (1961).

5.   T. B. Lewis and L. E. Nielsen, Trans. Soc. Rheol., 12, 421
     (1968).

6.   J. M. Burgers, Second Report on Viscosity and Plasticity,
     Nordemann, New York, 1938, p. 113.

7.   R. F. Landel, B. G. Moser, and A. J. Bauman, Proc. 4th
     Internat. Congr. Rheol., Part 2, E. H. Lee, Ed., Interscience,
     New York, 1965, p. 663.

8.   M. M. Cross, J. Colloid Interface Sci., 33, 30 (1970).

9.   M. M. Cross, Polymer Systems: Deformation and Flow,
     R. E. Wetton and R. W. Whorlow, Ed., Macmillan, London,
     1968, p. 263.

10. I. M. Krieger and T. J. Dougherty, Trans. Soc. Rheol., 3,
     137 (1959).

11. T. Gillespie, J. Colloid Sci., 22, 554 and 563 (1966).

12. N. Casson, Rheology of Disperse Systems, C. C. Mills, Ed.,
     Pergamon, Oxford, 1959, p. 84.

13. T. Matsumoto, A. Takashima, T. Masuda, and S. Onogi,
     Trans. Soc. Rheol., 14, 617 (1970).

14. J. N. Goodier, Phil.Mag., 22, 678 (1936).

15. H. M. Smallwood, J. Appl. Phys., 15, 758 (1944).

16. E. Guth, J. Appl. Phys., 16, 20 (1945).

17. Z. Hashin, Proc. 4th Internat. Congr. Rheol., Vol. 3,
     E. H. Lee, Ed., Interscience, New York, 1965, p. 30.

18. L. E. Nielsen, J. Composite Mater., 2, 120 (1968).

19. T. B. Lewis and L. E. Nielsen, J. Appl. Polymer Sci., 14
     1449 (1970).

20. E. H. Kerner, Proc. Phys. Soc., B69, 808 (1956).

21. Z. Hashin and S. Shtrikman, J. Mech. Phys. Solids, 11,
     127 (1963).

22. S. W. Tsai, U. S. Govt. Rept., AD 834851, 1968.

23. J. E. Ashton, J. C. Halpin, and P. H. Petit, Primer on
     Composite Analysis, Technomic, Stamford, Conn., 1969.

24. J. C. Halpin, J. Composite Mater., 3, 732 (1969).

25. L. E. Nielsen, J. Appl. Phys., 41, 4626 (1970).

26. H. A. Flocke, Kaut. Gummi Kunstst., 18, 717 (1965).

27. J. G. Brodnyan, Trans. Soc. Rheol., 12, 357 (1968).

28. K. H. Sweeny and R. D. Geckler, J. Appl. Phys., 25, 1135
     (1954).

29. G. F. Eveson, Rheology of Disperse Systems, C. C. Mills, Ed.,
     Pergamon, Oxford, 1959, p. 61.

30. R. J. Farris, Trans. Soc. Rheol., 12, 281 (1968).

31. L. C. E. Struik, H. W. Bree, and F. R. Schwarzl, Shear
     Modulus of Rubbers Containing Fillers with a Bimodal Size
     Distribution, U. S. Dept. Comm. Rept. AD 662897 (1967).

32. Y. Sato and J. Furukawa, Rubber Chem. Techn., 35, 857
     (1962), and 36, 1081 (1963).

33. L. E. Nielsen, Appl. Polymer Symposia, No. 12, 249 (1969).

34. T. Miyamoto, K. Kodama, and K. Shibayama, J. Polymer Sci.,
     A2, 8, 2095 (1970).

35. S. Miyata and T. Hata, Proc. 5th Internat. Congr. Rheol.,
     Vol. 3, S. Onogi, Ed., Univ. Tokyo Press, Tokyo, 1970, p. 71.

36. E. B. Atkinson and R. F. Eagling, Physical Properties of
     Polymers, Soc. Chem. Ind. Monograph No. 5, 1959, p. 197.

37. R. W. Gray and N. G. McCrum, J. Polymer Sci., A2, 7,
     1329 (1969).

38. L. E. Nielsen, Rheol. Acta, 13, 86 (1974). 6th Internat.
     Congr. Rheol, Lyon, France, Sept. 1972.

39. G. Holden, E. T. Bishop, and N. R. Legge, J. Polymer Sci.,
     C26, 37 (1969).

40. M. Takayanagi, Proc. 4th Internat. Congr. Rheol., Vol. 1,

     E. H. Lee and A. L. Copley, Ed., Wiley, New York, 1965, p.161.

41. D. H. Kaelble, Trans. Soc. Rheol., 15, 235 (1971).

42. B-L. Lee and L. E. Nielsen, J. Composite Mater., 6, 136 (1972).

43. L. E. Nielsen and T. B. Lewis, J. Polymer Sci., A2, 7,

     1705 (1969).

44. L. E. Nielsen, R. A. Wall, and P. G. Richmond, SPE J., 11,

     22 (Sept. 1955).

45. J. R. Joseph, J. L. Kardos, and L. E. Nielsen, J. Appl.

     Polymer Sci., 12, 1151 (1968).

46. M. Narkis and L. Nicholais, J. Appl. Polymer Sci., 15,

     469 (1971).

47. R. Bostwick and R. H. Carey, Ind. Eng. Chem., 42, 848 (1950).

48. G. V. Vinogradov, Yu. G. Yanovsky, and E. I. Frenkin,

     Rheol. Acta, 7, 277 (1968).

49. R. D. Boehme, J. Appl. Polymer Sci., 12, 1097 (1968).

50. Anonymous, Modern Plast., 43, #12, 102 (1966).

51. G. W. Becker and H. Oberst, Kolloid Zeit., 148, 6 (1956).

52. T. L. Smith, Trans. Soc. Rheol., 3, 113 (1959).

53. A. W. McKee, SPE J., 18, 186 (1962).

54. A. W. Brown, SPE J., 18, #10, 1259 (1962).

55. J. Economy, L. C. Wohrer, and V. I. Matkovich, SAMPE J., 5,

     #1, 23 (1969).

56. F. R. Barnet and J. Cuevas, Modern Plast., 44, #4, 161 (1966).

57. L. J. Cohen and O. Ishai, J. Compos. Mater., 1, 390 (1967).

58. K. C. Radford, J. Mater. Sci., 6, 1286 (1971).

59. S. Sahu and L. J. Broutman, Polymer Eng. Sci., 12, 91 (1972).

60. F. R. Schwarzl, H. W. Bree, C. J. Nederveen, G. A. Schwippert,

     L. C. E. Struik, and C. W. Van der Wal, Rheol. Acta, 5,

     270 (1966).

61. F. R. Schwarzl, H. W. Bree, G. A. Schwippert, L. C. E. Struik, and C. W. Van der Wal, Proc. 5th Internat. Congr. Rheol., Vol. 3, S. Onogi, Ed., Univ. Tokyo, Tokyo, 1970, p.3.

62. M. G. Sharma and W. F. St. Lawrence, Proc. 5th Internat. Congr. Rheol., Vol 3, S. Onogi, Ed., Univ. Tokyo, Tokyo, 1970, p. 47.

63. R. F. Landel, Trans. Soc. Rheol., 2, 53 (1958).

64. L. O. Amberg and A. E. Robinson, Ind. Eng. Chem., 53, 368 (1961).

65. A. R. Payne, J. Appl. Polymer Sci., 6, 368 (1962).

66. B. B. Boonstra and A. I. Medalia, Rubber Chem. Techn., 36, 115 (1963).

67. L. E. Nielsen, Trans. Soc. Rheol., 13, 141 (1969).

68. C. J. Nederveen and H. W. Bree, U. S. Dept. of Commerce Rept. AD 655634 (1967).

69. L. E. Nielsen, J. Appl. Polymer Sci., 10, 97 (1966).

70. L. Nicolais and M. Narkis, Polymer Eng. Sci., 11, 194 (1971).

71. R. J. Farris, J. Appl. Polymer Sci., 8, 25 (1964).

72. R. J. Farris, Trans. Soc. Rheol., 12, 303, 315 (1968).

73. K. C. Bryant and D. C. Bisset, Rubber Chem. Techn., 30 610 (1957).

74. F. R. Schwarzl, H. W. Bree, and C. J. Nederveen, Proc. 4th Internat. Congr. Rheol., Vol. 3, E. H. Lee, Ed., Interscience, New York, 1965, p. 241.

75. A. E. Oberth, Rubber Chem. Techn., 40, 1337 (1967).

76. R. Shuttleworth, Europ. Polymer J., 4, 31 (1968).

77. L. E. Nielsen, J. Composite Mater., 1, 100 (1967).

78. R. Sabia and F. R. Eirich, J. Polymer Sci., A2, 1909 (1964).

79. E. P. Plueddemann, H. A. Clark, L. E. Nelson, and K. R. Hoffman, Modern Plast., 39, #12, 135 (1962).

80. S. Sterman and J. G. Marsden, Polymer Eng. Sci., 6, 97 (1966).

81. S. Sterman and J. G. Marsden, Modern Plast. 43, #11, 133
     (1966).

82. B. M. Vanderbilt and J. J. Jaruzelski, Ind. Eng. Chem., Prod.
     Res. Dev., 1, 188 (1962).

83. L. P. Ziemianski, C. A. Pagano, and M. W. Ranney, Rubber
     World, 163, #1, 53 (1970).

84. E. L. Warrick and P. C. Lauterbur, Ind. Eng. Chem., 47,
     486 (1955).

85. F. M. Lewis, Rubber Chem. Techn., 35, 1222 (1962).

86. P. I. A. Martin, British Plast., 38, 95 (1965).

87. H. Alter, J. Appl. Polymer Sci., 9, 1525 (1965).

88. H. W. Kuhlmann, F. Wolter, and E. R. Mueller, Trans. SPE, 5,
     101 (1965).

89. J. N. Goodier, J. Appl. Mech. (Trans ASME), 55, A39 (1933).

90. A. A. Griffith, Phil. Trans. Royal Soc., London, A221, 163
     (1920-21).

91. B. B. Boonstra and A. I. Medalia, Rubber Age, 92, 892 (1963).

92. E. B. Prestridge, J. Appl. Polymer Sci., 7, 27 (1963).

93. G. P. Larson, Modern Plast., 35, 157 (May 1958).

94. A. G. Sands, R. C. Clark, and E. J. Kohn, U. S. Dept.
     Commerce Rept. AD 640054 (1966).

95. O. R. Strauch, SPE J., 25, #9, 38 (1969).

96. O. Ishai and S. R. Bodner, Trans. Soc. Rheol., 14, 253 (1970).

97. R. M. Gruver, U. S. Dept. Commerce Rept. AD 103538 (1956).

98. E. G. Dingman, SPE J., 17, 981 (1961).

99. R. N. Haward and J. Mann, Proc. Royal Soc., A282, 120 (1964).

100. K. Fletcher, R. N. Haward, and J. Mann, Chem. Ind., No. 45,
     1854 (1965).

101. K. Satake, J. Appl. Polymer Sci., 14, 1007 (1970).

102. K. C. Rusch and R. H. Beck, Jr., J. Polymer Sci., C30,
     447 (1970).

103. J-M. Charrier and R. J. P. Ranchoux, Polymer Eng. Sci., 11, 381 (1971).

104. M. Baer, J. Appl. Polymer Sci., 16, 1109 (1972).

105. G. L. Wilkes and R. S. Stein, J. Polymer Sci., A2, 7, 1525 (1969).

106. J. F. Beecher, L. Marker, R. D. Bradford, and S. L. Aggarwal, J. Polymer Sci., C26, 117 (1969).

107. G. S. Fielding-Russell, Rubber Chem. Techn., 45, 252 (1972).

108. S. Ye. Bresler, L. M. Pyrkov, S. Ya. Frenkel, L. A. Lauis, and S. I. Klenin, Polymer Sci. USSR (Engl. Transl.) 4, 89 (1963).

109. W. J. Frazer, Chem. Ind., No. 33, 1399 (1966).

110. H. Keskkula, Appl. Polymer Sympos., 15, 51 (1970).

111. T. T. Jones, British Plast., 33, 525 (1960).

112. A. N. Gent and A. G. Thomas, J. Appl. Polymer Sci., 1, 107 (1959).

113. A. N. Gent and A. G. Thomas, Rubber Chem. Techn., 36, 597 (1963).

114. V. A. Matonis, SPE J., 20, 1024 (1964).

115. K. C. Rusch, J. Appl. Polymer Sci., 13, 2297 (1969); 14, 1263 (1970).

116. S. Baxter and T. T. Jones, Plast. Polymer, 40, #146, 69 (1972).

117. C. J. Benning, Plastic Foams - Structure, Properties, and Applications, Vol. 2, Interscience, New York, 1969, p. 200.

118. A. N. Gent and A. G. Thomas, J. Appl. Polymer Sci., 2, 354 (1959).

119. R. H. Carey and E. A. Rogers, Modern Plast., 33, 139 (Aug. 1956).

120. L. C. Cessna, Polymer Eng. Sci., 11, 211 (1971).

121. R. F. Landel and T. L. Smith, ARS J., 31, 599 (1961).

122. L. C. E. Struik, H. W. Bree, and F. R. Schwarzl, Proc.
     Internat. Rubber Conf., Brighton, Maclaren & Sons, London,
     1967, p. 205.

123. S. N. Ganz and V. D. Parkhomenko, Polymer Mech. (Engl.
     Transl.), 1, #3, 39 (1966).

124. F. R. Schwarzl and H. W. Bree, U. S. Dept. Commerce Rept.,
     AD 700700 (1969).

125. L. E. Nielsen, J. Appl. Polymer Sci., 13, 1800 (1969).

126. E. G. Bobalek and R. M. Evans, SPE Trans., 1, 93 (1961).

127. G. R. Cotten and B. B. Boonstra, J. Appl. Polymer Sci., 9,
     3395 (1965).

128. K. C. Rusch, J. Macromol. Sci., B2, 421 (1968).

129. M. Shen and D. H. Kaelble, J. Polymer Sci., B8, 149 (1970).

130. M. L. Williams, R. F. Landel, and J. D. Ferry, J. Amer.
     Chem. Soc., 77, 3701 (1955).

131. C. K. Lim, R. E. Cohen, and N. W. Tschoegl, Adv. Chem.
     Series, 99, 397 (1971).

132. G. L. Ball and I. O. Salyer, J. Acoust. Soc. Amer., 39,
     663 (1966).

133. H. Oberst, L. Bohn, and F. Linhardt, Kunststoffe, 51, 495
     (1961).

134. H. Thurn, Kunststoffe, 50, 606 (1960).

135. A. Wambach and L. E. Nielsen, unpublished data, Washington
     University.

136. I. Galperin, J. Appl. Polymer Sci., 11, 1475 (1967).

137. A. Yim and L. E. St. Pierre, J. Polymer Sci., B7, 237 (1969).

138. Yu. S. Lipatov, T. E. Lipatova, Ya. P. Vasilieko, and
     L. M. Sergeyeva, Polymer Sci. USSR (Engl. transl.), 4, 920
     (1963).

139. Yu. S. Lipatov, _Trans. J. Plast. Inst._, 34, 83 (1966).

140. G. Kraus and J. T. Gruver, _J. Polymer Sci._, A2, 8, 571
     (1970).

141. D. H. Droste and A. T. DiBenedetto, _J. Appl. Polymer Sci._,
     13, 2149 (1969).

142. S. A. Shreiner, P. I. Zubov, T. A. Volkova, and I. I.
     Vokulonskaya, _Colloid J. USSR_ (Engl. Transl.), 26, #5, 541
     (1965).

143. A. R. Payne, _J. Appl. Polymer Sci._, 6, 57 (1962).

144. A. M. Gessler and A. R. Payne, _J. Appl. Polymer Sci._, 7,
     1815 (1963).

145. J. M. Lifshitz and A. Rotem, _J. Composite Mater._, 3,
     412 (1969).

146. R. Buchdahl and L. E. Nielsen, _J. Appl. Phys._, 21, 482
     (1950).

147. R. Buchdahl and L. E. Nielsen, _J. Polymer Sci._, 15, 1 (1955).

148. J. A. Blanchette and L. E. Nielsen, _J. Polymer Sci._, 20,
     317 (1956).

149. M. Baer, _J. Polymer Sci._, A2, 417 (1964).

150. E. Perry, _J. Appl. Polymer Sci._, 8, 2605 (1964).

151. R. J. Angelo, R. M. Ikeda, and M. L. Wallach, _Polymer_,
     6, 141 (1965).

152. K. Fujimoto and N. Yoshimura, _Rubber Chem. Techn._, 41,
     1109 (1968).

153. H. Keskkula and S. G. Turley, _J. Polymer Sci._, B7, 697
     (1969).

154. P. Bauer, J. Hennig, and G. Schreyer, _Angew. Makromol. Chem._,
     11, 145 (1970).

155. C. B. Buchnall and M. M. Hall, _J. Mater. Sci._, 6, 95 (1971).

156. G. Cigna, _J. Appl. Polymer Sci._, 14, 1781 (1970).

157. E. R. Wagner and L. M. Robeson, Rubber Chem. Techn., 43,
      1129 (1970).

158. M. Takayanagi, Memoirs Faculty Engineering, Kyushu Univ.,
      23, #1, 1 (1963).

159. G. M. Estes, S. L. Cooper, and A. V. Tobolsky, Rev. Macromol.
      Chem., C4, 313 (1970).

160. M. Matsuo, T. K. Kwei, D. Klempner, and H. L. Frisch,
      Polymer Eng. Sci., 10, 327 (1970).

161. G. Kraus, K. W. Rollmann, and J. T. Gruver, Macromol.,
      3, 92 (1970).

162. J. Rehner, Jr., Rubber Chem. Techn., 17, 865 (1944).

163. A. E. Oberth and R. S. Bruenner, Trans. Soc. Rheol., 9,
      165 (1965).

164. I. E. Neimark, A. A. Chuiko, and I. B. Slinyakova, SPE
      Trans., 2, 135 (1962).

165. W. J. Frissell, Plast. Techn., 2, 723 (1956).

166. E. A. Noga and R. T. Woodhams, SPE J., 26, #9, 23 (1970).

167. F. G. Krautz, SPE J., 27, #8, 74 (1971).

168. L. E. Nielsen, unpublished data.

169. P. H. Pinchbeck, Wear, 5, 85 (1962).

170. W. A. Glaeser, Wear, 6, 93 (1963).

171. Anonymous, Wear, 4, 479 (1961).

172. A. Schallamach, Wear, 1, 384 (1957), or Rubber Chem. Techn.,
      31, 982 (1958).

173. A. Schallamach, Proc. Phys. Soc., 67B, 883 (1954), or
      Rubber Chem. Techn., 28, 906 (1955).

174. C. J. Speerschneider and C. H. Li, Wear, 5, 392 (1962).

175. C. C. Lee, W. Rovatti, S. M. Skinner, and E. G. Bobalek,
      J. Appl. Polymer Sci., 9, 2047 (1965).

176. H. L. Parry and R. W. Hewitt, Ind. Eng. Chem., 49, 1103 (1957).

177. P. W. Libby, J. Iannicelli, and C. R. McGill, <u>Rubber Chem</u>.
      <u>Techn</u>., 40, 1598 (1967).

178. P. S. Turner, <u>J. Res. Nat. Bur. Stds</u>., 37, 239 (1946).

179. J. P. Thomas, U. S. Dept. Commerce Rept. AD 287826.

180. R. A. Shapery, <u>J. Composite Mater</u>., 2, 380 (1968).

Chapter 8

Fiber-Filled Composites and Other Composites

I. Introduction

Most of the materials traditionally considered as composites have used fibers as the filler phase. These include
glass fibers in polyesters and epoxies, glass fabric laminates,
and filament-wound vessels. Other fiber-filled composites
include asbestos fibers in phenolic resins and chopped glass
fibers in numerous thermoplastic materials such as polystyrene
and nylons. Recent developments are boron and graphite fibers
in epoxy resins or in high temperature resins such as the
polyimides. Super strong small single crystal fibers of alumina
or silicon carbide are called whiskers, and they offer some
promise in aerospace applications (1-3).

The importance of fiber-filled composites arises largely
from the fact that such materials can have unusually high
strength and stiffness for a given weight of material. The
specific strength (tensile strength/density) and the specific
modulus (modulus/density) can surpass the values for even the
best of the metals. The superior values of composites are
illustrated in Table 1. When polymer composites are compared
to unfilled polymers, the improvements offered by composites are
spectacular. Many of the fiber-filled composites are anisotropic
with tremendous strength in one direction; this can be used to
advantage in certain applications by proper design.

453

Table 1

Specific Modulus and Strength of Some Materials

Material	Specific Modulus (inches)	Specific Strength (inches)
Aluminum	1×10^8	1×10^5
Stainless steel	1.1×10^8	8.8×10^5
Polystyrene	1.1×10^7	1.85×10^5
Epoxy resin	1.1×10^7	2.2×10^5
Uniaxial glass - epoxy composite $\phi_2 = .7$	9.2×10^7	2.6×10^6
Uniaxial boron - epoxy composite $\phi_2 = .7$	5.9×10^8	3.7×10^6
Uniaxial graphite - epoxy composite. High modulus fiber, $\phi_2 = .6$	4.9×10^8	2.1×10^6
Uniaxial graphite - epoxy composite. Low modulus fiber, $\phi_2 = .6$	3.0×10^8	3.4×10^6

$$\text{Specific Property} = \frac{\text{Property in lbs/in}^2 \text{ (psi)}}{\text{Density in lbs/in}^3} = \text{inches.}$$

Density (lbs/in^3)= 0.036 x Density (g/cm^3).

ϕ_2 = volume fraction of fibers.

Fibers are used in a variety of fabrication techniques (3-6).
These include: 1. Impregnated mats of fibers. 2. Laminates of
sheets and woven fabrics. 3. Filament winding of resin-coated
continuous fibers around an axis of rotation to form a vessel.
4. Injection molding of polymers containing short fibers.

II. Moduli of Fiber-Filled Composites

Most fiber-filled composites are anisotropic, and as

discussed in Chapter 2, such materials have at least 5 or 6
independent elastic moduli so that their properties are
different in different directions. Often all the fibers are
aligned in one direction to give a uniaxially oriented material
such as illustrated in Figure 1 of Chapter 2. Of the 5 or 6
moduli, four are considered the most important in most situations.
These are the following: 1. The longitudinal Young's modulus E_L
in which the load is applied parallel to the fibers. 2. The
transverse Young's modulus E_T in which the load is applied
perpendicular to the fibers. 3. The longitudinal-transverse
shear modulus G_{LT} in which the shearing stress in the polymer
acts in a direction along the fibers. 4. The transverse shear
modulus G_{TT} in which the shearing stress is applied perpendicular
to the fibers.

Many equations have been proposed for estimating these
moduli (7-19). Only a few of the simplest or most accurate
equations will be discussed for these uniaxially oriented
systems. In the longitudinal direction, a tensile force tends
to stretch the fiber and the matrix the same amount. Therefore,
for very long fibers, the longitudinal Young's modulus in
tension is given accurately by:

$$E_L = E_1 \phi_1 + E_2 \phi_2 \qquad\qquad (1)$$

The moduli of the matrix and fibers are E_1 and E_2, respectively,
and the corresponding volume fractions of the two phases are
ϕ_1 and ϕ_2. The top curve of Figure 1 is a plot of equation 1
for the case where $E_2/E_1 = 25$ (glass fibers in an epoxy resin).

The transverse Young's modulus E_T has been estimated by
many equations (7-17). The most convenient of these equations

is the Halpin-Tsai (13-15) equations as modified by Nielsen (20, 21):

$$\frac{E_T}{E_1} = \frac{1 + AB\phi_2}{1 - B\psi\phi_2} \tag{2}$$

where

$$A = 0.5, \qquad B = \frac{E_2/E_1 - 1}{E_2/E_1 + A} \tag{3}$$

and

$$\psi \doteq 1 + \left(\frac{1 - \phi_m}{\phi_m^2}\right)\phi_2 . \tag{4}$$

The factor ψ takes into account the maximum packing fraction ϕ_m of the fibers as discussed in Chapter 7. For cubic packing of fibers, $\phi_m = 0.785$, while for hexagonal packing, $\phi_m = 0.907$; in general ϕ_m will lie between these limits near the random close packing case where $\phi_2 = 0.82$. The lowest curve of Figure 1 illustrates the expected variation of E_T with concentration of glass fibers in an epoxy resin. Compared to E_L, E_T is very small; that is, fibers are not very effective in increasing the modulus in a direction perpendicular to their length.

The longitudinal-transverse shear modulus G_{LT} can be estimated from (13-15, 20):

$$\frac{G_{LT}}{G_1} = \frac{1 + AB\phi_2}{1 - B\psi\phi_2} \tag{5}$$

where $A = 1.0$, and B and ψ are given by the same expressions as equations 3 and 4, except that E_2/E_1 of equation 3 is replaced by G_2/G_1, the modulus ratio of the two phases. The middle curve of Figure 1 shows that $\frac{G_{LT}}{G_1}$ is much smaller than $\frac{E_L}{E_1}$ but

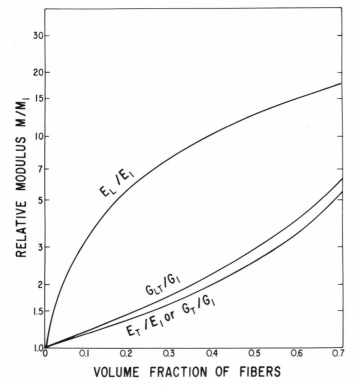

Fig. 1

Relative moduli as a function of volume fraction of fibers
for uniaxially oriented fiber-filled composites for the case
of glass fibers in epoxy resins in which the modulus of the
fibers is 25 times the modulus of the matrix. Maximum
packing fraction of the fibers is assumed to be 0.85 in
calculating G_{LT}, G_{TT}, and E_T.

---

somewhat greater than E_T/E_1.

The transverse shear modulus G_{TT} can be estimated from

$$\frac{G_{TT}}{G_1} = \frac{1 + AB\phi_2}{1 - B\psi\phi_2} \qquad (6)$$

where A = 0.5, and B and ψ are defined by equations 3 and 4 with

E_2/E_1 replaced by G_2/G_1. Figure 1, or a comparison of equations 2 and 6, shows that E_T/E_1 and G_{TT}/G_1 are essentially the same.

As pointed out in Chapter 7, all moduli can be calculated by the use of the modified Halpin-Tsai (20,21) equations

$$\frac{M}{M_1} = \frac{1 + AB\phi_2}{1 - B\psi\phi_2} .$$

(7)

For fiber-filled composites, the values of the factor A are given in Table 2. It will be recalled from Chapter 7 that A is related to the Einstein coefficient k_E by the equation, $A = k_E - 1$.

The rule of mixtures (Equation 1) only holds for the longitudinal Young's modulus E_L in the case of very long fibers; oriented short fibers give smaller moduli in a polymer matrix. Figure 2 illustrates the expected behavior of the relative modulus as a function of the aspect ratio (ratio of length to diameter of the fiber) for the case where the fiber has a modulus 100 times that of the matrix. The sigmoidal shaped curves are a result of the factor A changing from 1.5 for spheres to infinity for very long fibers. Aspect ratios greater than 100 are required to realize the full potentiality of the fibers in a composite. Experimental results on short fiber composites, in which the fibers were fairly well uniaxially oriented, confirm the prediction that aspect ratios of over 100 are required to obtain maximum strength and modulus (22,23).

Equations 1 and 2 or Figure 1 show that there is a tremendous change in the modulus when the test direction is rotated 90 degrees so that E_L becomes transformed into E_T. The equation for predicting the Young's modulus E_θ at any angle θ from the

Table 2

Values of A for Fiber-Filled and Ribbon Composites

Type of Composite	Modulus	A
Uniaxial Orientation (Long)	E_L	2L/D
Uniaxial Orientation (Transverse)	E_T	0.5
Uniaxial Orientation	G_{LT}	1.0
Uniaxial Orientation	G_{TT}	0.5
Uniaxial Orientation (Bulk)	B	0
Random Orientation; 3-D	G for L/D = 4	2.08
Random Orientation; 3-D	G for L/D = 6	2.84
Random Orientation; 3-D	G for L/D = 8	3.80
Random Orientation; 3-D	G for L/D = 10	4.93
Random Orientation; 3-D	G for L/D = 12	6.20
Random Orientation; 3-D	G for L/D = 15	8.38
Random Orientation; 3-D	G for L/D = ∞	∞
Ribbon-Filled (Longitudinal)	E_L	∞
Ribbon-Filled (Transverse)	E_T	2 w/t
Ribbon-Filled (Transverse)	E_{TT}	0
Ribbon-Filled	G_{LT}	$(w/t)^{\sqrt{3}}$ (?)
Ribbon-Filled	$G_{LT'}$	0
Ribbon-Filled	G_{TT}	0

L/D = aspect ratio of fibers = length/diameter.
w/t = width/thickness of ribbons.

fiber direction is (24):

$$\frac{1}{E_\theta} = \frac{\cos^4\theta}{E_L} + \frac{\sin^4\theta}{E_T} + \left(\frac{1}{G_{LT}} - \frac{2\nu_{LT}}{E_L}\right)\sin^2\theta\cos^2\theta \qquad (8)$$

where ν_{LT} is the Poisson's ratio of the composite for a tensile

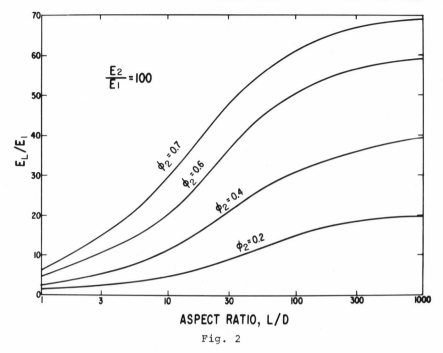

ASPECT RATIO, L/D

Fig. 2

Relative longitudinal Young's modulus as a function of
aspect ratio for discontinuous fibers for the case in
which $E_2/E_1 = 100$.

---

load applied parallel to the fibers. Figure 3A is a plot of
equation 8 for the case of a boron fiber-epoxy composite containing about 65 volume percent fibers (25). The figure indicates
that only slight misalignment of the fibers with respect to the
direction of applied load results in a drastic decrease in the
modulus.

The shear modulus G_θ also changes with angle:

$$\frac{1}{G_\theta} = \frac{1}{G_{LT}} + 4\left(\frac{1 + \nu_{LT}}{E_L} + \frac{1 + \nu_{TL}}{E_T} - \frac{1}{G_{LT}}\right)\sin^2\theta\cos^2\theta \qquad (9)$$

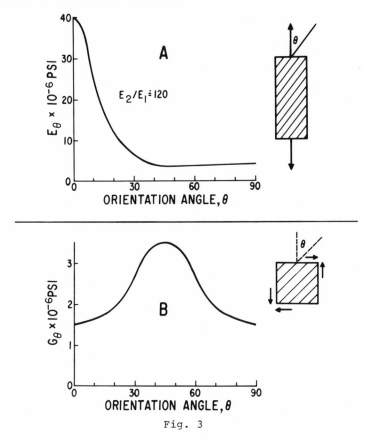

Fig. 3

A. Young's modulus E_θ of aligned fiber composites as a
function of the angle between the fiber axis and the tensile
stress. $E_2/E_1 = 120$, the approximate value for boron fiber-
epoxy composites containing 65 volume percent fibers.
B. The longitudinal shear modulus versus the orientation
angle for the case of $G_2/G_1 = 120$ and $\phi_2 = 0.65$.

where ν_{TL} is the Poisson's ratio for a load applied perpendicular

to the direction of the fibers. The two Poisson's ratios are

related by the equation:

$$\frac{\nu_{LT}}{\nu_{TL}} = \frac{E_L}{E_T} .$$

(10)

Figure 3B shows G_θ, the longitudinal shear modulus at angle θ, for a typical boron fiber-epoxy composite. The shear modulus goes through a large maximum at 45 degrees where the shear in the matrix transfers the greatest amount of force to the fibers.

Although uniaxially oriented fiber composites have very high moduli in one direction, the other moduli are low. In most practical applications it is difficult to design a part so that a large stress is applied in only one direction. Therefore, to get good properties in at least two or three directions, fibers can be randomly oriented, or several layers of uniaxially oriented fibers can be stacked or cross-plied at different angles to form laminates. Such composites are nearly isotropic in a plane as illustrated in Figure 2 of Chapter 2 for biaxial orthotropic materials. A composite containing long fibers randomly oriented in a plane has a high Young's modulus for any direction a load is applied in this plane. Nielsen and Chen (26) developed a method of calculating Young's modulus for such a composite. Their theoretical results agree with some experimental studies (27) but in other cases the theoretical results are lower than the experimental ones (28-30). Tsai (25,31) developed a simpler method of calculating Young's modulus of composites containing fibers which are randomly oriented in a plane. His equation is:

$$E_{2D} \doteq \frac{3}{8} E_L + \frac{5}{8} E_T. \tag{11}$$

In this equation the longitudinal Young's modulus E_L and the transverse modulus E_T can either be experimental values obtained from uniaxially oriented fiber composites, or they can be estimated from equations 1 and 2. Figure 4 compares uniaxially oriented fiber composites with composites containing very long

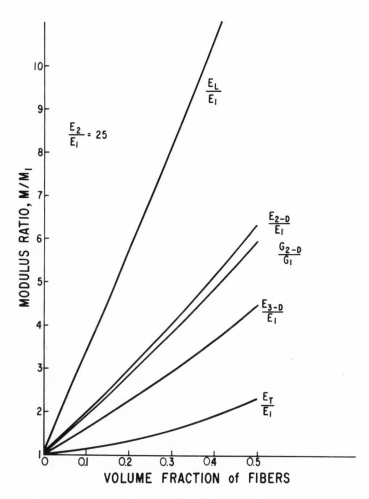

Fig. 4

Relative moduli as a function of fiber concentration for
$E_2/E_1 = 25$. A comparison of uniaxial composites with
composites in which the fibers are randomly oriented in
two or three directions.

fibers randomly oriented in one plane for the case where the
fibers have a modulus 25 times that of the polymer matrix, i.e.,
$E_2/E_1 = 25$. This is approximately the case of glass fibers in
an epoxy matrix. Although the modulus of the random composite
is high compared to that of the matrix, the modulus is much lower
than E_L of a uniaxially oriented composite. Thus, in order to
achieve a high modulus in all directions in a plane, there is a
considerable sacrifice in the maximum possible modulus E_L.

The shear modulus of a composite in which the fibers are
randomly oriented in a plane is approximately (14,31)

$$G_{2D} \doteq \frac{1}{8} E_L + \frac{1}{4} E_T \ . \tag{12}$$

A plot of G_{2D}/G_1 is shown in Figure 4 also.

Fibers also may be oriented randomly in three dimensions to
give truly isotropic materials, although this is generally
difficult to achieve experimentally. An approximate equation
for Young's modulus in this case is (30):

$$E_{3D} \doteq \frac{1}{5} E_L + \frac{4}{5} E_T \ . \tag{13}$$

Figure 4 illustrates this equation for the case where $E_2/E_1 = 25$.
In order to achieve the same properties in all directions, there
is a very great sacrifice in maximum achievable modulus.
Nielsen (32) believes that equation 13 predicts values which are
too large for truly randomly oriented three dimensional composites
when the concentration of fibers is below about 40 v/o. He
proposes:

$$\log E_{3D} = \phi_1 \log E_1 + \phi_2 \log E_2 \ . \tag{14}$$

It has been nearly impossible to prepare experimentally composites
in which the fibers are randomly oriented in three directions.
The fabrication techniques nearly always partially align the

fibers in a plane. Thus, the relative merits of equations 13 and 14 have not been adequately tested experimentally.

A number of experimental studies on the moduli of fiber-filled composites indicate that most of the above theoretical equations are reasonably accurate. These studies include the work by Lees (23), Anderson and Lavengood (22), and Noga and Woodhams (27), Lee (29), and Bernardo (33).

III. Strength of Fiber-Filled Composites

A. Uniaxially Oriented Fibers

In spite of its great practical importance, the strength and stress-strain behavior of fiber-filled composites is not nearly as clearly understood as the moduli of such materials. The fracture phenomena of fiber-filled composites are terribly complex, not only because of anisotropy and heterogeneity but because of several possible modes of fracture and the great importance of interfacial adhesion, dewetting, perfection of fiber alignment, stress concentration at the ends of fibers, the degree of overlap of the ends of adjacent fibers, and the relative brittle or ductile nature of the components. Only in the case of infinitely long fibers aligned in one direction and tested in tension parallel to the fibers is the strength given by a simple relationship. In this special case, the rule of mixtures holds:

$$\sigma_{BL} = \sigma_{B1}\, \phi_1 + \sigma_{B2}\, \phi_2. \tag{15}$$

In this equation σ_{B1} and σ_{B2} are the tensile strength of the matrix and fibers, respectively while σ_{BL} is the longitudinal tensile strength of the composite.

For uniaxially oriented fiber composites there are at least three important modes of failure and three important strengths. These strengths are the longitudinal tensile strength σ_{BL}, the transverse tensile strength σ_{BT}, and the shear strength σ_{BS}. The relative importance of these strengths depends, among other factors, upon the angle between the fibers and the applied load. Between 0° and about 5° where a tensile load is approximately parallel to the fibers, the longitudinal tensile strength is the important factor in determining the mode of failure. For fiber orientation angles θ between about 5° and 45° the important factor determining the strength and mode of failure of the composite is the shear strength σ_{BS}. At higher angles the transverse strength tends to determine the mode of failure. For most fiber-filled composites, σ_{BL} is much greater than the tensile strength of the matrix σ_{B1} since fibers are broken. The shear strength of the composite is comparable to the shear strength of the matrix. The transverse tensile strength σ_{BT} is generally less than the tensile strength of the matrix material— often roughly $\sigma_{B1}/2$. An equation which takes into account all of these factors and which often agrees reasonably well with experimental data as a function of orientation angle θ is (25):

$$\frac{1}{\sigma_{B\theta}^2} = \frac{\cos^4\theta}{\sigma_{BL}^2} + \left(\frac{1}{\sigma_{BS}^2} - \frac{1}{\sigma_{BL}^2}\right)\cos^2\theta\sin^2\theta + \frac{\sin^4\theta}{\sigma_{BT}^2} \quad . \quad (16)$$

The tensile strength at an angle θ between the fiber direction and the applied load is $\sigma_{B\theta}$. Equation 16 shows that the tensile strength decreases dramatically as the angle θ increases. Equations similar to some of the different terms in equation 16 have been proposed by Jackson and Cratchley (34) and by

Ashkenazi (35). In general, transverse tensile strength and shear strength are determined by the strength of the matrix since few, if any, fibers are broken.

Not all the experimental studies agree with the predictions of equation 16. Another proposed equation is (36):

$$\sigma_{B\theta} = \frac{\sigma_{BT}}{\sin\theta} \qquad (17)$$

This simple equation was found to hold for a number of different kinds of composites as long as $\theta \geq 10°$. Figure 5 illustrates the tensile (flexural) strength as a function of the fiber orientation angle for two composites which obey equation 17 (36).

The tensile strength of composites can be greatly affected by such factors as the perfection of packing and alignment of the fibers and by imperfections such as voids. Paul and Thomson (37) found that the longitudinal strength of filament wound composites could be doubled in some cases by the elimination of voids. Points of contact between different fibers are points of stress concentration which can be especially damaging to transverse strengths (3,38).

Composites containing very long or continuous fibers can be made by such fabrication methods as filament winding. However, other fabrication techniques such as injection molding require shorter discontinuous fibers. Even if all the fibers are carefully oriented in one direction, discontinuous fiber composites are not as strong as continuous fiber composites. The reasons for this decrease in strength are: 1. Appreciable lengths near each end of the fibers are ineffective in transmitting load from the matrix to the fibers. 2. The fiber ends act as stress concentrators. 3. Fibers which do not overlap one another

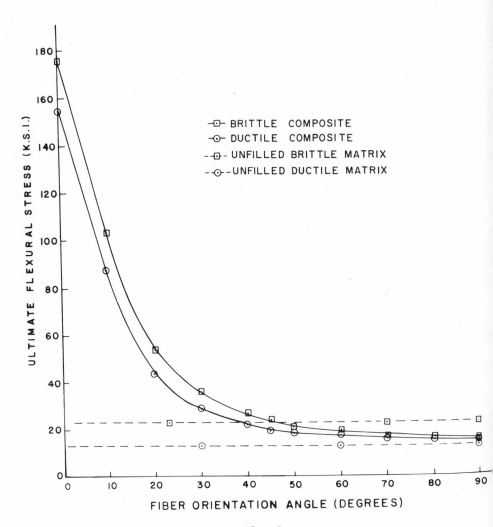

Fig. 5

The flexural strength of an aligned glass fiber-epoxy
composite as a function of the angle between the fibers
and the applied stress. [Reprinted from Ishai, Anderson,
and Lavengood, J. Mater., 5, 184 (1970).]

appreciably cannot contribute to strengthening the composite.

4. In general, it is impossible to achieve as perfect orientation with short fibers as with continuous fibers.

Many studies, both experimental and theoretical, have been made on oriented discontinuous fiber composites. Theoretical studies include the work of Dow (39), Sutton (40), Outwater (41), Kelly (42), Rosen (17,43), Chen (44), Allen (45), Cottrell (46), Riley (47), Piggott (48), Tarnopol'skii (49) and Rosen and Dow (50). A few of the experimental investigations are those of Sutton, Rosen, and Flom (1), Anderson and Lavengood (22), and Lavengood and Ishai (51).

In short fiber or discontinuous fiber composites the polymer is the only continuous phase. Longitudinal tensile stresses are applied to the fibers through shearing stresses in the matrix (3, 17, 39-50). These shearing stresses in the matrix are a maximum near the ends of the fibers and gradually decrease to zero away from the ends. The tensile loads in the fibers are zero at the ends and gradually increase to a plateau in the central portion of the fibers. Thus, the part of the fibers near the ends carry less load than the middle section. The sum of the length of the fiber on each end required for the tensile load to reach its plateau or maximum value is often called the critical or ineffective fiber length L_c since the end portion of the fibers are ineffective in carrying the load. In other words, a fiber must have a length of at least L_c to achieve the maximum stress in the fiber. The critical fiber length depends upon such factors as the relative moduli of the two phases, the strength of the interfacial bond, the shear strength of the matrix, and

the tensile strength of the fiber. In the special case of
perfect adhesion, in which either the matrix or the fibers break
before the interfacial bond, if the matrix shows a plastic
yield behavior,

$$L_C = D_2 \, \sigma_{B2}/2\tau_{B1}. \qquad (18)$$

In equation 18, D_2 is the fiber diameter, σ_{B_2} is the tensile
strength of the fiber, and τ_{B1} is the shear strength of the
matrix. In this special case, if $L > L_C$, the tensile strength
of the composite, as given by a modified rule of mixtures,
should be:

$$\sigma_{BL} \doteq \sigma_{B2} \, \phi_2 \left(1 - \frac{L_C}{2L}\right) + \sigma_{B1} \, \phi_1 . \qquad (19)$$

The total length of the fiber is L. Poor adhesion increases
the critical fiber length since mechanical friction at the
interface must take the place of adhesion (41). Although some
theories predict L_C lengths which correspond to aspect ratios L/D
as low as 10, experimental values of L_C are much greater and
require aspect ratios of 100 or even 1000 to achieve maximum
longitudinal tensile strength.

The portion of a fiber that is adjacent to the end of
another fiber must carry more load than the rest of the fiber (44).
This is one of the reasons why composites containing discontinuous fibers can never be as strong as composites containing
continuous fibers. The theory of Riley (47) predicts that
composites containing discontinuous fibers can never have
longitudinal tensile strengths greater than 6/7 of those of
continuous fiber composites because of the detrimental effects
due to fiber ends.

The strength of the interfacial bond between the two phases
is an important factor in determining the strength of a composite,
especially the transverse strength. The longitudinal tensile
strength is affected by the strength of the interfacial bond
only in the case of relatively short fibers. The transverse
strength σ_{BT} is generally less than the strength of the matrix
σ_{B1}. However, in some kinds of composites, good adhesive bonding
gives a somewhat higher transverse tensile strength than does
poor bonding (52,53). In other cases of good adhesion, the fibers
restrain the matrix, giving rise to biaxial stresses and reduced
elongations to break; under these conditions, the composite with
poor adhesion may have the higher transverse strength. The
theory of Cooper and Kelly (52) predicts

$$\sigma_{BT} \doteq \sigma_{B1} \left[1 - 2\left(\frac{\phi_2}{\pi}\right)^{1/2} \right] + 2\sigma_i \left(\frac{\phi_2}{\pi}\right)^{1/2} . \tag{20}$$

where σ_i is the strength of the interfacial bond.

The concept of the strength of the interfacial bond is not
always clear. If there is perfect adhesion, the matrix or the
filler breaks before the interfacial bond. If there is no
adhesion, essentially no work is required to separate the
surfaces of the matrix and filler phases even though the two
surfaces may appear to be in contact. However, even in the case
of no adhesion, work is required to pull a fiber out of a block
of the matrix because of the squeezing force exerted on the fiber
as a result of the mismatch in coefficients of the thermal
expansion and the cooling down of the composite from the fabrication temperature. Between perfect adhesion and no adhesion
there, of course, can be many gradations of partial adhesion.

Uniaxial fiber-filled composites can have very high longitudinal tensile strengths, but the longitudinal compressive
strength is generally less because of a buckling of the fibers (3,
54-56). The smaller the diameter of the fibers the greater is
the buckling and the lower is the compressive strength. Voids
and poor adhesion are especially detrimental to compressive
strength. In certain cases where the fibers buckle, it has been
predicted that the compressive strength should be given by (52):

$$\sigma_{BL} \doteq \frac{G_1}{1 - \phi_2} \quad . \tag{21}$$

Transverse compressive strength is limited by the strength
of the matrix and so is less than the longitudinal compressive
strength (3). However, the transverse compressive strength is
considerably greater than the transverse tensile strength as
shown in Table 3 for 72 volume percent aligned glass fibers in
an epoxy resin. The pure resin in this case probably has a
tensile strength of less than 10,000 psi. Boron, which forms
large diameter fibers and which has a Young's modulus six times

Table 3

Strength of Uniaxial Glass Fiber Composites

Direction	Tensile Strength (psi)	Compressive Strength (psi)
Longitudinal	275,000	200,000
Transverse	8,000	20,000

that of glass, makes composites with unusually high compressive
strengths up to 350,000 psi (3).

The so-called interlaminar shear strength is another measure
of strength of composites. It is generally measured as a
flexural test on short beams, so there is a large shearing force
inside the beam which tends to produce failure by a longitudinal
splitting of the beam. Interlaminar shear strength increases
with the tensile or shear strength of the matrix, and it decreases
with an increase in void content (57). If nearly all the voids
can be eliminated, the interlaminar shear strength can be increased
as much as 100 percent over normal composites containing 0.5
percent or more of void space (58).

The different kinds of strengths of unidirectional composites
with an epoxy matrix are summarized in Table 4 (59). The

Table 4

Strength of Unidirectional Fibrous Composites

| Fiber | ϕ_2 | Longitudinal | | Transverse | | Shear Strength |
		Tensile	Compression	Tensile	Compression	
Boron	.50	210	195	8.1	26.4	12.1
E-Glass	.50	157	101	4.0	20.0	6.0
Carbon (Thornel 25)	.50	92	67	1.0	21.0	4.0
Carbon (Modmor)	.50	150	130	8.0	20.0	11.0

Strengths are in thousands of psi.

longitudinal strength properties increase with concentration of
fibers.   The shear and transverse strengths tend to decrease
with fiber concentration (59).

B.   Strength of Randomly Oriented Fiber Composites & Laminates
          Uniaxially oriented fiber composites generally have
desirable properties only in the direction of the fiber axis.   By
randomly orienting fibers in a plane or by making multi-layered
laminates in which the fibers in the various layers have different orientation directions, composites can be constructed
which are essentially isotropic in a plane; that is, such composites have desirable properties in all directions in a plane.
If fibers are aligned in all three directions, desirable properties
can be achieved in three dimensions.   However, to achieve good
properties in two or three directions, there must be a sacrifice
compared to the longitudinal direction of a uniaxially oriented
fiber composite.   The greatest sacrifice is generally in the
tensile modulus with a somewhat smaller decrease in tensile
strength.

     Objects made by commercial processes from polymers filled
with short fibers have the fibers partially randomly arranged
and partially oriented.   In the laboratory, attempts have been
made to approach random two or three dimensional composites (23,
27, 29, 30, 33, 60-63).   Typical of the results are those of
Bernardo (33) for short glass fibers in polyethylene as given
in Table 5 and the data of Lee (29) for short glass fibers in
polystyrene in Table 6.   Young's modulus and tensile strength are
increased dramatically by the fibers.   However, the increases
are not as great as would be expected for similar composites

Table 5

Mechanical Properties of Randomly Oriented Glass

Fiber-Filled High Density Polyethylene

Property	Weight	Percent	Glass	Fibers*
	0	10	20	30
Tensile Strength (psi)	3700	6060	8840	10130
Flexural Strength (psi)	3000	6410	9750	12290
Flexural Modulus (psi)	125,000	352,000	584,000	795,000
Heat Distortion Temp. at 66 psi, °F	160	240	264	266
Tensile Impact (ft-lb/sq in)	90	60	48	41
Drop Ball Impact (in-lb)	> 160	35	25	15
Izod Impact, Notched (ft-lb/in of notch)	0.9	—	—	2.3

*Fibers: 1/4 inch strands before processing

containing infinitely long fibers. The improvements are greater

for polyethylene than for polystyrene except for Izod impact

strength. Two points should be noted when considering the data

in Tables 5 and 6. First, the fibers are not truly randomly

oriented but undoubtedly are partly uniaxially or biaxially

oriented. Second, although the fibers were initially 1/4 inch

long, many of them were broken during the processing of the

polymer and during the molding of the specimens. The first

Table 6

Mechanical Properties of Polystyrene Filled with Short

Glass Fibers Randomly Oriented

Property	Weight	Percent	Glass	Fibers*
	0	20	30	40
Flexural Strength $(10^{-3}$ psi)	8.4	12.9	15.9	18.1
Flexural Modulus $(10^{-5}$psi)	4.4	7.9	9.4	10.9
Ixod Impact Strength (ft lb/in of notch)	0.2	6.2	8.5	12.1

*Fibers: 1/4 inch chopped strands before processing.
Test temperature = 23°C.

factor tends to increase the strength while the second factor reduces the strength.

It is difficult to achieve control over the kind and degree of orientation by such fabrication processes as injection molding (64). Much better control of properties in any direction in a plane is possible through the use of laminates. Typical laminates alternate the layers by 90° (cross-ply) or by 60° (quasi-isotropic). With quasi-isotropic laminates the properties are nearly the same in all directions. Cross-ply laminates have properties which are dependent upon the angle of testing as illustrated in Table 7 (65). Cross-ply laminates with brittle matrices have tensile stress-strain curves similar to the one shown schematically in Figure 6 if the specimen is oriented such that the stress in half of the layers is parallel to the fibers

Table 7

Moduli of Cross-Ply Laminates

70% Boron Filaments in Polymer

Fiber Orientation & Direction of Stress	Tension Modulus	Compression Modulus	Shear Modulus	Poisson's Ratios
1 ply 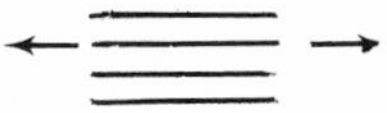	40×10^6	38×10^6	1.0×10^6	$\nu_{LT} = 0.24$ $\nu_{TL} = 0.02$
2 plies 	20×10^6	20×10^6	1.8×10^6	
2 plies 	4×10^6	4×10^6	12×10^6	$\nu_{LT} = \nu_{TL}$ $= 0.84$

Moduli in PSI

in these layers. The stress-strain curves often show a break
where the elongation becomes great enough to form cracks in the
layers in which the fibers are oriented perpendicular to the
stress. Beyond the break, essentially all the load is carried by

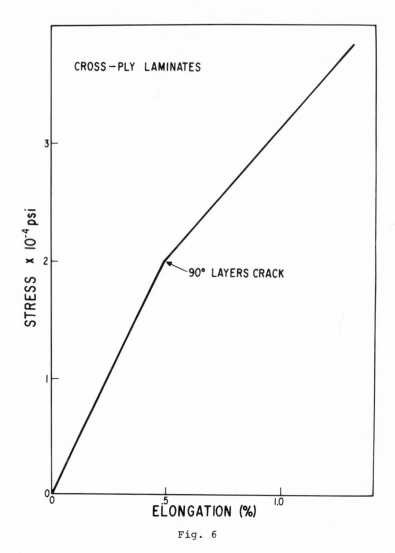

Fig. 6

Stress-strain curve of a cross-ply laminate in which half
of the fibers are parallel to the tensile stress.

the layers in which the fibers are parallel to the stress.

In many laminates, including tire cord fabrics, fabrics rather than unwoven fibers are used. In still other laminates, such as those found in the melamine resin table tops, paper sheets are used. The mechanical properties of laminates are reviewed in several books and articles (6, 66-68).

IV.   Other Properties

A.   Creep

Creep is reduced greatly by the addition of fibers to a matrix (69-71). As a first approximation the creep of a composite compared to that of the unfilled polymer should be reduced by about the same factor as the ratio of the two moduli of the materials. That is,

$$\varepsilon(t) \doteq \varepsilon_1(t) E_1/E. \tag{22}$$

$\varepsilon(t)$ is the creep of the composite at any time t, and $\varepsilon_1(t)$ is the corresponding creep of the unfilled matrix. Thus, if the creep behavior of the unfilled polymer is known and if the ratio of the moduli for the unfilled to filled polymer has been measured, an estimate of the creep of the fiber-filled composite can be made. However, the validity of equation 22 must be fully established for each particular system of fiber-filled composites before its use can be justified. The Young's moduli of fiber-filled composites strongly depend upon the kind and exact degree of fiber orientation. Slight variations between the specimens used for measuring the modulus and those used for the creep

experiments can result in errors of hundreds of percent, for
instance. In some experiments the creep of fiber-filled polymers
was less than that predicted by equation 22 (72). Other equations
have been proposed which predict greater reduction in creep than
does equation 22 (73-75). Equation 22 also should not be valid
after interfacial fracture (dewetting) occurs or if cracks develop
in the composite during creep; in such cases the creep should
greatly increase over the rate expected from equation 22. Silane
treatment of glass fibers can cut the creep rate, especially
after long test times, probably because of improved adhesion (70).
Experiments show that transverse creep is much greater than
longitudinal creep for uniaxially oriented fiber composites.

B. Fatigue

The fatigue behavior of fiber-filled composites is complex and not clearly understood. However, fatigue damage
generally is associated with the generation of cracks in the
matrix, or with dewetting and the destruction of the polymer-
fiber bonding, or by a combination of the two effects (76-78).
Fatigue life greatly decreases as the applied stress is increased.
Ductile matrices tend to give longer fatigue life than brittle
matrices. Up to aspect ratios of about 200, fatigue life increases
with the length of the fibers (76). Heat build-up can be another
major factor in decreasing fatigue life at high frequencies (79,
80). The mechanical damping of a composite, especially near the
interface, generates heat which cannot be dissipated easily at
high frequencies and high loads. As the temperature rises, the
damping increases still more, and the polymer strength and
stiffness decrease; catastrophic failure can follow quickly.

The fatigue of cross-ply laminates differs from that of single ply uniaxial fiber composites. Lamination changes the stress fields around the fibers. Cracks tend to develop first in the layers in which the fibers are oriented approximately perpendicular to the applied stress. Stresses are concentrated especially where two adjacent fibers appear to touch.

It has been observed that as cracks develop, the elastic modulus decreases, and the mechanical damping increases (81). Thus, dynamic mechanical tests might be considered as a useful technique for monitoring fatigue. If the changes are gradual in the dynamic mechanical properties, an object can be removed from service before there is danger of catastrophic failure. However, Nielsen (72) has found for several types of composites that most of the changes in dynamic mechanical properties take place just before failure occurs. In such a situation, it is improbable that impending failure would be detected in time to remove the damaged composite from use before it failed.

C. Heat Distortion Temperature

One of the most striking effects due to fibers in composites is the great increase in heat distortion temperature. This effect is illustrated in Table 5 (33) and in Figure 7 (27). The heat distortion temperature generally is increased more for crystalline than for amorphous polymers (70). For crystalline polymers the heat distortion temperature may approach the melting point when filled with fibers while amorphous polymers soften near the glass transition temperature or somewhat higher. The importance of the modulus and the shape of the modulus-temperature curve in determining the heat distortion temperature was discussed

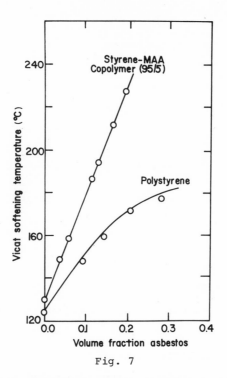

Fig. 7

Vicat softening temperature of composites containing
randomly oriented asbestos fibers in either polystyrene
or a copolymer of styrene (95%) and methacrylic acid (5%).
[Reprinted from Noga and Woodhams, SPE J., 26, #9, 23
(1970).]

in Chapter 6. For amorphous materials the increase in heat

distortion temperature is more of an apparent increase than a

real increase since the increase results from a decrease in

creep rate due to the higher modulus rather than from a true

increase in the softening temperature or glass transition

temperature. Above the glass transition temperature the viscosity

of the system, rather than the modulus, may be the factor that

is important, so high molecular weight and good interfacial

adhesion tend to raise the apparent softening temperature of
amorphous polymers. The increase in heat distortion temperature
of crystalline polymers on the addition of fibers mostly is due
to the increase in modulus.

D. Impact Strength

The impact strength of composites is even more complex
than that of unfilled polymers because of the part played by the
fibers and the interface in addition to the polymer. Correlations
which correspond to reality may be difficult to establish, and
one kind of impact test may contradict the results of another
type of test. For a material to be very tough and to have a high
impact strength, in general there must be some mechanism for
spreading the stored energy to be absorbed throughout as large a
volume of material as possible. If the energy is concentrated
in a small volume, the material fails in a brittle manner, and
the impact strength is low.

Fibers give rise to at least two mechanisms for the dissipation of energy: 1. Fibers may pull out of the matrix and
dissipate energy by mechanical friction. At the same time the
pulling out of the fibers prevents localization of stresses in
one area along the fiber (52,82). 2. Controlled dewetting of
the fibers, as illustrated in Figure 8, dissipates energy in
the dewetting process, spreads the region of stress concentration
throughout a larger region, and tends to stop the propogation
of the crack (83). Fibers also tend to reduce the impact
strength by at least two mechanisms: 1. Fibers generally
drastically reduce the elongation to break and thus may reduce
the area under the stress-strain curve. 2. Stress concentrations
occur at regions around fiber ends, areas of poor adhesion, and

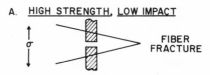

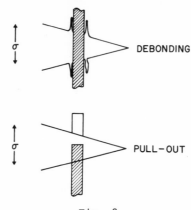

Fig. 8

Schematic diagram of the behavior of fiber-filled composites near the tip of a growing crack. The fibers can: A. Fracture; B. Debond or pull out of the matrix.

regions where fibers contact one another. Thus, depending upon the nature of the composite and the type of impact test, fibers can cause the apparent impact strength to either increase or decrease.

If the impact load is applied parallel to the fibers, highest impact strengths are obtained if the adhesion is relatively poor and if the fibers are short (about equal to the ineffective fiber length) so that maximum energy can be dissipated by mechanical friction during the pull-out process and by debonding of the fibers (84-86). Very long fibers with good adhesion

decrease the impact strength at least for tough matrices largely
because of the greatly reduced elongation to break and the
reduced plastic flow of the matrix (87). However, if the load is
applied perpendicular to the fibers, good adhesion is required
for even moderate impact strength (88). For uniaxial composites
the transverse impact strength is generally lower than the
longitudinal impact strength. The transverse impact strength
also is generally lower than that of the pure matrix material
since in this direction the toughening mechanisms possible for
fibers are inoperative.

The energy dissipated by forming a unit amount of new
surface by either debonding or by fiber pull-out can be estimated
theoretically (86). For pull-out:

$$\gamma = \frac{\sigma_{B2} \, L_C^2 \, \phi_2}{12L} \quad , \quad (L > L_C) \tag{23}$$

$$\gamma = \frac{\sigma_{B2} \, L^2 \, \phi_2}{12L_C} \quad , \quad (L < L_C) . \tag{24}$$

For debonding:

$$\gamma = \frac{\sigma_{B2}^2 \, L_D \, \phi_2}{4E_2} \tag{25}$$

In these equations, γ is the fracture surface energy, that is, the
energy dissipated in forming a unit amount of new surface, σ_{B2}
is the tensile strength of the fibers, L is the length of the
fibers, L_C is the critical "ineffective" length of the fibers as
defined by equation 18 and L_D is the debonded length of the
fibers. If pull-out is the major mechanism of energy dissipation,

the impact strength should be a maximum when the length of the
fibers is equal to L_c. Debonding as a result of poor adhesion
makes a composite less sensitive to notches and cracks (89).
Thus, the factors, such as pull-out and debonding, which increase
the impact strength are the same ones which tend to reduce the
breaking strength of a fiber-filled composite.

The impact strength of polyethylene containing randomly
oriented glass fibers is illustrated by the data of Bernardo
in Table 5 (33). Similar data for glass fiber-filled polystyrene are shown in Table 6 (29). In these tables only the
notched Izod impact strength increased with fiber content, the
tensile impact and drop ball impact both decreased. The tensile
and drop ball impact strengths reflect the decreased elongation
to break on the addition of fibers while the notched Izod impact
strength is sensitive to the decreased ease of crack propogation
when fibers are present. Thus, as pointed out in Chapter 5,
different impact tests really measure different properties. One
must be careful to use an impact test which correlates with the
particular practical application of interest. By changing the
length of the fibers and the strength of the interfacial bonding,
all the tests might have shown improvement on the addition of
fibers. However, it is difficult to improve the impact strength
of tough polymers such as polyethylene by adding fibers; more
often the impact strength may actually decrease. The greatest
improvement in impact strength by the use of fibers is with very
brittle matrices (29,87,90). For instance, random fibers in
polystyrene increase its notched Izod impact strength from about
0.25 to about 2.9 foot lbs. per inch of notch at 35 weight
percent glass fibers (91). On the other hand, an unfilled

polycarbonate is ductile and has a very high impact strength
approaching 16 ft lbs/in notch. Polycarbonate filled with
glass fibers has an Izod impact strength of about 3 at a fiber
concentration of 20 percent. The impact strength of polymers,
especially brittle ones, can be improved greatly by using
ductile wires or metal screens instead of brittle glass fibers (92,
93).

E. Coefficients of Thermal Expansion

Uniaxially oriented fiber composites have two (or in
unusual cases three) coefficients of thermal expansion. In the
longitudinal direction, the coefficient of expansion α_L is small
because of the mechanical restraints imposed by the fibers,
which have a small coefficient compared to a polymer matrix.
In the transverse direction, the coefficient of expansion α_T is
larger, and at low concentrations of fibers, the coefficient
even can be greater than that of the unfilled polymer. The
reason for the high value is because the rigid fibers prevent
much expansion of the matrix in the longitudinal direction, so
the matrix is forced to expand more than normal in the transverse
direction.

Schapery (94) has reviewed the literature and has derived
relatively simple, yet quite accurate, expressions for the
coefficients of expansion. The longitudinal coefficient of
thermal expansion is:

$$\alpha_L \doteq \frac{\alpha_1 E_1 \phi_1 + \alpha_2 E_2 \phi_2}{E_1 \phi_1 + E_2 \phi_2} \tag{26}$$

This equation assumes that Poisson's ratios of the components

are not too far apart. The transverse coefficient of expansion
is:

$$\alpha_T \doteq (1 + \nu_1)\alpha_1\phi_1 + (1 + \nu_2)\alpha_2\phi_2 - \alpha_L\bar{\nu} \qquad (27)$$

where α_L is the longitudinal coefficient, which is given very
closely by equation 26, and $\bar{\nu}$ is the Poisson's ratio of the
composite as closely approximated by

$$\bar{\nu} \doteq \nu_1\phi_1 + \nu_2\phi_2 . \qquad (28)$$

At volume fractions of fibers greater than about 0.2 or 0.3,
equation 27 is approximated closely by

$$\alpha_T \doteq (1 + \nu_1)\alpha_1\phi_1 + \alpha_2\phi_2 . \qquad (29)$$

The coefficients of expansion as a function of volume fraction
of fibers as predicted by equations 26, 27 and 29 are plotted
in Figure 9 for the following case:

Matrix	Fiber
$\alpha_1 = 6 \times 10^{-5}/°C$	$\alpha_2 = 0.5 \times 10^{-5}/°C$
$E_1 = 5 \times 10^5$ psi	$E_2 = 10 \times 10^6$ psi
$\nu_1 = 0.35$	$\nu_2 = 0.20$

These values are typical for glass fibers in polymers. From
Figure 9 it is obvious that the coefficients of expansion, like
the elastic moduli, are very anisotropic in nature for aligned
fiber composites. As a result of this anisotropy, large
thermally induced stresses may occur in the matrix between
lamallae in cross-ply or other types of laminates.

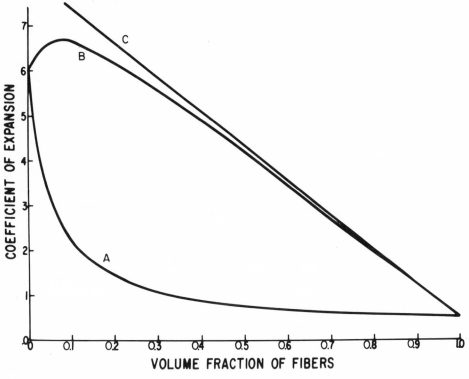

Fig. 9

Thermal coefficients of expansion for a uniaxial fiber
composite. Curve A corresponds to equation 26. Curve B
corresponds to equation 27. Curve C corresponds to
equation 29. Coefficient of volume expansion of the
fibers is 0.5 x 10^{-5}/°C while that of the matrix is 6 x
10^{-5}/°C. The corresponding Young's moduli are 10 x 10^{6}
and 5 x 10^{5} psi.

———————————

The coefficient of thermal expansion for a composite in

which the fibers are randomly oriented in three dimensions

should be

$$\alpha_{3D} \doteq \frac{\alpha_L + 2\alpha_T}{3} \tag{30}$$

The values of α_L and α_T can be estimated from equations 26 and 27.

V.   Ribbon-Filled Composites

The same techniques such as filament winding that are used to make uniaxially oriented fiber-filled composites can be used to fabricate composites containing aligned ribbons. A ribbon can be defined as a fiber with a cross section which has a width much greater than its thickness. The cross section is generally rectangular in shape, but it can be elliptical, for instance. There are several possible advantages of ribbon (or tape) composites over composites containing fibers with a circular cross section. Ribbon composites can have high strength and rigidity in the direction perpendicular to the ribbons in the plane of the sheet. Thus, such composites are much more isotropic in the plane of a sheet than are fiber-filled composites. Ribbon composites also tend to be very resistant to puncture by sharp objects. A third advantage is their greatly decreased permeability to gases and liquids compared to polymers or other kinds of composites. In order to get through a ribbon composite, a diffusing molecule must follow a long tortuous path to get around the impermeable ribbons (95).

Theoretical calculations have shown the great potential of ribbon composites, and these predictions have been verified for the moduli of such materials many times. However, only recently have the experimental strengths of ribbon composites approached the theoretical values because nearly all the past work used matrices which did not fulfill all the requirements for such composites. Matrix property requirements are much more stringent for ribbon composites than for fiber composites. These requirements will be discussed in later paragraphs.

A schematic drawing of a ribbon composite is shown in Figure 10. The volume fraction of ribbons in such a composite is given by:

$$\phi_2 = \frac{1}{(1 + D/t)(2 - B_T/W)} \cdot \qquad (31)$$

In this equation W and t are the width and thickness of the ribbons, D is the thickness of the polymer layer between layers of ribbons, and B_T is total overlap of both edges of a given ribbon with the two ribbons in either the next layer above or below. In the symmetrical case shown in Figure 10, $B_T = 2B$ where B is the amount of overlap of ribbons.

Ribbon composites have six elastic moduli as illustrated in Figure 11 (96). In the case of very wide ribbons (large aspect ratio W/t), the moduli are approximately given by simple

RIBBON COMPOSITES

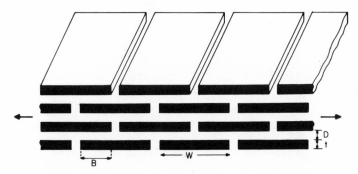

Fig. 10

Schematic diagram of a ribbon-filled composite. The view shows primarily the ends of the ribbons.

RIBBON COMPOSITES

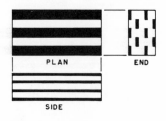

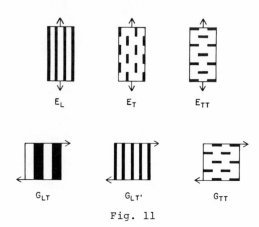

Fig. 11

Schematic diagram showing the six elastic moduli of a ribbon composite.

equations. The longitudinal and transverse Young's moduli, E_L and E_T, are

$$E_L = E_T = E_1\phi_1 + E_2\phi_2 \; .$$ (32)

The longitudinal-transverse shear modulus G_{LT} also is given by the rule of mixtures:

$$G_{LT} = G_1\phi_1 + G_2\phi_2 \; .$$ (33)

The other three moduli are given by the inverse rule of mixtures:

$$\frac{1}{E_{TT}} = \frac{\phi_1}{E_1} + \frac{\phi_2}{E_2} \tag{34}$$

$$\frac{1}{G_{LT'}} = \frac{1}{G_{TT}} = \frac{\phi_1}{G_1} + \frac{\phi_2}{G_2} \quad . \tag{35}$$

Thus, in contrast to unidirectional fiber-filled materials which have only one high modulus, ribbon-filled materials can have three large moduli.

If the aspect ratio of the ribbons is not very large, the transverse Young's modulus E_T and the longitudinal shear modulus G_{LT} are less than what is predicted by the rule of mixtures. In this case, the effect of aspect ratio can be predicted by the Halpin-Tsai equations

$$\frac{M}{M_1} = \frac{1 + AB\phi_2}{1 - B\phi_2} \tag{36}$$

$$B = \frac{M_2/M_1 - 1}{M_2/M_1 + A} \tag{37}$$

For the case $M = E_T$, $A = 2W/t$, and for $M = G_{LT}$, $A \doteq (W/t)^{\sqrt{3}}$ (14,97). An aspect ratio of about 10 to 100 is generally needed to approach the maximum modulus. The greater the difference in the moduli of the ribbons and matrix the greater must the aspect ratio be to achieve a high modulus. The values of A for all the moduli of ribbon composites are listed in Table 2.

It has been assumed that ribbon composites should have a high transverse tensile strength, and computer calculations

verify this assumption (96). However, experimental tests have
generally given low strengths (97). If the interfacial bonding
is weak, the strength decreases rapidly with ribbon concentration (96). However, even with good adhesion, the experimental
values may be low because the matrix does not have the required
properties. The following conditions must be fulfilled to
achieve high strength (98): 1. There must be excellent adhesion
between the polymer and the ribbons. 2. The matrix must be
ductile with a high ultimate elongation in order to minimize
the effect of stress concentration due to thermal stresses from
the fabrication process. In addition, there must be enough
elongation left over to transmit fully the stresses from the
polymer to the ribbons. 3. There must be adequate overlap of
the ribbons to get all the possible stress transmitted to the
ribbons. This requires an aspect ratio greater than some
critical value. 4. A high perfection is required in the
fabrication process in order to maintain a regular arrangement
of the ribbons to be sure that all areas of overlap are above
a critical value. Also, there must be few if any voids or
areas of poor adhesion. 5. For highest strength, the tensile
or shear strength of the matrix should be greater than its
yield strength. 6. The composite should fracture by transverse
breaking of the ribbons rather than shear failure of the matrix.
The matrix is subjected to a complex multiaxial state of stress
rather than simple shear, but the lap shear test (ASTM D-1002 or
C-273) is a good practical test to evaluate the shear strength
σ_S of the polymer (99).

In order that the composites fail by transverse fracture of
ribbons, the ratio B/t must exceed the value given in the

following equation (98):

$$B/t \geq \frac{x}{y} \left(\frac{\sigma_{B2}}{\sigma_{BS}} \right) \tag{38}$$

In this relation, σ_{B2} is the tensile strength of the ribbons, σ_{BS} is the shear strength of the matrix as measured by a lap shear test, y is the number of layers of ribbon required for the lay-up pattern to be repeated, and x is the minimum number of ribbons that actually carry stress in a thickness equal to the repeat thickness of the lay-up pattern. The ratio x/y is the minimum fraction of ribbons carrying load in the entire thickness of a given section; in Figure 10, x/y = 1/2. The minimum overlap B of adjacent layers must be less than half the width of the ribbons. In Figure 10 the maximum transverse tensile strength is one half the maximum longitudinal tensile strength. If the aspect ratio W/t is great enough, however, lay-up patterns can be devised to give transverse strengths which approach the longitudinal strength so that ribbon composites can be nearly isotropic in the plane of the ribbons. The maximum transverse tensile strength of a ribbon composite is

$$\sigma_B = \frac{x\sigma_{B2}t + y\sigma_{B1}D}{y(t+D)} \doteq \left(\frac{x}{y}\right)\left(\frac{t}{t+D}\right)\sigma_{B2} \cdot \tag{39}$$

The tensile strength of the matrix is σ_{B1}. Equation 39 becomes the rule of mixtures as x/y approaches 1.0. By using the proper matrix polymer, composites have been made which have transverse tensile strengths over forty times that of the matrix, and in the fracture process the ribbons are split longitudinally (98). This high strength contrasts with unidirectional fiber-filled composites in which the transverse tensile strength is generally considerably less than that of the matrix. Ribbon-filled polymers also may have higher strengths than cross-ply and similar laminates.

VI. Other Types of Composites

A. Flake-Filled Polymers

Polymers filled with flakes have many of the character-istics of ribbon-filled composites. Typical flake fillers include mica, kaolin, graphite, glass flakes, aluminum flakes, and aluminum diboride. By most fabrication techniques, the flakes will be more or less oriented in a plane, so such materials often have the behavior of biaxially oriented materials. Materials with planar orientation of the flakes have extremely high resistance to the permeation of gases and liquids (95,100). The reason for this low permeability is because of the long tortuous path that the permeating molecules must take to go around the impermeable flakes. Flake composites also have strong resistance to puncturing by sharp objects (101). Flake-filled polymers have unusually high moduli compared to most other particulate-filled composites (100, 102-107). The tensile modulus measured in any direction parallel to the plane of orientation and the shear modulus may approach values predicted by the rule of mixtures. Attempts have been made to predict theoretically the moduli as a function of aspect ratio (length divided by thickness) and other factors (108, 109).

It is difficult to achieve the perfection of flake orienta-tion and overlap that is required for high strength. Misaligned flakes and regions of insufficient overlap of adjacent flakes

create defects which greatly reduce strength. For high strength,
the matrix also must fulfill the same requirements as for good
ribbon composites. Entrapped air can be a serious problem in
flake composites. An air bubble may be squeezed between two
flakes to create a sheet of air which effectively destroys the
adhesion between the flakes and which acts as a very strong
stress concentrator. Most flake composites are brittle with
low impact strength. However, such materials may be quite
insensitive to notches and cracks (106). The low notch
sensitivity probably results from the large number of imperfections already built into these materials.

Flake-filled elastomers and plastics often have high
mechanical damping (110-113). For this reason, vibration
damping materials generally contain flake fillers (111-113).
Part of this damping may result from one layer of a flake, such
as mica or graphite, sliding over another layer when the
material is deformed.

B. Composites with Thick Interlayers

In most composites there is a mismatch of the properties, such as the moduli and coefficients of expansion, of the
two components at the interface. This mismatch introduces
stresses at the interface which tend to reduce the strength and
other properties because the stresses may result in the formation of cracks or in debonding or dewetting. There are at
least two possible approaches for solving the problems resulting
from the stresses introduced at the interface: 1. A "graded
seal" approach can be used in which the properties of a thick
interfacial layer gradually change from those of one component
to those of the other component. 2. An interlayer of a softer,

ductile material can be placed between the filler and matrix phases. This ductile interlayer can relieve some of the stresses by deforming without breaking either itself or the adhesive bond to the matrix and filler phases. These interlayers are much thicker than those formed by treating the filler with silanes, for instance.

Several attempts have been made to coat the filler surfaces so as to form an interlayer (114-117). Dramatic improvements in a number of properties have resulted. The transverse tensile strength of aligned fiber composites may be nearly doubled when an interlayer of an epoxy resin is applied to glass fibers which are then imbedded in another epoxy resin (114). The longitudinal tensile strength of the same composite could be increased by fifty percent. An elastomeric interlayer on glass spheres in an epoxy resin increases the tensile strength about 20 percent over that of the same composite without the interlayer (115). It is essential that the interlayer have good adhesion to both the filler and the matrix. An interlayer may increase fatigue life by a factor of ten to a hundred times over that of a similar composite without the interlayer. The impact strength may be improved also by an interlayer (117).

Interlayers may improve properties by several possible mechanisms: 1. The interlayer protects the surface of the fiber during fabrication and thus increases the measured strength of the fiber. 2. In the "graded seal" type of composites, the induced thermal stresses are reduced by a better match of the thermal coefficients of expansion. 3. If the interlayer is very ductile, it can relieve stress concentrations by deforming without breaking. Thus, the interlayer tends to prevent dewetting and crack formation around the filler particles.

4. Stress concentration is reduced by preventing one fiber or filler particle from touching another one. Stress concentration factors are very high at points of contact (38). Theoretical studies related to interlayers have been made by Alfrey (118) and by Matonis (119).

C. Interpenetrating Network Composites

Few good examples of interpenetrating or interlocking network composites have been studied. One reason for the lack of data is the difficulty in fabricating such composites. Examples of interlocking network composites are: 1. Open-celled foams of one material filled with another material. 2. Wire mats which have been sintered together at cross-over points and which are impregnated with a polymer or other matrix material. 3. Polymer-polymer blends in the concentration range in which phase inversion occurs.

An example of a filled foam has been described by White and Van Vlack (120). Parikh, Moreen, and Williams (121) studied impregnated metal fiber mats. An important parameter determining the mechanical properties of the filled mats was the spacing between cross-over points of the wires. This is somewhat analogous to the kinetic theory of rubber elasticity in which the molecular weight between crosslinks is the important parameter. Many examples of polymer-polymer interpenetrating networks have been prepared (122-128). These materials can be made by such techniques as mechanically mixing of two polymers or by swelling a crosslinked rubber with a monomer and subsequently polymerizing the mixture. In these mixtures, both phases are simultaneously continuous.

Apparently no attempts have been made to explain the
mechanical properties of interpenetrating network composites
theoretically. However, if the network structure is random so
that the composites are isotropic, the moduli probably can be
estimated with reasonable accuracy by the logarithmic rule of
mixtures (32):

$$\log M = \phi_1 \log M_1 + \phi_2 \log M_2 \quad . \qquad (40)$$

The modulus M can be either Young's modulus or the shear modulus.

VII. Summary

Fiber-filled composites may be characterized by anisotropy
and unusually high strength and stiffness in one or more
directions. All of the 5 or 6 independent moduli can be
estimated reasonably accurately by simple equations for uniaxially oriented composites. The moduli of laminated composites
and of composites containing randomly oriented fibers also can
be estimated. The strength, however, generally can be estimated
only crudely. Some properties, such as longitudinal tensile
strength, are determined primarily by the properties of the
fibers. Other properties, such as the transverse tensile
strength and interlaminar shear strength, are determined largely
by the properties of the matrix.

Tensile strength and impact strength are affected by the
length of the fibers and by the strength of the adhesive bond
between the fibers and the matrix. To achieve high strength,
the fibers must be lengthened as the strength of the adhesive
bond decreases. On the other hand, impact strengths tend to
increase as the strength of the bond decreases and as the fiber

length decreases to a limiting value.

Ribbon-filled and flake-filled composites can have a great
advantage over aligned fiber-filled composites because of near
isotropy in a plane. However, ribbon and flake composites
require matrices that must have very special properties in
order to achieve the optimum high strengths. In addition,
these composites are difficult to fabricate without introducing
imperfections which are very detrimental to strength. Many
properties comparable to those of ribbon and flake composites
generally can be obtained with fibers by laminating layers of
fibers oriented in several directions or by randomly orienting
fibers in a plane.

Interpenetrating network composites represent an unexplored
field. These materials may have some very useful mechanical
properties.

VIII. Problems

1. Compare the shear modulus as a function of composition for
    a polymer filled with glass spheres with the shear modulus
    G_{LT} of the same polymer filled with oriented glass fibers.
    $G_2/G_1 = 25$. $\phi_m = 0.64$ for the spheres, and $\phi_m = 0.82$ for
    the fibers.

2. Estimate the longitudinal Young's modulus of a composite
    consisting of oriented glass fibers in an epoxy matrix as a
    function of the aspect ratio of the fibers. Calculate for
    the cases of $\phi_2 = 0.3$ and $\phi_2 = 0.6$. $E_2/E_1 = 25$. Assume $\phi_m = 1$.

3. Long glass fibers are randomly oriented in a plane in a
    composite in which $E_2/E_1 = 120$. Estimate Young's modulus
    as a function of concentration of the fibers.

4. A composite consists of aligned fibers in a rubber matrix.
    How much greater is the longitudinal Young's modulus than
    the transverse Young's modulus at a volume fraction of fibers
    of 0.6? $E_2/E_1 = 10^4$. $E_1 = 10^7$ dynes/cm^2. Assume $\phi_m = 1$.

5. Everything is the same as in problem 4 except $\phi_m = 0.82$.

6. What is the expected longitudinal tensile strength of an
    aligned fiber composite made by filament winding? The
    composite contains 65 volume percent fibers with a tensile
    strength of 250,000 psi. The matrix has a tensile strength
    of 12,000 psi.

7. Estimate the longitudinal and transverse Young's moduli of
    a composite containing 75 weight percent of aligned fibers.
    The density of the matrix is 1.0, and the density of the
    fibers is 2.5. $E_1 = 2.5 \times 10^{10}$ dynes/cm^2, and $E_2 = 10^7$ psi.
    These values are typical of glass fibers in polystyrene.

8. How much does the relative transverse Young's modulus E_T/E_1
    as a function of composition differ for aligned fiber
    composites in which the fibers have a hexagonal packing
    in one case and cubic packing in the other case? Assume
    $E_2/E_1 = 100$.

9. A polymer contains a filler in the form of short oriented
    rods. Two creep tests are made: (a) The load is applied
    parallel to the rods. (b) The load is applied perpendicular
    to the rods. How does the creep differ in the two cases?
    If the rods have an aspect ratio L/d of 10, what is the
    approximate ratio of the creep in the two directions at
    any time?

10. A weak, brittle fiber of low coefficient of thermal
    expansion is put in a thermoset resin which is cured at

200°C. At room temperature will the induced thermal stresses tend to break the fibers under tension, or will the fibers tend to buckle?

11. Sketch the lay-up pattern for a ribbon-filled composite in which 2/3 of the ribbons at any point in the cross section must carry a transverse tensile load, i.e., $x/y = 2/3$.

12. A composite consists of 50 volume percent of aligned glass fibers with a Young's modulus of 10^7 psi in a matrix with a Young's modulus of 5×10^5 psi. What are the Young's modulus and the shear modulus of this composite when measured at an angle of 45° to the fiber direction?

13. One composite consists of long uniaxially oriented fibers in a rubber matrix. Another composite is a randomly oriented interpenetrating network structure. Plot the longitudinal and transverse Young's moduli as a function of composition for the first composite and the Young's modulus as a function of composition for the second composite. The Young's moduli of the components are 10^6 N/m^2 for the rubber and 10^{10} N/m^2 for the other component in both composites.

14. In going from an uniaxially oriented fiber-filled composite to a composite in which the fibers are randomly oriented in a plane, the relative modulus often decreases more than the relative tensile strength. Why?

IX. References

1. W. H. Sutton, B. W. Rosen, and D. G. Flom, SPE J. 20, 1203 (1964).

2.   R. L. Mehan, W. H. Sutton, and J. A. Herzog, AIAA J., 4,
     1889 (1966).

3.   L. J. Broutman and R. H. Krock, Modern Composite Materials,
     Addison-Wesley, Reading, Mass., 1967.

4.   P. Morgan, Glass Reinforced Plastics, Iliffe, London, 1961.

5.   S. S. Oleesky and J. G. Mohr, Handbook of Reinforced
     Plastics, Reinhold, New York, 1964.

6.   D. J. Duffin, Laminated Plastics, Reinhold, New York, 1966.

7.   S. W. Tsai, Structural Behavior of Composite Materials,
     NASA Rept. CR-71 (1964).

8.   Z. Hashin and B. W. Rosen, J. Appl. Mech., 31E, 223 (1964).

9.   Z. Hashin, AIAA J., 4, 1411 (1966).

10. J. J. Hermans, Proc. Koninkl. Nederl. Akademie Van
     Wetenschappen, Amsterdam, 70B, 1 (1967).

11. J. M. Whitney, Textile Res. J., 37, 1008 (1967).

12. C. C. Chamis and G. P. Sendeckyj, J. Composite Mater., 2,
     332 (1968).

13. S. W. Tsai, U. S. Dept. Commerce Rept. AD834851 (1968).

14. J. E. Ashton, J. C. Halpin, and P. H. Petit, Primer on
     Composite Analysis, Technomic, Stamford, Conn., 1969.

15. J. C. Halpin, J. Composite Mater., 3, 732 (1969).

16. T. S. Chow and J. J. Hermans, J. Composite Mater., 3,
     382 (1969).

17. B. W. Rosen, Proc. Royal Soc., A319, 79 (1970).

18. G. P. Sendeckyj, J. Composite Mater., 4, 500 (1970).

19. H. T. Corten, Engineering Design for Plastics, E. Baer, Ed.,
     Van Nostrand Reinhold, New York, 1964, p. 869.

20. L. E. Nielsen, J. Appl. Phys., 41, 4626 (1970).

21. T. B. Lewis and L. E. Nielsen, J. Appl. Polymer Sci., 14,
     1449 (1970).

22. R. M. Anderson and R. E. Lavengood, SPE J., 24, #3, 20 (1968).

23. J. K. Lees, Polymer Eng. Sci., 8, 186 and 195 (1968).

24. N. J. Hoff, Engineering Laminates, A. G. H. Dietz, Ed.,
     Wiley, New York, 1949, p. 15.

25. S. W. Tsai, Mechanics of Composite Materials, Air Force
     Materials Lab. Rept. AFML-TR-66-149 (1966).

26. L. E. Nielsen and P. E. Chen, J. Mater., 3, 352 (1968).

27. E. A. Noga and R. T. Woodhams, SPE J., 26, #9, 23 (1970).

28. J. C. Halpin and N. J. Pagano, J. Composite Mater., 3,
     720 (1969).

29. L-H. Lee, Polymer Eng. Sci., 9, 213 (1969).

30. R. E. Lavengood and L. A. Goettler, U. S. Dept. Commerce
     Rept. AD886372 (1971).

31. S. W. Tsai and N. J. Pagano, Composite Materials Workshop,
     S. W. Tsai, J. C. Halpin and N. J. Pagano, Ed., Technomic,
     Stamford, Conn., 1968, p. 233.

32. L. E. Nielsen, Rheol. Acta, 13, 86 (1974).

33. A. C. Bernardo, SPE J., 26, #10, 39 (1970).

34. P. W. Jackson and D. Cratchley, J. Mech. Phys. Solids,
     14, 49 (1966).

35. E. K. Ashkenazi, Polymer Mech., 1, 60 (1966). (Engl.
     Transl. from Russian.)

36. O. Ishai, R. M. Anderson, and R. E. Lavengood, J. Mater.,
     5, 184 (1970).

37. J. T. Paul, Jr. and J. B. Thomson, Modern Plastics, 43,
     #4, 145 (1965).

38. J. A. Kies, U. S. Dept. Commerce Rept. AD274560 (1962).

39. N. F. Dow, General Electric Co., Rept. TIS R63 SD61, 1963.

40. W. H. Sutton and J. Chorné, Fiber Composite Materials,
     Amer. Soc. for Metals, Metals Park, Ohio, 1965, p. 173.

41. J. O. Outwater, Jr., Modern Plastics, 33, #7, 156 (1956).

42. A. Kelly and W. R. Tyson, High Strength Materials,
    V. F. Zackay, Ed., Wiley, New York, 1965, p. 578.

43. B. W. Rosen, AIAA J., 2, 1985 (1964).

44. P. E. Chen, Polymer Eng. Sci., 11, 51 (1971).

45. H. G. Allen, J. Phys., D5, 331 (1972).

46. A. H. Cottrell, Proc. Royal Soc., A282, 2 (1964).

47. V. R. Riley, J. Composite Mater., 2, 436 (1968).

48. M. R. Piggott, Acta Metallurgy, 14, 1429 (1966).

49. Yu. M. Tarnopol'skii and T. Ya. Kintsis, Polymer Mech., 1,
    #1, 72 (1965)(Engl. transl. from Russian.)

50. B. W. Rosen and N. F. Dow, Fracture, Vol. 7, H. Liebowitz,
    Ed., Academic Press, New York, 1972, p. 611.

51. R. E. Lavengood and O. Isahi, J. Mater., 5, 684 (1970).

52. G. A. Cooper and A. Kelly, ASTM, Spec. Tech. Publ., No. 452,
    Amer. Soc. Testing Materials, Philadelphia, Pa., 1969,
    p. 90.

53. J. M. Lin, P. E. Chen, and A. T. DiBenedetto, Polymer Eng.
    Sci., 11, 344 (1971).

54. B. W. Rosen, Fiber Composite Materials, Amer. Soc. for
    Metals, Metals Park, Ohio, 1965, p. 37.

55. M. A. Sadowsky, S. L. Pu, and M. A. Hussain, J. Appl. Mech.,
    E34, 1011 (1967).

56. E. Moncunill de Ferran and B. Harris, J. Composite Mater.,
    4, 62 (1970).

57. I. Petker, SPE Trans., 5, 49 (1965).

58. W. D. Bascom and J. B. Romans, Ind. Eng. Chem. (Prod. Res.
    Devel.), 7, 172 (1968).

59. C. C. Chamis, ASTM Spec. Tech. Publ. No. 460, Amer. Soc.
    for Testing Materials, Philadelphia, Pa., 1969, p. 336.

60. V. A. Kargin, T. I. Sogolova, and T. K. Metelskaya, Rubber
    Chem. Techn., 36, 111 (1963).

61. V. Karpov and M. Kaufman, British Plastics, 38, 498 (1965).

62. G. F. Hardy and H. L. Wagner, J. Appl. Polymer Sci., 13,
    961 (1969).

63. M. P. Wagner, Rubber World, 164, #5, 46 (1971).

64. L. A. Goettler, Modern Plastics, 47, #4, 140 (1970).

65. F. J. Filippi, Air Force Materials Lab, Monthly Progress
    Rept. #5, Feb. 1966.

66. A. G. H. Dietz, Engineering Laminates, Wiley, New York,
    1949.

67. A. G. H. Dietz, Composite Engineering Laminates, MIT Press,
    Cambridge, Mass., 1969.

68. G. B. Parsons, Modern Plastics, 29, 129 (Oct. 1951).

69. S. Turner, British Plastics, 38, 44 (1965).

70. F. G. Krautz, SPE J., 27, #8, 74 (1971).

71. F. Y. Soliman, ASTM Spec. Tech. Publ., No. 460, 1969, p. 254.

72. L. E. Nielsen, Unpublished data.

73. S. T. Mileiko, J. Mater. Sci., 5, 254 (1970).

74. D. McLean, J. Mater. Sci., 7, 98 (1971).

75. A. Kelly and K. N. Street, Proc. Royal Soc., A328,
    283 (1972).

76. R. E. Lavengood and L. B. Gulbransen, Polymer Eng. Sci., 9,
    365 (1969).

77. G. M. Nordby, U. S. Dept. Commerce Rept., AD 623128 (1965).

78. E. Hagerup, J. Appl. Polymer Sci., 7, 1093 (1963).

79. L. C. Cessna, J. A. Levens, and J. B. Thomson, Polymer
    Eng. Sci., 9, 339 (1969).

80. J. W. Dally and L. J. Broutman, J. Composite Mater.,
    1, 424 (1967).

81. A. T. DiBenedetto, J. V. Gauchel, R. L. Thomas, and J. W. Barlow, _J. Mater._, 7, 211 (1972).

82. A. Kelly, _Proc. Royal Soc._, A319, 95 (1970).

83. J. Cook and J. E. Gordon, _Proc. Royal Soc._, A282, 508 (1964).

84. G. A. Cooper, _J. Mater. Sci._, 5, 645 (1970).

85. M. R. Piggott, _J. Mater. Sci._, 5, 669 (1970).

86. D. C. Phillips and A. S. Tetelman, _Composites_, 3, 216 (1972).

87. F. G. Krautz, _Advances in Chemistry_, 99, 452 (1971).

88. J. G. Morley, _Proc. Royal Soc._, A319, 117 (1970).

89. P. W. R. Beaumont and D. C. Phillips, _J. Composite Mater._, 6, 32 (1972).

90. M. A. Ali and F. J. Grimer, _J. Mater. Sci._, 4, 389 (1969).

91. T. P. Murphy, _Preprint 833F_, meeting of Soc. Automotive Eng., Detroit, Mich., Mar. 30-April 3, 1964.

92. A. Wrzesien, _Composites_, 3, 172 (1972).

93. G. A. Cooper and J. M. Sillwood, _J. Mater. Sci._, 7, 325 (1972).

94. R. A. Shapery, _J. Composite Mater._, 2, 380 (1968).

95. L. E. Nielsen, _J. Macromol. Sci._, A1, 929 (1967).

96. P. E. Chen and L. E. Nielsen, _Kolloid Zeit. & Zeit. Fur Polymer_, 235, 1174 (1969).

97. J. C. Halpin and R. L. Thomas, _J. Composite Mater._, 2, 488 (1968).

98. T. B. Lewis and L. E. Nielsen, U. S. Patent No. 3,790,438.

99. _ASTM Standards_, Part 16, Amer. Soc. for Testing and Materials, Philadelphia, Pa.

100. A. W. Brown, _SPE J._, 18, #10, 1259 (1962).

101. G. Rugger, _SPE Techn. Papers_, 3, 393 (1957).

102. L. E. Nielsen, R. A. Wall, and P. G. Richmond, _SPE J._, 11, #7 22 (1955).

103. R. M. Gruver, U. S. Dept. Commerce Dept. AD 103538
      (1956).

104. J. J. Aclin, U. S. Dept. Commerce Rept. AD 233969
      (1960).

105. E. G. Dingman, SPE J., 17, 981 (1961).

106. D. Stevens, U. S. Dept. Commerce Rept. AD 274332 (1962).

107. J. Economy, L. C. Wohrer, and V. I. Matkovich, SAMPE J.,
      5, #1 23 (1969).

108. T. T. Wu, Internat. J. Solids Structure, 2, 1 (1966)

109. G. E. Padawer and N. Beecher, Polymer Eng. Sci., 10,
      185 (1970).

110. L. E. Nielsen, Trans. Soc. Rheol., 13, 141 (1969).

111. G. L. Ball and I. O. Salyer, J. Acoust. Soc. Amer., 39,
      663 (1966).

112. H. O. Oberst, L. Bohn, and F. Linhardt, Kunststoffe, 51,
      495 (1961).

113. H. Thurn, Kunststoffe, 50, 606 (1960).

114. R. E. Lavengood, M. J. Michno, and J. D. Fairing, Dept. of
      Commerce Rept. AD776592.

115. A. S. Kenyon, J. Colloid Interface Sci., 27, 761 (1968).

116. G. J. Fallick, H. J. Bixler, R. A. Marsella, F. F. Garner,
      and E. M. Fettes, Modern Plastics, 45, #5, 143 (1968).

117. M. Xanthos and R. T. Woodhams, J. Appl. Polymer Sci., 16,
      381 (1972).

118. T. Alfrey, Jr., High Strength Materials, V. F. Zackay, Ed.,
      Wiley, New York, 1965, p. 769.

119. V. Matonis, Polymer Eng. Sci., 9, 100 (1969).

120. P. L. White and L. H. Van Vlack, Polymer Eng. Sci., 10,
      293 (1970).

121. N. M. Parikh, H. A. Moreen, and A. J. Williams, U. S.
      Dept. Commerce Rept. AD 255992 (1961).

122. L. H. Sperling and D. W. Friedman, J. Polymer Sci., A2,
      7, 425 (1969).

123. L. H. Sperling, H. F. George, V. Huelck, and D. A. Thomas,
      J. Appl. Polymer Sci., 14, 2815 (1970).

124. V. Huelck, D. A. Thomas, and L. H. Sperling, Macromol.,
      5, 348 (1972).

125. M. Matsuo, T. K. Kwei, D. Klempner, and H. L. Frisch,
      Polymer Eng. Sci., 10, 327 (1970).

126. J. M. Starita, Trans. Soc. Rheol., 16, 339 (1972).

127. L. H. Sperling, V. Huelck, and D. A. Thomas, Polymer
      Networks, Structure and Mechanical Properties, A. J.
      Chompff and S. Newman, Ed., Plenum Press, New York,
      1971, p. 435.

128. H. L. Frisch, D. Klempner, K. C. Frisch, and T. K.
      Kwei, Polymer Networks, Structure and Mechanical Properties,
      A. J. Chompff and S. Newman, Ed., Plenum Press, New
      York, 1971, p. 451.

Appendix I

Chemical Structure of Common Polymers

1. Polyethylene

$$-\overset{\underset{\displaystyle H}{|}}{\underset{\underset{\displaystyle H}{|}}{C}}-\overset{\underset{\displaystyle H}{|}}{\underset{\underset{\displaystyle H}{|}}{C}}-$$

2. Polystyrene

$$-\overset{\underset{\displaystyle H}{|}}{\underset{\underset{\displaystyle H}{|}}{C}}-\overset{\underset{\displaystyle H}{|}}{\underset{\underset{\displaystyle C_6H_5}{|}}{C}}-$$

3. Polyvinyl chloride

$$-\overset{\underset{\displaystyle H}{|}}{\underset{\underset{\displaystyle H}{|}}{C}}-\overset{\underset{\displaystyle H}{|}}{\underset{\underset{\displaystyle Cl}{|}}{C}}-$$

4. Polymethyl methacrylate

$$-\overset{\underset{\displaystyle H}{|}}{\underset{\underset{\displaystyle H}{|}}{C}}-\overset{\underset{\displaystyle CH_3}{|}}{\underset{\underset{\displaystyle C-O-CH_3}{|}}{C}}-$$
$$\underset{\displaystyle O}{\|}$$

5. Polypropylene

$$-\overset{\underset{\displaystyle H}{|}}{\underset{\underset{\displaystyle H}{|}}{C}}-\overset{\underset{\displaystyle H}{|}}{\underset{\underset{\displaystyle CH_3}{|}}{C}}-$$

6. Polybutadiene (1;4 addition)

$$-\overset{\underset{\displaystyle H}{|}}{\underset{\underset{\displaystyle H}{|}}{C}}-\overset{\displaystyle H}{C}=\overset{\displaystyle H}{C}-\overset{\underset{\displaystyle H}{|}}{\underset{\underset{\displaystyle H}{|}}{C}}-$$

7. Polyoxymethylene

$$-\overset{\underset{\displaystyle H}{|}}{\underset{\underset{\displaystyle H}{|}}{C}}-O-$$

8. Polyvinyl methyl ether

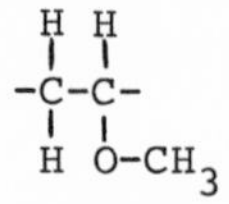

$$\begin{array}{c} H \quad H \\ | \quad\; | \\ -C-C- \\ | \quad\; | \\ H \;\; O-CH_3 \end{array}$$

9. Polydimethyl siloxane

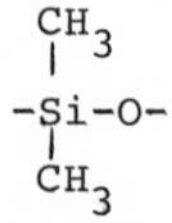

$$\begin{array}{c} CH_3 \\ | \\ -Si-O- \\ | \\ CH_3 \end{array}$$

10. Polyvinylidene
    fluoride

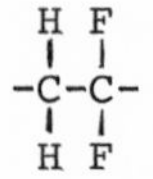

$$\begin{array}{c} H \quad F \\ | \quad\; | \\ -C-C- \\ | \quad\; | \\ H \quad F \end{array}$$

11. Polycarbonate of
    bisphenol-A

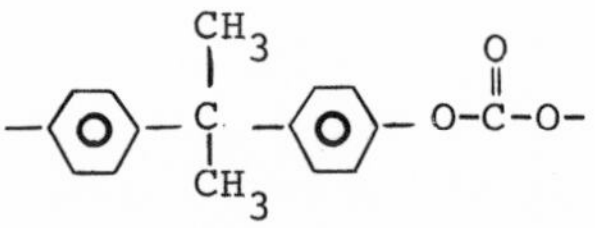

12. Polyethylene terephthalate

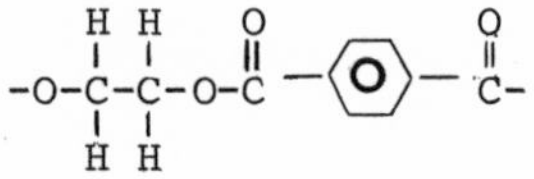

13. Polycaprolactam
        (Nylon 6)

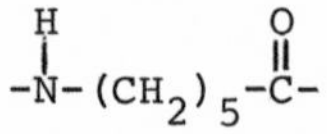

14. Polyhexamethylene adipate
        (Nylon 6-6)

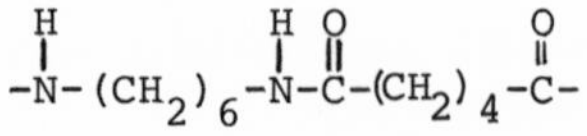

15. Polyphenylene oxide
        (Poly-2,6-dimethylphenylene oxide)

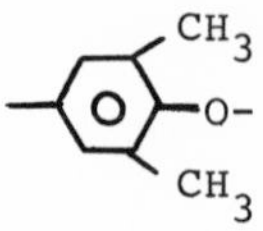

Appendix II

Conversion Factors for Moduli, Stress, and Viscosity

To Convert From	To	Multiply by
Newtons/meter^2 (N/m^2)	dynes/cm^2	10.00
dynes/cm^2	newtons/meter^2 (N/m^2)	0.100
psi	N/m^2	6.895×10^3
N/m^2	psi	1.450×10^{-4}
dynes/cm^2	kg/cm^2	1.020×10^{-6}
dynes/cm^2	kg/sq. mm	1.020×10^{-8}
kg/sq.mm	dynes/cm^2	9.806×10^7
dynes/cm^2	psi	1.450×10^{-5}
psi	dynes/cm^2	6.895×10^4
psi	kg/sq.mm	7.03×10^{-4}
kg/sq.mm	psi	1.422×10^3
dynes/cm^2	atmospheres	9.869×10^{-7}
atmospheres	dynes/cm^2	1.013×10^6
atmospheres	N/m^2	1.013×10^5
psi	atmospheres	6.81×10^{-2}
dynes/cm^2	bars	1.00×10^{-6}
psi	bars	6.895×10^{-2}
g/denier	dynes/cm^2	8.83×10^8 ρ*
g/denier	psi	1.28×10^4 ρ*
bars	N/m^2	1.00×10^5

*ρ = density

To Convert From	To	Multiply by
kg/cm^2	N/m^2	9.807×10^4
poise	$N \cdot S/m^2$	1.000×10^{-1}
stokes	m^2/S	1.000×10^{-4}
dynes	newtons (N)	1.000×10^{-5}

Appendix III

Glass Transition Temperature and Melting Points of Polymers

Polymer	T_g (°C)	T_m (°C)
Polyethylene	-120 (-130)	137, (141)
Polypropylene (isotactic)	-10	176 (182)
Polyisobutylene	-70 (-73)	128 (.5)?
Polyisoprene (cis)	-73	28 (36)
Polyisoprene (trans)	-60	74 (65)
Poly 1,4-cis-butadiene	-108 (-95)	1
Poly 1,4-trans butadiene	-83 (-18)	148 (92)
Poly 1,2-butadiene (isotactic)	-4	120
Poly-1-butene	-25	132 (126)
Poly-1-pentene	-40	75 (130)
Poly-1-octene	-65	-38
Poly-4-methyl pentene-1	29	250
Polyoxymethylene	-83 (-50)	181 (198)
Polyethylene oxide	-66 (-53)	66
Polyvinyl methyl ether	-13 (-20)	144
Polyvinyl ethyl ether	-25 (-42)	86
Polyvinyl-n-butyl ether	-52 (-55)	64
Polyvinyl isobutyl ether	-27 (-18)	115 (165)
Polyvinyl tert. butyl ether	88	260
Polydimethyl siloxane	-123	-40
Polystyrene (atactic)	100 (105)	-

515

Polymer	T_g (°C)	T_m (°C)
Polystyrene (isotactic)	100	240 (250)
Poly α-methyl styrene	192 (180)	
Poly o-methyl styrene	119 (125)	> 360
Poly m-methyl styrene	72 (82)	215
Poly p-methyl styrene	110 (126)	
Poly p-phenyl styrene	138	
Poly p-chloro styrene	128	
Poly 2,5-dichloro styrene	130 (115)	
Poly α-vinyl naphthalene	162	360
Polymethyl acrylate	3 (6)	
Polyethyl acrylate	-24	
Polyacrylic acid	106 (97)	
Poly (zinc acrylate)	> 300	
Polymethyl methacrylate (syndiotactic)	115 (105)	> 200
Polymethyl methacrylate (isotactic)	45 (55)	160
Polyethyl methacrylate	65	
Poly n-propyl methacrylate	35	
Poly n-butyl methacrylate	21	
Poly n-hexyl methacrylate	-5	
Poly n-octyl methacrylate	-20	
Polyvinyl fluoride	40 (-20)	200
Polyvinyl chloride	87 (81)	227 (273)
Polyvinylidene fluoride	-40 (-46)	
Polyvinylidene chloride	-19 (-17)	198 (190)
Poly-1,2-dichloroethylene	145	
Polychloroprene	-50	80 (115)
Polytetrafluoroethylene	126 ? (-65)	327 (330)

Polymer	T_g (°C)	T_m (°C)
Polyacrylonitrile (syndiotactic)	104 (130)	317
Polymethacrylonitrile	120	
Polyvinyl acetate	28	
Polyvinyl carbazole	208 (150)	
Polyvinyl formal	105	
Polyvinyl butyral	49 (59)	
Cellulose triacetate	105 ?	306
Ethyl cellulose	43	
Polyvinyl alcohol	85	870 ?
Poly(bisphenol-A carbonate)	150	267 (220)
Polyethylene terephthalate	69	265 (325)
Polytetramethylene terephthalate	40	232
Nylon 3		260
Nylon 5		223
Nylon 6 (Polycaprolactam)	50 (40)	225 (219)
Nylon 10	42	177 (192)
Nylon 11	43 (46)	189 (194)
Nylon 12	42	179
Nylon 66 (Polyhexamethylene adipamide)	50 (57)	265 (260)
Nylon 6-10 (Polyhexamethylene sebacamide)	40 (44)	227 (233)
Poly-2,6-dimethyl phenylene oxide	220 (210)	481
Poly p-xylene		375
Polyvinyl pyrrolidone	86	
Polyacenaphthylene	321	

Note: Parenthesis indicate alternate values reported in the literature.

Appendix IV

Relations Between Engineering Moduli and Tensor Moduli and Tensor Compliances For Anisotropic Materials

The generalized Hooke's law in tensor notation has 36 elements. Symmetry reduces these 36 elements to 21 independent elements in the most complex cases. For uniaxially and biaxially oriented polymers there are 5 independent elements as a result of a plane of symmetry. This plane of symmetry is perpendicular to the direction of orientation for uniaxial orientation as is evident from Figure 1 of Chapter 2. For biaxial orientation the plane of symmetry is parallel to the plane of orientation. These 5 tensor elements can be expressed in terms of 5 independent engineering moduli. However, the relationships are simpler if the engineering moduli are expressed in terms of tensor compliances rather than the tensor moduli. The inverse generalized Hooke's law in terms of compliances S_{ij} is:

$$\varepsilon_i = \begin{vmatrix} S_{11} & S_{12} & S_{13} & S_{14} & S_{15} & S_{16} \\ S_{21} & S_{22} & S_{23} & S_{24} & S_{25} & S_{26} \\ S_{31} & S_{32} & S_{33} & S_{34} & S_{35} & S_{36} \\ S_{41} & S_{42} & S_{43} & S_{44} & S_{45} & S_{46} \\ S_{51} & S_{52} & S_{53} & S_{54} & S_{55} & S_{56} \\ S_{61} & S_{62} & S_{63} & S_{64} & S_{65} & S_{66} \end{vmatrix} \sigma_j \qquad i,j = 1 \cdots 6. \tag{1}$$

ε_i is the strain in the i direction, and σ_j is the stress in the
j direction. S_{ij} is the strain in the i direction resulting
from a stress in the j direction. For uniaxially and biaxially
anisotropic materials this reduces to:

$$
\varepsilon_i =
\begin{vmatrix}
S_{11} & S_{12} & S_{13} & 0 & 0 & 0 \\
S_{12} & S_{11} & S_{13} & 0 & 0 & 0 \\
S_{13} & S_{13} & S_{33} & 0 & 0 & 0 \\
0 & 0 & 0 & S_{44} & 0 & 0 \\
0 & 0 & 0 & 0 & S_{44} & 0 \\
0 & 0 & 0 & 0 & 0 & S_{66}
\end{vmatrix}
\sigma_j
\qquad (2)
$$

written out in long hand, this becomes:

$$\varepsilon_1 = S_{11}\,\sigma_1 + S_{12}\,\sigma_2 + S_{13}\,\sigma_3 .$$

$$\varepsilon_2 = S_{12}\,\sigma_1 + S_{11}\,\sigma_2 + S_{13}\,\sigma_3 .$$

$$\varepsilon_3 = S_{13}\,\sigma_1 + S_{13}\,\sigma_2 + S_{33}\,\sigma_3 . \qquad (3)$$

$$\varepsilon_{13} = \varepsilon_{23} = S_{44}\,\gamma_{13}$$

$$\varepsilon_{12} = S_{66}\,\gamma_{12}$$

where γ_{13} is the shearing force for planes normal to the plane
of symmetry, and γ_{12} is the shearing force in the plane of
symmetry.

For uniaxial orientation, the directions 1 and 2 refer
to the directions perpendicular to the direction of orientation,
and 3 refers to the direction of orientation. The compliance

S_{44} refers to the longitudinal-transverse shear coordinate or to shear in planes normal to the plane of symmetry. The compliance S_{66} refers to shear in the plane of symmetry, that is, the transverse-transverse shear coordinate. The engineering moduli for uniaxially oriented materials are:

$$E_L = 1/S_{33} \tag{4}$$

$$E_T = 1/S_{11} \tag{5}$$

$$G_{LT} = 1/S_{44} \tag{6}$$

$$G_{TT} = 1/S_{66} \tag{7}$$

$$\nu_{LT} = -S_{13}/S_{33} = -S_{23}/S_{33} \tag{8}$$

$$\nu_{TT} = -S_{12}/S_{11} \tag{9}$$

$$\nu_{TL} = -S_{13}/S_{11} \tag{10}$$

ν_{LT} is the Poisson's ratio characteristic of contractions within the plane of symmetry due to forces in the direction of orientation. ν_{TT} is the Poisson's ratio which is due to contractions within the plane of symmetry due to forces applied within the same plane, that is, ν_{TT} is the transverse contraction per unit width in direction 2 produced by a load in the other transverse direction (direction 1) divided by the elongation in direction 1.

The moduli also can be expressed by other relations such as:

$$\frac{\nu_{LT}}{E_L} = \frac{\nu_{TL}}{E_T} \tag{11}$$

$$S_{66} = 2(S_{11} - S_{12}) \tag{12}$$

or

$$G_{TT} = \frac{E_T}{2(1 + \nu_{TT})} \tag{13}$$

$$\frac{4}{E_{45°}} = S_{11} + S_{33} + S_{44} + 2S_{13} = \frac{(1 - 2\nu_{LT})}{E_L} + \frac{1}{E_T} + \frac{1}{G_{LT}} \tag{14}$$

$E_{45°}$ is the Young's modulus measured at 45° to the orientation direction.

$$\frac{4}{G_{45°}} = 4S_{11} - 2S_{12} - 4S_{13} + 2S_{33} + S_{44} = \frac{2}{E_T} + \frac{2}{E_L} + \frac{1}{G_{TT}} + \frac{1}{G_{LT}}$$

$$+ \frac{4\nu_{TL}}{E_T} \quad . \tag{15}$$

$$G_{45°} = \frac{E_L E_T}{E_T(1 + 2\nu_{LT}) + E_L} \tag{16}$$

$G_{45°}$ is analogous to G_{LT}, but the axis of torque is 45° to the axis of orientation. If $E_L \gg E_T$, then

$$G_{45°} \doteq E_T \quad . \tag{17}$$

In general $G_{45°}$ is slightly less than G_{LT}; a typical value of $G_{45°}/G_{LT} \simeq 0.9$. Shear moduli can be measured in which the axis of twist is perpendicular to the direction of orientation. This modulus $G_{90°}$ is given by:

$$\frac{1}{G_{90°}} = \frac{1}{2}(S_{44} + S_{66}) = \frac{1}{2}(S_{44} + 2S_{11} - 2S_{12}) \tag{18}$$

Similar relationships hold for biaxially oriented materials in which the plane of symmetry is parallel to the plane of orientation as shown in Figure 2 of Chapter 2. Some of these relationships are:

$$E_P = 1/S_{11} = 1/S_{22} \tag{19}$$

$$E_T = 1/S_{33} \tag{20}$$

$$G_T = 1/S_{44} \tag{21}$$

$$G_P = 1/S_{66} \quad . \tag{22}$$

The engineering moduli can be expressed in terms of tensor moduli C_{ij} rather than in terms of the tensor compliances S_{ij}. For uniaxially anisotropic materials,

$$C_{11} = E_T/(1 - \nu_{LT} \nu_{TL}) \tag{23}$$

$$C_{33} = E_L/(1 - \nu_{LT} \nu_{TL}) \tag{24}$$

$$C_{44} = G_{LT} \tag{25}$$

$$C_{13} = \nu_{LT} E_L/(1 - \nu_{LT} \nu_{TL}) \tag{26}$$

$$C_{66} = G_{TT} \quad . \tag{27}$$

APPENDIX V

List of Symbols

Numbers refer to the first chapter in which the symbol appears.

a   A constant   3

a   Length of a crack   5

A   Cross sectional area, or area of a shear face   1

A   A constant related to the Einstein coefficient in equations for the moduli of composites   7

A_i Amplitude of the i th oscillation in free vibrations   1

A_i A constant related to the Einstein coefficient in equations for the moduli of inverted composite systems   7

a_T Williams-Landel-Ferry time-temperature shift factor   3

B   Bulk modulus   1

B   A constant related to the ratio of the moduli of the components of composites   7

B   Overlap of edges of ribbons in adjacent layers in ribbon-filled composites   8

B_i A constant related to the ratio of the moduli of the components of inverted composite systems   7

B_T Total overlap (sum of both edges) of ribbons in adjacent layers in ribbon-filled composites   8

B_1 Bulk modulus of the matrix phase of composites   7

B_2 Bulk modulus of the filler phase of composites   7

C   Width of test specimen of rectangular cross section   2

C   Length of a tear   5

C_X Number of moles of tetrafunctional crosslinking agent per
      unit volume of polymer   4

C_{ij} Stress in the i direction resulting from a strain in the j
         direction. An element of the modulus matrix Appendix IV.

d   Distance between anion and cation in polyelectrolytes   4

d   Diameter of spherical filler particles in a composite   7

D   Thickness of test specimen with rectangular cross section   1

D   Distance between shearing surfaces (Figure 2)   1

D   Diameter of specimen with a circular cross section   2

D   Thickness of polymer layer between layers of ribbons in
      ribbon-filled composites   8

DB   Decibel   1

E   Young's modulus   1

$E_r(t)$ Stress relaxation modulus as a function of time   3

E'   Real part of complex dynamic Young's modulus   1

E"   Loss modulus or imaginary part of dynamic Young's modulus   1

E"/E' Dissipation factor; a damping term equivalent to tan δ 1

E_L Longitudinal Young's modulus of uniaxially oriented polymers
      and aligned fiber-filled composites   2

E_P Young's modulus in the plane of a biaxially oriented polymer
      or two dimensional fiber-filled composite   2

E_T Transverse Young's modulus of uniaxially oriented polymers
      or aligned fiber composites   2

E_U Young's modulus of unoriented unfilled polymer   4

E_1, E_2 Moduli of springs of a 4-element model   3

E_1 Young's modulus of the spherical indentor in a Hertz
      indentation test   6

E_2 Young's modulus of the material with a flat surface in a
       Hertz indentation test   6

E_1 Young's modulus of the continuous phase in a composite   7

E_2 Young's modulus of the dispersed phase in a composite   7

E_{2D} Young's modulus in the plane of the sheet of a biaxial
       composite in which fibers are randomly oriented in a plane   8

E_{3D} Young's modulus of composites in which fibers are randomly
       oriented in three directions   8

f   Frequency in cycles/second or Hz   1

f_R Resonance frequency 1

F   Force 1

g   Acceleration of gravity   6

G   Shear modulus   1

G*   Complex dynamic shear modulus   1

G'   Real part of the complex dynamic shear modulus   1

G"   Loss modulus or the imaginary part of the complex dynamic
       shear modulus   1

G"/G' Dissipation factor for dynamic mechanical tests in shear;
       a damping term equivalent to tan δ   1

G_C Critical stress energy release rate   5

G_P One of the shear moduli of biaxially oriented anisotropic
       materials; see Figure 2, Chapter 2.   2

G_T One of the shear moduli of biaxially oriented anisotropic
       materials. See Figure 2, Chapter 2.   2

G_{LT} Longitudinal-transverse shear modulus of a uniaxial
       anisotropic material. See Figure 1, Chapter 2.   2

G_{TT} Transverse-transverse shear modulus of a uniaxial anisotropic
       material. See Figure 1, Chapter 2.   2

G_1 Shear modulus of the continuous (matrix) phase in a composite   7

G_2 Shear modulus of the dispersed phase in a composite   7

G_{2D} Shear modulus in the plane of the sheet for composites with fibers randomly oriented in a plane   8

h   Depth of penetration or indentation   6

H   Heat energy dissipated per cycle per unit volume of material during a dynamic mechanical test   1

H_B Hysteresis energy to break   5

$H(\tau)$ Distribution of relaxation times   3

i $\sqrt{-1}$ 1

I   Polar moment of inertia   2

J   Compliance   1

J*   Complex compliance   1

J'   Real part of complex compliance   1

J"   Imaginary part of the complex compliance   1

J_0 Compliance at stresses low enough for the compliance to be independent of the applied stress   3

J_e Steady state creep compliance   3

k   Boltzmann's constant   5

k_E Einstein coefficient   7

K   A constant   1

K   Rate of strain = $d\varepsilon/dt$ 5

K_C Critical stress intensity factor   5

L   Length of specimen   1

L_0 Initial length of a test specimen   1

L_C Critical or ineffective fiber length in fiber-filled composites   8

L_D Debonded length of fiber during fracture of fiber-filled
        composites   8

$L(\tau)$ Distribution of retardation times   3

m   Mass of specimen   2

m   A constant of the Cross equation   7

M   Mass on end of a specimen   2

M   An elastic modulus   2

M   Molecular weight   3

M_o Molecular weight of a monomeric unit   1

M_c Molecular weight between crosslinked points   1

M_e Molecular weight between entanglement points   3

M_x Molecular weight of the trifunctional crosslinked atoms plus
        their attached hydrogen atoms; generally 26.   4

$\bar{M}_n$ Number average molecular weight   1

$\bar{M}_w$ Weight average molecular weight   3

M_1 Elastic modulus of the matrix of composites   7

M_2 Elastic modulus of the dispersed phase in composites   7

n   A constant   1

n   A constant in the Nutting equation   3

n_c Number average number of atoms in polymer backbone between
        crosslinks   1

n_i Mole fraction of group i   1

N   Number of segments in a polymer chain   3

N   Number of cycles to cause failure in a fatigue test   6

N   Newtons   Appendix II.

N_o Avogadro's number   3

P   Period of oscillation in seconds   1

P_i Stress-biased probability of chain rupture   5

P_m Maximum pressure in the Hertz penetration of a sphere into a flat surface   6

q   Swelling ratio   3

q   Electrical charge on counterion of polyelectrolyte   4

Q   Q-Factor, tan δ 1

r   Radius of curvature at the tip of a crack or notch   5

r   Radius of circle of contact when a sphere is pressed into a flat surface   6

$\overline{r^2}$ Mean-square distance between network juncture points   4

$\overline{r_o^2}$ Mean-square end-to-end distance of network chains in free space   4

R   Gas constant   1

R   Resilience   1

R   Radius of a circular specimen or sphere   2

S   Shear displacement   1

S_{ij} Strain in the i direction resulting from a stress in the j direction.   An element of the compliance matrix.   Appendix IV.

t   Time   3

t   Thickness of ribbons in ribbon-filled composites   8

t_{b} Time to break   5

T   Temperature, generally °K   1

T_F Flex temperature; temperature at which shear modulus is 45,000 psi   6

T_g Glass transition temperature   1

T_{go} Glass transition temperature of uncrosslinked polymer of same chemical composition as a crosslinked one   1

T_{gA} Glass transition temperature of polymer A   1

T_{gg} Secondary glass transition temperature   4

T_m Melting point, generally °K   1

T_m° Melting point of pure homopolymer of very high molecular weight   1

T_O Reference temperature, generally °K   3

T_4 Temperature at which the shear modulus is 10^4 psi   6

U_B Energy to break   5

U_t Tearing energy   5

v Velocity   2

$\bar{v}$ Specific volume   3

$\bar{v}_a$ Specific volume of amorphous glass   5

$\bar{v}_c$ Specific volume of crystalline phase   5

V Volume   1

V_O Original volume   1

V_1 Molar volume of solvent   1

V_L Volume of matrix liquid that is entrapped within and on surface of an aggregate   7

V_S Actual volume of the spheres making up an aggregate   7

V_u Molar volume of a polymer repeat unit   1

w_O A collision parameter in fracture theory   5

w_c Degree of crystallinity   4

W Total strain energy in a specimen during a tearing test   5

W Normal load in a friction test   6

W Width of ribbons in ribbon-filled composites   8

W_i Weight fraction of component i   1

x Minimum number of ribbons in a ribbon-filled composite that actually carry stress in a thickness equal to the repeat thickness of the lay-up pattern   8

X_A Mole fraction of component A   1

X_C Mole fraction of the monomeric units which are crosslinked in a polymer   1

X_X Approximate mole fraction of crosslinked atoms   4

y Number of layers of ribbons in a ribbon-filled composite required for the lay-up pattern to be repeated   8

Y Deflection or displacement of a beam resulting from an applied force   2

Z_e Average number of atoms in backbone between entanglements   3

Z_w Weight average number of atoms in the backbone of a polymer chain   3

α (alpha) Volume coefficient of thermal expansion   1

α-transition T_g of amorphous polymers; a crystalline transition in crystalline polymers   4

α_c Volume coefficient of thermal expansion of a crystal   5

α_i Difference in the volume coefficients of thermal expansion in the liquid and glassy states of component i   1

α_g Volume coefficient of thermal expansion of a polymer in the glassy state   1

α_ℓ Volume coefficient of thermal expansion of a polymer in the liquid or rubbery state   1

α_L Volume coefficient of thermal expansion in the longitudinal direction for aligned fiber composites   8

α_T Volume coefficient of thermal expansion in the transverse direction for aligned fiber composites   8

α_1 Volume coefficient of thermal expansion of the continuous (matrix) phase in composites   7

α_2 Volume coefficient of thermal expansion of the filler (discontinuous) phase in composites   7

β (beta) A constant of the Nutting equation   3

γ (gamma) Shear strain   1

γ The work required to form a unit area of new surface during fracture   5

$\dot{\gamma}$ Rate of shear   4

δ (delta)   The phase difference between stress and strain in dynamic mechanical tests   1

δ Solubility parameter   4

tan δ Dissipation factor, a damping term   1

Δ Logarithmic decrement, a damping term   1

ΔH Energy of activation or heat of reaction   4

ΔH_u Heat of fusion per mole of crystalline repeat unit   1

ε (epsilon)   Strain   1

ε_B Strain at break; ultimate elongation   1

ε_B^o Elongation to break of the matrix phase (unfilled) of a composite   7

ε_L Strain in longitudinal direction   2

ε_T Strain in direction perpendicular to the applied stress; transverse strain   1

ε_Y Elongation or strain at yield point   1

ε_o Initial strain   3

ζ (zeta)   Segmental friction factor   3

η (eta)   Viscosity of a liquid, polymer melt, or suspension   3

η^* Complex viscosity   1

η' Real part of complex viscosity   1

η'' Imaginary part of complex viscosity   1

η_a Apparent viscosity of a polymer melt   4

η_i Viscosity of a blend made up of fractions of different molecular weight   3

η_c Consistency of a polymer melt   4

η_o Viscosity at reference temperature T_o 3

η_o Viscosity at zero rate of shear   4

η_1 Viscosity of the matrix liquid of a suspension   7

η_2, η_3 Viscosity of dashpots in a 4-element model   3

η_∞ Limiting viscosity at very high rates of shear   7

θ (theta) Shear angle, (Figure 2, Chapter 1)   1

θ Angle from the direction of applied stress   5

θ Angle between direction of aligned fibers and applied
   stress in fiber-filled composites   7

λ (lambda) Extension ratio, L/L_o 5

λ_i A shift factor for component i in polymer mixtures. Sometimes
   λ_i is the ratio of the number average molecular weight of a
   blend to the number average molecular weight of component i
   3

Λ Activation volume in the fracture process   5

μ (mu) Geometric shape factor in torsion of beams (See Chapter 2,
   Table 3.)   2

μ Coefficient of friction   6

μ_r Coefficient of rolling friction   6

ν (nu) Poisson's ratio   1

ν_e Effective number of crosslinked chains per unit volume   5

ν_1 Poisson's ratio of the continuous phase in composites   7

ν_{LT} Poisson's ratio for the force applied in the longitudinal
   direction of a uniaxial material   2

ν_{TL} Poisson's ratio for the force applied in the transverse
   direction of a uniaxial anisotropic material   2

ρ (rho) Density   3

ρ_o Density at reference temperature T_o 3

σ (sigma) Stress   1

σ_s Shear stress   1

σ_B Tensile strength or stress to break   1

σ_c Critical stress characterizing stress dependence of creep   3

σ_c Stress on a single polymer chain   5

σ_h Maximum tensile stress at edge of circle of contact in a Hertz penetration test   6

σ_i Strength of the interfacial bond in fiber-filled composites   8

σ_m Maximum stress at the tip of a crack   5

σ_t Tangential stress at the edge of a hole   5

σ_o Initial stress, or the applied stress   3

σ_{BO} Tensile strength of a polymer with infinite (very high) molecular weight   5

σ_{BL} Stress to break an aligned fiber-filled composite in the longitudinal direction   8

σ_{BS} Shear strength of matrix in a composite   8

σ_{BT} Tensile strength of aligned fiber composites in a direction perpendicular to the fibers   8

σ_{yo} Yield stress of the matrix phase of a composite   7

σ_{B1} Tensile strength of the matrix phase of a composite   8

σ_{B2} Tensile strength of the fibers in a composite   8

$\sigma_{B\theta}$ Tensile strength of an aligned fiber composite measured at an angle θ between the applied stress and the fibers   8

τ(tau)   Relaxation time, or retardation time   3

ϕ_a(phi)   Volume fraction of an aggregate that is made up of solid spheres   7

ϕ_A Volume fraction of monomeric unit A   1

ϕ_m Maximum packing fraction of filler particles   7

ϕ_m' Maximum packing fraction of the dispersed (low modulus) phase in inverted composite systems   7

ϕ_1 Volume fraction of the matrix (continuous phase) in composite materials   7

ϕ_2 Volume fraction of the filler (discontinuous) phase in
composites   7

χ(chi) Nearest neighbor interaction parameter which determines
the solubility behavior of a polymer in a liquid   1

ψ(psi) Specific damping capacity   1

ψ A reduced concentration factor which takes into account
the maximum packing fraction of the filler phase in
calculations of the moduli of composites   7

ω(omega) Angular frequency in radians per second   1

Ω A constant in the Cross equation   7

AUTHOR INDEX

Numbers in parentheses are reference numbers and indicate that an author's work is referred to although his name is not cited in the text. Underlined numbers give the page on which the complete reference is listed.

A

Abitz, W., 27(89) 36
Aclin, J. J., 496(104), 509
Adachi, T., 116(157), 136
Adams, C. H., 314,315,317(261), 339
Adams, G., 197(232), 246
Adams, N., 354(62), 374
Aggarwal, S. L., 59(71), 66,
    123, 138, 217(313), 251,
    294(169), 335, 416,428(106), 448
Aiken, W., 118, 119(165), 137
Ainbinder, S. B., 270(35), 329
Ajroldi, G., 171(133), 241
Aklonis, J. J., 218(338), 252,
    366, 376
Albert, W., 216(306), 250, 293(153),
    334
Alfrey, Jr., T., 4(2), 32, 80,
    92(30), 129, 113, 119(147), 136,
    118, 119(165), 137, 499(118), 509
Ali, M. A., 486(90), 508
Allen, G., 229(388), 255
Allen, H. G., 469, 506
Allen, V. R., 99(97), 133
Allison, S. W., 285, 300(120), 333
Alter, H., 411(87), 447
Ambartsumyan, S. A., 198(241), 247
Amberg, L. O., 406(64), 446
Ambrose, E. J., 198(250), 247
Anderson, A. A., 285(112), 332
Anderson, R. M., 458(22), 465,
    467(36), 469, 505
Andrew, E. R., 201(271), 248
Andrews, E. H., 351, 352(39), 373
Andrews, J. M., 265, 300(14), 328
Andrews, R. D., 198(243), 247,
    225(378), 254
Angelo, R. J., 59(75), 66, 217(312),
    251, 428(151), 450
Angier, D. J., 294(155), 334
Arends, C. B., 294(157), 334
Arisawa, K., 84(37), 130
Armeniades, C. D., 139, 187(29), 236,
    201, 202, 225(239), 247, 201,
    202, 229(268), 248
Armstrong, G. M., 343(9), 372
Arnold, R. G., 278(60), 330
Asada, J., 83(22), 83, 113, 114(25),
    129, 84(38), 130, 167(121), 240
Ashkenazi, E. K., 467, 505
Ashton, J. E., 39, 40(2), 62, 198(242),
    247, 388(23), 444, 455, 456, 464,
    493(14), 504
Atack, D., 355(66), 374

Atkinson, E. B., 59(67), 66, 214, 216
    (290), 250, 284(100), 332, 395,
    428(36), 444
Axilrod, B. M., 290, 292(133), 290,
    292(135), 333

B

Baccaredda, M., 59(74), 66, 195, 224
    (214), 245, 216(307), 250, 215
    222(325), 215, 222, 229(326), 251,
    222(353), 253, 224(367), 254,
    229(384), 255
Backman, D. K., 93(79), 132
Baer, E., 139, 187(29), 236, 187, 229
    (176), 243, 201, 202, 225(239),
    247, 201, 202, 229(268), 248
    270(33,38), 329
Baer, M., 59(73), 66, 216(310), 251,
    294, 318(163), 335, 319(271), 339,
    415(104), 448, 428(149), 450
Bailey, J., 285, 290(108), 332
Ball, G. L., 423(132), 449, 497(111),
    509
Ballman, R. L., 100(99), 133, 285, 289,
    314, 315, 317(109), 332, 290(127),
    333
Ballou, J. W., 139, 198, 204(31), 236
Balwit, J. S., 273, 275(48), 330
Bares, J., 84(41), 130
Barish, L., 281(78), 331
Barker, Jr., R. E., 218, 229(337), 252
Barlow, D. A., 356(80), 375
Barlow, J. W., 481(81), 508
Barnet, F. R., 406(56), 445
Bartenev, G. M., 355(72), 355, 356
    (74), 356(78), 375
Bartoe, W. F., 363, 367(100), 376
Bascom, W. D., 473(58), 506
Battaerd, H. A. J., 294(170), 335
Bauer, P., 58(60), 65, 216(301), 250,
    428(154), 450
Bauman, A. J., 383(7), 443
Bauwens-Crowet, C., 302(217), 337
Bauwens, J-C., 302(217), 337
Baxter, S., 416(116), 448
Beaman, R. G., 31(97), 37
Beardmore, P., 292, 306(145), 334
Beaumont, P. W. R., 486(89), 508
Beck, H. N., 283(92), 331
Beck, Jr., R. H., 294(159), 334,
    301, 307(201), 336, 415(102), 447
Becker, G. W., 93(77,78), 116, 132,
    194(203), 245, 406(51), 445
Beecher, J. F., 59(71), 66, 123,

537

138, 217(313), 251, 294(169),
335, 416, 428(106), 448
Beecher, N., 496(109), 509
Bekkedahl, N., 19(21), 33
Bell, J. P., 23(60), 35, 175, 177
(140), 241
Bely, V. A., 356(76), 375
Benbow, J. J., 297(177), 335
Bender, B. W., 319(270), 339
Benning, C. J., 417(117), 448
Berezknitskiy, L. T., 305(226), 337
Berg, R. M., 347(19,23), 372
Berge, J. W., 139(14), 235
Bergen, Jr., R. L., 84(35), 130,
92(62), 131
Bernardo, A. C., 465, 474, 481(33),
486, 505
Bernhardt, E. C., 363(101), 376
Berry, G. C., 52(31), 64, 97, 99,
105(92), 104(106), 133
Berry, J. P., 109, 135, 297
(178-180), 335
Bersch, C. F., 121(183), 138
Bevilacqua, E. M., 319(268), 339
Bhateja, S. K., 270(32), 329
Binder, G., 301(196), 336
Birnboim, M. H., 139(52), 237
Bischoff, J., 84(28), 129
Bishop, E. T., 59(69), 66, 217
(316), 251, 292, 294(143),
334, 397, 429(39), 444
Bisset, D. C., 409(73), 446
Bixler, H. J., 498(116), 509
Blanchette, J. A., 59(66), 66,
216(302), 250, 428(148), 450
Blasenbrey, S., 223(364), 254
Bobalek, E. G., 421(126), 449,
434(175), 457
Bodner, S. R., 414(96), 447
Boehme, R. D. 406, 425(49), 445
Boerma, J., 275, 281, 317(53), 330
Boettner, R. C., 348, 351, 352(29),
373
Bohn, L., 195, 218, 225(228), 246
313, 314(247), 338, 318(266),
339, 423(133), 449, 497(112), 509
Bondi, A., 111, 113(146), 136, 185,
186(168), 243
Bonnin, M. J., 120(181), 138
Boonstra, B. B., 406, 411, 413(66),
446, 413(91), 447, 421(127), 449
Boor, L., 363, 367(100), 376
Booth, C., 229(388), 255
Borders, A. M., 292, 293(141), 334
Bostwick, R., 406, 411(47), 445
Boundy, R. H., 343(17), 372
Bowden, F. P., 353, 354, 356(51), 374
Boyer, R. F., 19(29), 22(41), 34
22(48), 35, 31(98), 37, 187,
215, 218, 222(172), 243, 216(309),
251, 222(363), 254, 273 330, 314
(253), 338, 314, 319, 320(260),
339, 343(17), 372
Boyer-Kawenoki, F., 58(52), 65,
193(200), 245
Bradford, R. D., 59(71), 66, 123, 138,
217(313), 251, 294(169), 335, 416,
428(106), 448
Bragaw, C. G., 292, 302, 306, 319(147),
334

Brandrup, J., 206(281), 249
Brashkin, M. A., 341(6), 372
Brauer, G. M., 19(23), 34
Bree, H. W., 393(31), 444, 406, 422(60)
445, 405, 409, 411(74), 446, 419
(122,124), 449
Bresler, S. Ye., 294(167), 335,
416(108), 448
Breuer, H., 139, 224(19), 235, 169,
225(123), 240
Brillouin, L., 228(379), 254
Brodnyan, J. G., 393(27), 444
Brooks, R. E., 281(80,84), 331
Broutman, L. J., 349, 352(35), 373
406, 409(59), 445, 453, 454,
467, 469, 472, 473(3), 504,
480(80), 507
Brower, F. M., 273(43), 329
Brown, A. W., 406, 414(54), 445,
496(100), 508
Brown, G. M., 118(164), 137
Brown, J. E., 198, 209, 210, 216
(248), 247
Brown, N., 285(121,122), 290(122),
333, 299(191), 336
Bruenner, R.S., 431(163), 451
Brunt, N. A., 118(172), 137,
320(274), 339, 361(93), 375
Bryant, K. C., 409(73), 446
Bryant, W. M. D., 27(87), 36,
281(83), 331
Buccaredda, M., 59(74), 66
Buchdahl, R., 26(69), 35, 56(43),
64, 58(53), 65, 78,89,102(13),
128, 95(82), 132, 97(93,94),
133, 118(167), 119, 137,
139(41), 237, 158, 159(73),
238, 165, 198, 202(109), 240,
189(195), 244, 214(287), 249,
216, 225(291), 250, 215, 226
(330), 218, 222(340), 252,
222(356), 253, 223, 228(365),
254, 272, 273, 317(39), 329,
284(97), 285(106), 332, 294,
314, 318(161), 334, 294, 314,
318(162), 335, 299(190), 336,
428(146), 450
Buckley, D. J., 293(149), 334
Bucknall, C. B., 292, 302(140),
296, 302, 306(146), 334,
313(250), 338, 428(155), 450
Buckser, S., 275(54), 330
Bueche, A. M., 273, 275(48), 330
355(67), 374
Bueche, F., 19, 23, 25, 26(33), 34,
25(65), 35, 52(30), 63, 76, 97,
99, 105(9), 128, 97(90,91), 99
(96), 104(105), 108(91), 133,
105(113), 134, 108(127), 135,
111(143), 136, 176, 189(143),
242, 185(163), 243, 265(19),
328, 278(62), 279(66), 279
(67,68), 280(67,68), 330
Buenker, R. J., 198, 199,200(260),
248
Bulgin, D., 362(98), 376
Bullman, G. W., 108(130), 135
Burgers, J. M., 383(6), 391, 443
Burns, H., 308(234), 338

Busse, W. F., 100(100), 133
Bussink, J., 218, 219, 224(339),
   252, 314(254), 339

Butta, E., 59(74), 66, 195, 224
   (214), 245, 216(307), 250,
   215, 222(325), 215, 222,
   229(326), 251, 222(353),
   253, 229(384), 255

                    C

Caldwell, J. R., 118(168,169), 137
   195(224,225), 246, 284(102,103),
   332
Campbell, D., 305(222), 337
Cannon, C. G., 283(94), 332
Canter, N. H., 164(100), 239
Carey, R. H., 92(64), 114, 131,
   352(50), 374, 406, 411(47),
   445, 418(119), 448
Carswell, T. S., 262(5), 328
Case, L. C., 279(63,64), 330
Cassie, A. B. D., 351, 352(43), 373
Casson, N., 386, 443
Catsiff, E., 79(14), 128, 84(28),
   84, 92(30), 129, 84(33), 130,
   116(155), 136
Cayrol, B., 229(385), 255
Cessna, L. C., 419, 420(120), 448
   480(79), 507
Chae, Y., 197, 229(231), 246
Chalidze, V. N., 302(218), 337
Chamis, C. C. 455(12), 504, 473,
   474(59), 506
Chang, M. S., 279(65), 330
Chapoy, L. L., 366, 376
Chappel, F. P., 198(253), 247,
   283(94), 332
Charch, W. H., 198(257), 248
Charrier, J-M., 292, 294(144), 334,
   415(103), 448
Chartoff, R. P., 104(109), 134
Cheatham, R. G., 119(177,178), 120
   (177,178), 138, 285, 290(107),
   332
Chen, P. E., 297, 307(183), 335,
   462, 505, 469, 470(44), 471(53),
   506, 491, 494(96), 508
Chernyshev, B. M., 139(37), 236
Chinai, S. N., 57(51), 65, 193,
   209(201), 245
Chompff, A. J., 100(98), 133
Chorné, J., 469(39), 505
Chow, T. S., 455(16), 504
Christiansen, A. W., 270(38), 329
Chu, W. H., 267, 279, 280(24), 329
Chuiko, A. A., 431(164), 451
Chung, C.I., 222(355), 253
Cigna, G., 58(58), 65, 217(317),
   251, 319, 320(272), 339, 428
   (156), 450
Cirlin, E. H., 195, 197(218), 245
Cizek, A. W., 360(90), 375
Clamroth, R., 162(98), 239
Clark, H. A., 409(79), 446
Clark, R. C., 414(94), 447
Clash, Jr., R. F., 347(19,23), 372
Claver, G. C., 294, 318(163), 335
Clayton, D., 292, 302(140), 334

Cleereman, K. J., 290, 292(136),
   333, 343, 344(16), 372
Clegg, P. L., 92, 94(63), 131
Clendinning, R. A., 218, 224(341),
   252
Cocks, G. G., 140(20), 235
Cohen, L. J., 406(57), 445
Cohen, L. A., 308(242), 338
Cohen, R. E., 122(185), 138,
   422(131), 449
Cohen, V., 290, 292(133), 333
Colwell, R. E., 160(79), 238
Combs, R. L., 104(108), 134
Conant, F. S., 353(52), 374
Cook, J., 483(83), 508
Cook, N. P., 369(120), 377
Cooper, G. A., 471, 472,
   483(52), 506, 484(84),
   487(93), 508
Cooper, S. L., 59(70), 66, 217
   (314), 251, 294, 335, 429
   (159), 451
Coover, H. W., 104(108), 134
Corten, H. T., 298(188), 336,
   455(19), 504
Cotten, G. R., 421(127), 449
Cottrell, A. H., 299(189), 336,
   469 506
Cox, W. P., 56(42), 64, 160(77),
   160, 161(78), 238, 170(125),
   171(129), 241, 343(12), 372
Cramer, W. S., 17(9), 33
Cratchley, D., 466(34), 505
Crissman, J. M., 194, 222(206),
   245, 215, 219(323), 251
Cross, M. M., 384(8,9), 443
Crowet, C., 265(16), 328
Crozier, R. N., 347(26), 373
Crugnola, A., 113, 114(149), 136
Cuddihy, E. F., 229(391), 255
Cuevas, J., 406(56), 445
Cuff, G., 47(13), 62, 89, 92(43), 130
Cummings, J. D., 92(65), 131
Curtis, J. W., 285(118), 333
Cuthrell, R. E., 181(157), 242

                    D

Daane, J. H., 202(273), 248, 218,
   229(337), 252
Dally, J. W., 349, 352(35), 373,
   480(80), 507
Dammont, F. R., 110(138), 135, 215,
   229(328), 252
Danilov, V. G., 341(5), 372
Danilova, M. P., 341(5), 372
Danusso, F., 113, 114(149), 136
Darin, S. R., 278, 279, 280(59), 330
Darlington, M. W., 119, 120(179),
   138, 202(269), 248
Date, M., 139(59), 237
Datsyshin, A. P., 305(226), 337
Davies, G. R., 202(278), 249
De Coste, J. B., 354, 357(64), 374
Deeley, C. W. 194, 215, 222(205),
   245, 348, 351, 352(32), 373
de Farran,E. Moncunill, 472(56), 506
Den Hartog, J. P., 48(22), 63
Dekking, P., 139, 219, 222(9), 235
de Morton, M.E., 139(21), 236

de **Petris**, S.,195, 224(214), 245,
    215, 222, 229(326), 251, 229
    (384), 255
Desper, C. R., 198(255), 248
Deutsch, K., 219(343), 252
De Vries,K. L., 93(79), 132, 302,
    303(220), 305(224,225), 337
De Witt, T. W., 139(50), 237, 161
    (80), 238
Diamant, Y., 23, 24(59), 35
Di Benedetto, A. T., 24, 35, 46(12),
    62, 263, 284, 301, 307(6), 265,
    301, 307(15), 265(17), 328, 425
    (141), 450, 471(53), 506, 481
    (81), 508
Dietz, A. G. H., 119, 120(177, 178),
    138, 265(12,13,17), 267(17), 328
    285, 290(107), 332, 479(66,67),
    507
Dillon, J. H., 48(29), 63, 139(5),
    235, 139(63), 238, 348(28), 373
Di Marzio, E. A., 19(30), 34, 24, 35
Dingman, E. G., 414(98), 447, 496
    (105), 509
Dixon, R. R., 89, 92(44), 130
Dobry, A., 58(52), 65, 193(200),
    245
Dodge, C. W. H., 23(54), 35,
    177(147), 242
Dougherty, T. J., 386, 443
Dow, N. F., 469, 505, 469, 506
Doyle, M. E., 283(90), 331
Drexler, L. H., 97(87), 132
Droste, D. H., 425(141), 450
Drumm, M. F., 23(54), 35, 177
    (147), 242
Duckett, R. A., 285, 290(122),
    290(129), 333
Dudek, T. J., 139(24), 236, 278
    (62), 279, 280(68), 330
Duffin, D. J., 454, 479(6), 504
Dukes, W. H., 261(3), 328
Duling, I. N., 197(233), 246
Dumbleton, J. H., 84(29), 129,
    169(124), 240, 198(263), 248
Dunell, B. A., 48(29), 63, 139(63),
    159(75), 159(76), 238
Dunn, C. M. R., 120(181), 138
Dzyura, E. A., 52(34), 64, 170(128)
    241

                        E

Eagling, R. F., 59(67), 66, 214,
    216(290), 250, 284(100), 332,
    395, 428(36), 444
Eby, R. K., 229(389), 255
Ecker, R., 58(54), 65, 216(293),
    250
Eckert, R.E., 265(9), 328
Economy, J., 406(55), 445, 496
    (107), 509
Edwards, R. H., 306(230), 338
Einstein, A., 381, 391, 442
Eirich, F. R., 119, 137, 119(175),
    138, 409(78), 446
Eisenberg, A., 19(34,35), 34, 206,
    207, 208(285), 249, 229(385),
    255

Eldridge, J. E., 165(111), 240
Elkin, A. I., 355(72,74), 356(74),
    375
Elliott, A., 198(250), 247
Elyash, L. J., 273(52), 330
Emmett, R. A., 293(151), 334
Enders, D. H., 94(81), 132
Engelter, C., 92(60), 131
Enjoji, H., 187, 188(182), 244
Epps, L., 224(372), 254
Erhardt, P., 283(87), 331
Estes, G. M., 59(70), 66, 217(314),
    251, 294, 335, 429(159), 451
Evans, H. C., 293(148), 334
Evans, R. M., 421(126), 449
Eveson, G. F., 393(29), 444
Eyerer, P., 367(113), 376
Eyring, H., 90(46,47), 130, 302
    (213), 337

                        F

Fairing, J. D., 498(114), 509
Fallick, G. J., 498(116), 509
Faraday, C. S. N., 202(277), 249
Farlie, E. D., 109, 135
Farnham, A. G., 218, 224(341), 252
Farris, R. J., 393(30), 444, 409
    (71,72), 446
Farrow, G., 225(373), 254
Faucher, J. A., 83, 116(20), 129
    118(170), 137, 195, 224(226),
    246, 215(327), 251, 224(371),
    254, 284, 318(104), 332
Fedors, R. F., 279(69), 330, 320
    (275), 339
Ferry, J. D., 4, 11, 12(3), 33, 48, 52
    (24), 63, 67, 75, 76(1), 76(10),
    79, 97, 100, 106(1), 109, 114(15),
    122, 128, 97(95), 100(103), 133,
    107(123), 134, 109(134,135), 135
    139, 156, 157(2), 171, 192(1),
    235, 139(49,52), 237, 150, 172(66),
    150(67), 157(68), 238, 165(110),
    240, 171(130-132), 172, 174(137),
    241, 195, 215(220), 246, 306(229),
    337, 422(130), 449
Fettes, E. M., 294(155), 334, 498
    (116), 509
Fielding-Russell, G. S., 139(40,58),
    237, 217(332), 252, 416(107), 448
Fields, J. E., 206(283), 249
Filippi, F. J., 476(65), 507
Findley, W. N., 47(16,17,21), 63
    90(51,52), 92(52,67), 94, 114,
    131, 116, 137
Fisch, W., 23(62), 35
Fischer, E. W., 27(84), 36
Fitchmun, D. R., 188(192), 244
Fitzgerald, E. R., 139(49), 237
Fitzgerald, W. E., 19, 21(28), 34,
    206(282), 249
Fitzhugh, A. F., 347(26), 373
Fletcher, K., 294(156), 334,
    415(100), 447
Flocke, H. A., 23(61), 35, 167,
    182, 187(117), 240, 222
    (359, 360), 253, 392(26), 444

Flom, D. G., 354, 355, 356(58),
    355(67), 355, 356(68), 374,
    453(1), 503, 469, 506
Flory, P. J., 19, 23(32), 34,
    23(50), 35, 27(90), 30(92,93),
    36, 97(88), 133, 107(124), 134
    107(125), 135, 111(144), 136,
    176(141), 241, 185(162), 243,
    273(45,46), 274, 329, 275(56),
    278(58), 330
Foden, E., 352(48), 374
Ford, R. W., 281(82), 331
Fort, Jr., T., 354, 356(59), 374
Fortner, C. P., 290(134), 333
Fox, A., 116, 137
Fox, T. G., 19, 23(32), 34, 23
    (50,53), 35, 52(31,32), 64,
    97(88,89,92,95), 99(92,97),
    105(92), 133
Frazer, W. J., 273(52), 330, 294
    (158), 334, 416(109), 448
Freeston, Jr., W. D., 265(10), 328,
    301(197), 336
French, D. M., 279(65), 330
Frenkel, S. Ya. 294(167), 335,
    416(108), 448
Frenkin, E. I., 406(48), 445
Friedman, D. W., 499(122), 510
Frisch, K. C., 499(128), 510
Frisch, H. L., 188(191,194), 244,
    216(308), 250, 429(160), 451,
    499(125,128), 510
Frissell, W. J., 431, 434(165), 451
Frosini, V., 59(74), 66, 195, 224
    (214), 245, 201, 202(267), 248,
    216(307), 250, 215(325,326), 222
    (325,326), 229(326), 251, 222(353),
    253, 229(384), 255
Fujii, T., 161(82), 239
Fujiki, T., 187(181), 244
Fujimoto, K., 58(59), 65, 216(297),
    250, 293(150), 334, 428, 429
    (152), 450
Fujimoto, T., 100, 101(104), 133
Fujino, K., 58(61), 65, 83(21), 129,
    84(32), 130, 113, 114, 116(148),
    136, 139(25), 236, 216(296), 250
Fujioka, K., 308, 317(238), 338
Fujisawa, T., 83(22), 129
Fujita, H., 105(115), 134
Fukada, E., 139(59), 237
Fukui, Y., 83(22), 83, 113, 114(25),
    129, 84(38), 130, 167(121), 240
Fulcher, K. U., 217(332), 252
Funt, B. L., 19(26), 34
Fuoss, R. M., 19(25), 34, 225(375),
    254
Furno, F. J., 369(120), 377
Furukawa, J., 394, 444
Fuschillo, N., 217(335), 252

                    G

Gabaraeva, A. D., 285(113), 332
Galperin, I., 425(136), 449
Ganz, S. N., 419(123), 449
Garbuglio, C., 171(133), 241
Garfield, L. J., 105(112), 134

Garner, F. F., 498(116), 509
Gauchel, J. V., 481(81), 508
Gavan, F. M., 359(83), 360(83,89), 375
Geckler, R. D., 393(28), 444
Gee, G., 26(73), 36
Gehman, S. D., 139(5), 235, 139(47,54),
    237, 162(85,86), 239, 347(20),
    372, 369(117), 376
Geil, P. H., 27(81), 36, 114(154), 136,
    283(96), 332, 285(124), 333
Gent, A. N., 118(163), 137, 139(45),
    237, 272, 301(40), 329, 301(202),
    336, 321(281), 340, 355, 356(73),
    361, 362(92), 375, 416(112,113),
    418(118), 448
George, D., 292(139), 334
George, H. F., 122(186), 139, 499(123),
    510
Gerngross, O., 27(89), 36
Gesinski, L., 92(73), 132
Gessler, A. M., 162, 163, 164(90),
    239, 428(144), 450
Gezalov, M. A., 302, 303(209), 337
Gezovich, D. M., 285(124), 333
Ghersa, P., 284(101), 332
Gibbs, J. H., 19(30), 34, 197(232),
    246
Gieniewski, C., 90, 92(56), 92(70), 131
Gillespie, T., 386, 443
Gillham, J. K., 139(27,28,30), 167(27),
    236, 224(372), 254, 229(393), 255
Giusti, P., 224(367), 254
Glaeser, W. A., 353(55), 374, 433
    (170), 451
Goettler, L. A., 462, 464, 474
    (30), 505, 476(64), 507
Gohn, G. R., 92(65), 131, 116,
    137
Goldstein, M., 19(31), 34, 90
    (54), 131, 197(234), 246
Goodier, J. N., 121(182), 138,
    296(173,174), 306(174),
    335, 386(14), 443, 413,
    431(89), 447
Goppel, J. M., 273, 313, 317
    (51), 330
Gorchahova, V. M., 341(4), 372
Gordon, G. A., 194, 218(208),
    245
Gordon, J. E., 483(83), 508
Gordon, M., 25,26(66), 35
Gouza, J. J., 359,363(87), 364,
    375
Granato, A. V., 228(381), 255
Gratch, S., 52(32), 64
Gray, R. W., 186(170),243, 395,
    424(37), 444
Grechanovskii, U. A., 52(34), 64,
    170(128), 241
Greensmith, H. W., 265(20), 328,
    321(278,279), 340
Gregory, R. K., 47(18), 63
Griffith, A. A., 296(176), 335,
    413(90), 447
Grimer, F. J., 486(90), 508
Groeninckx, G., 84, 113, 114(40),
    130, 113(151), 116, 136
Grosch, K. A., 354, 355(60), 374
Gruenwald, G., 369(116), 376

Gruver, J. T., 58(57), 65, 104
  (107), 105(111), 134, 216(300),
  250, 425(140), 450, 429(161),
  451
Gruver, R. M., 414(97), 447, 496
  (103), 509
Guicking, H. D., 22(44), 34
Guillet, J. E., 104(108), 134
Guimon, C., 162, 163(93), 239
Guir, K. E., 162(86), 239
Gulbransen, L. B., 480(76), 507
Gupta, R. P., 228(382), 255
Gupta, V. D., 111(141), 135, 185
  (165), 243, 202(278), 249
Guth, E., 48(27), 63, 386(16), 443

H

Haaf, W. R., 302(211), 337
Hagerup, E., 480(78), 507
Haldon, R. A., 222, 225(357), 253
Hali, W. F., 218, 224(341), 252
Hall, M. M., 428(155), 450
Halpin, J. C., 185(169), 243, 267(26),
  329, 279(66), 330, 388(23,24), 444
  455(14,15), 456(14,15), 464, 493(14)
  504, 462(28), 505, 493, 494(97),
  508
Ham, J. S., 104(110), 134
Hamada, M., 362(97), 376
Hammer, C. F., 281, 282(79), 331
Hammock, T. J., 225(378), 254
Hammond, R. J., 56(47), 64
Handler, F., 320(273), 339
Hansen, J. E., 281(80), 331
Harada, T., 84(37), 130
Harding, J., 347(24), 372
Hardy, G. F., 474(62)507
Hargreaves, E., 285, 287(114), 332
Harper, R., 139(50), 237
Harris, B., 472(56), 506
Harris, M., 273(41,42), 329, 352(47),
  374
Harris, W. D., 43(6), 62
Hartley, P. N., 26(73), 36
Harwood, J. A. C., 280(71), 331
Hashimoto, F., 195,225(230), 246
Hashin, Z., 386(17), 387, 443, 455
  (8,9), 504
Hata, T., 58(60), 65, 214, 216(289),
  249, 395, 416, 428, 429(35), 444
Haward, R. N., 105(114), 134, 294
  (156), 334, 301(203), 336, 319
  (269), 339, 415(99,100), 416(99),
  447
Hayakawa, K., 362(97), 376
Hayes, R. A., 21(37), 34
Hearle, J. W. S., 352(49), 374
Hearmon, R. F., 39(1), 40(1), 62,
  198(240), 247
Heffelfinger, C. J., 285(119), 333
Heider, J. E., 162, 163(92), 239
Heinze, H. D., 23(56), 35, 177(151),
  242
Heijboer, J., 139,219,222(9), 235,
  215(320,321,322), 223,224(320),
  224(321,322), 218(329,342), 219,
  224(339), 252, 219, 222(351), 253,
  224(366,368), 254,314(254,255), 339

Heller, W. R., 228(380), 255
Hellwege, K. H., 26(71), 36, 197, 201,
  204(236), 246, 204(274), 249
Helmer, J. D., 26(70), 35
Hendus, H., 59(68), 66
Hennig, J., 58(64), 65, 198(261),
  200, 248, 216(301), 250, 290(128),
  333, 418(154), 450
Henry, R. L., 335, 356(73), 375
Herbert, J. B. M., 26(73), 36
Hermann, K., 27(89), 36
Hermans, J. J., 455(10,16), 504
Herwig, H. U., 58(55), 65, 216
  (292), 250
Herzog, J. A., 453(2), 504
Hess, L. D., 292, 293(141), 334
Hewitt, R. W., 434(176), 451
Heydemann, P., 22(44), 34
Hill, F. B., 278(60), 330
Hillier, K. W., 164(103,104), 240
Hilyard, N. C., 356, 357(79), 375
Hirai, T., 93(76), 132
Hirose, H., 84(37), 130
Hobbs, L. M., 104(106), 133
Hoegberg, H., 171(130), 241, 314,
  315(262), 339
Hoff, E. A. W., 92, 94(63), 131,
  219(343), 252, 219, 222
  (350), 253
Hoff, N. J., 459(24), 505
Hoffman, K. R., 409(79), 446
Hofmann, W., 23(62), 35
Holden, G., 59(69), 66, 217(316),
  251, 292, 294(143), 334,
  397, 429(39), 444
Holik, A. S., 301(207), 337
Holliday, L., 198, 200, 205(265),
  206, 248, 285(125), 333
Homes, G. A., 265(16), 328, 302
  (217), 337
Homma, T., 109(134), 135
Hopkins, I. L., 56(49), 65
Horino, T., 83(21), 129, 113,
  114, 116(148), 136, 139
  (25), 236
Horio, M., 139(32), 236, 281
  (74), 283, 331
Horsley, R. A., 295, 309, 312,
  313(172), 335, 318(267), 339
Hoseman, R., 27(88), 36
Howlett, R. M., 293(152), 334
Hsiao, C. C., 46(11), 62, 92(69),
  131, 260(2), 328
Hsu, B., 93(75), 132
Huelck, V., 122(186), 138, 499(123,
  124,127), 510
Hulse, G., 317(264), 339
Hunt, B.I., 217(336), 252
Hunt, Jr., R. H., 344(18), 372
Hurst, D. A., 292(138), 333
Hurst, S. J., 229(388), 255
Hussain, M. A., 472(55), 506

I

Iannicelli, J., 434(117), 452
Ibaragi, T., 161(81), 239
Ikeda, R. M., 59(75), 66, 217(312),
  251, 428(151), 450

Illers, K-H., 26(68), 35, 59(68), 66
    139(10,11,19), 224(19), 229(10),
    235, 169, 225(123), 240, 194(204),
    195(204,215), 215,222(204,215),
    245, 195(223), 246
Imada, K., 198, 200(264), 248
Immergut, E. H., 206(281), 249
Ingram, P., 27(85), 36
Inoue, M., 283(89), 331, 285(117),
    333
Ioffe, A. F., 302, 303(209), 337
Irie, F., 229(387), 255
Irwin, G. R., 17(17), 33, 298(186),
    336
Isaksen, R. A., 171(129), 241
Ishai, O., 46(12), 62, 90, 92(55),
    131, 265(11,17), 267(17), 328,
    406(57), 445, 414(96), 447, 467(36)
    505, 469(51), 506
Ishida, Y., 225(377), 254, 229(387),
    255
Ishikawa, M., 84(37), 130
Ito, H., 229(387), 255
Ito, K., 263(7), 328, 367(112), 376,
    369(119), 377
Itoh, T., 283(86), 331
Iyo, Y., 216(299), 250

J

Jackson, G. B., 119(176), 138, 285,
    289, 314, 315, 317(109), 332,
    314, 315, 317(261), 339
Jackson, J. B., 194, 195, 197(207),
    245
Jackson, P. W., 466(34), 505
Jackson, Jr., W. J., 118(168,169),
    137, 195(224,225), 246, 284(102,
    103), 332
Jacobs, H., 169, 195, 197, 222(122),
    240
Jaeckel, K., 301(194), 336
James, D. I., 357(82), 375
Janáček, J., 109(135), 135, 195
    (212,213), 197(213), 245, 195
    (220, 221), 215(220,221), 219
    (220), 246, 219(349), 253
Jansson, J-F., 148(65), 238
Jaruzelski, J. J., 409(82), 447
Jenekel, E., 58(55), 65, 139(10,11),
    229(10), 235, 169, 195, 197,
    222(122), 240, 175(138), 241,
    195, 215, 222(215), 245, 216
    (292), 250
Jishage, M., 285(117), 333
Johari, G. P., 197(234), 246
Johnson, J. F., 52(33), 64
Johnson, K. L., 367(110), 376
Johnson, R. H., 197(233), 246
Johnson, R. N., 218, 224(341),
    252
Johnston, T. L., 348, 351, 352(29),
    373
Johnston, W. V., 26(74), 36
Jones, M., 351, 352(43), 373
Jones, P. J., 162(85), 239
Jones, T. T., 58(56), 65, 216(304),
    250, 313, 314, 320(249), 338,
    416(111,116), 448

Jopling, D. W., 367(109), 376
Joseph, J. J., 55(40), 64
Joseph, J. R., 406(45), 445
Juliano, P. C., 294(168), 335
Juve, A. E., 361(94), 375
Juve, R. D., 292, 293(141), 334

K

Kaelble, D. H., 59(77), 66, 122
    (184), 138, 217(315), 251,
    397(41), 429(41), 445, 422
    (129), 449
Kainradl, P., 320(273), 339
Kaiser, R., 26(71), 36, 197, 201,
    204(236), 246, 204(274), 249
Kajiyama, T., 198, 200(264), 248,
    222(361), 253
Kallas, P. H., 360(90), 375
Kambour, R. P., 301(205,206), 336,
    301(207), 302(211), 337
Kanig, G., 23(52), 35, 53, 54(36),
    64, 177, 180(148), 242
Karam, H. J., 343, 344(16), 372
Karas, G. C., 314, 320(257), 339
Kardos, J. L., 55(40), 64, 185(169),
    243, 406(45), 445
Kargin, V. A., 283(91), 331, 474
    (60), 507
Karpov, V., 474(61), 507
Kasahara, T., 314(256), 339
Kästner, S., 177(155), 242
Kato, H., 161(82), 239
Katz, D., 23, 24(59), 35, 53(37), 64
    176, 177(145), 242, 347(21,22)
    372
Kaufman, M., 474(61), 507
Kauzmann, W., 19(20), 33, 90(46), 130
Kawaguchi, T., 195(222), 246, 222(358),
    253
Kawai, H., 58(61), 65, 83(21), 129,
    84(32), 130, 139(25), 236, 216
    (296), 250, 283(86), 331
Ke, B., 19(22), 33
Keedy, D. A., 283(86), 331
Keith, H. D., 27(86), 36, 281, 282(73),
    283, 331
Keller, A., 27(83), 36, 285(115), 332
Kelley, F. N., 25(65), 35, 105(103),
    134, 297(185), 336
Kelly, A., 469, 471, 472, 483(52),
    506, 480(75), 507, 483(82), 508
Kennedy, W. D., 343(9), 372
Kenyon, A. S., 23(57), 35, 110(136),
    135, 167, 177, 180, 181, 229(113),
    240, 284(105), 332, 489(115), 509
Kerner, E. H., 387, 435(20), 443
Keskkula, H., 167(120), 240, 216(309),
    251, 294, 319(160), 334, 294, 302,
    306, 318(164), 335, 314(260,263),
    315, 317(263), 319, 320(260), 339,
    416(110), 448, 428(153), 450
Khosla, G., 116, 137
Kies, J. A., 467, 499(38), 505
Kim, K. Y., 160(79), 238
Kimball, Jr., A. L., 139(43), 237
Kin, L., 273(43), 329
King, A. L., 164(108), 240
King, G., 194, 195(202), 245

Kinjo, N., 195, 225(230), 246
Kintsis, T. Ya., 469(49), 506
Kitagawa, K., 172(135), 241
Klempner, D., 216(308), 250, 429(160), 451, 499(125,128), 510
Klenin, S. I., 294(167),335, 416(108), 448
Kline, D. E., 139(42), 237, 177(150), 242, 194, 222(205), 245, 222, 229 (352), 253
Kline, J. M. 139(48), 237
Knight, G. J., 31(99), 37
Knowles, J. K., 265(13), 328
Koch, P. J., 290(131), 333, 301, 307 (200), 336
Koch, T. A., 281, 282(79), 331
Kodama, K., 212, 214, 217(286), 249, 395, 416, 428, 429(34), 444
Kodama, M., 219,(347), 253
Kohn, E. J., 414(94), 447
Kojima, K., 285(116), 333
Kolarik, J., 195(212), 245, 195, 215(221), 246
Kollinsky, F., 191, 193, 209, 216(198), 244
Kolsky, H., 164(103), 240
Komatsu, T., 195, 225(230), 246
Kondo, Y., 313, 319, 320(251), 338
Koo, G. P., 351(44), 373, 351, 352(45), 374
Koppehele, H. P., 93, 120(74), 132
Koppelmann, J., 139(12), 235, 139(57), 237, 219(344, 345), 253
Koretskaya, T. A., 283(91), 331
Korshak, V. V., 341(5), 372
Korsukov, V. E., 302,303(221), 337
Kosaka, Y., 187(181), 244
Kosiyama, K., 47(15), 63, 116 (156), 136
Kovacs, A. J., 47(19,20), 63, 165(110), 240
Kragh, A. M., 366, 376
Kraus, G., 56, 57(50), 58(57), 65, 104(107), 105(111), 134, 191, 193, 209, 216(199), 244, 216(300), 250, 425(140), 450, 429(161), 451
Krautz, F. G., 431(167), 451, 479-481(70), 507, 485, 486 (87), 508
Kravtsov, A. I., 341(2), 372
Krieger, I. M., 386, 443
Krigbaum, W. R., 111(145), 136, 185(167), 243
Krock, R. H., 453, 454, 467, 469, 472, 473(3), 504
Kuenzle, O., 139(13), 235
Kuhlmann, H. W., 411(88), 447
Kuhn, W., 139(13), 235
Kuhre, C. J., 283(90), 331
Kuksenko, V. S., 302(208, 209, 221), 303(208, 209, 221), 337
Kuphal, K., 26(71), 36, 197, 201, 204(236), 246, 204(274), 249

Kuramoto, N., 116, 137
Kurata, M., 83(19), 129
Kuriyama, I., 139, 187(29), 236
Kurz, J., 195(209), 245, 224(370), 254
Kwai, H., 113, 114, 116(148), 136
Kwei, T. K., 110(138), 135, 188(191, 194), 244, 216(308), 250, 215, 229(328), 252, 429(160), 451, 499(125,128), 510

L

Ladizesky, N. H., 202(279), 249
Laka, M. G., 270(35), 329
Lake, G. J., 321(280), 340, 351(37), 373
Lancaster, J. K., 359, 361, 362(86), 375
Lanceley, H. A., 26(73), 36
Landel, R. F., 76(10), 79, 100, 109, 114(15), 122, 128, 150, 172(66), 238, 279(69), 330, 320(275), 339, 383(7), 443, 406(63), 446, 419(121) 422(130), 425(121), 449
Lang, G., 367(113), 376
Langley, N. R., 107(122,123), 134, 174(136,137), 241
Lark, R. F., 265(8), 328
Larson, G. P., 414, 430(93), 447
Lauis, L. A., 294(167), 335, 416(108), 448
Lauterbur, P. C., 411(84), 447
Lavengood, R. E., 458(22), 462, 464(30), 465, 467(36), 469, 474(30), 505, 469(51), 506, 498(114), 509
Lavrentev, V. V., 356(78), 375
Lawrence, R. R., 347(25), 373
Lawton, E. J., 273, 275(48), 330
Lawton, R. W., 164(108), 240
Lazan, B. J., 162(83,84), 239, 350(36), 373
Lazar, L. S., 348, 352(33), 373
Lazurkin, J. S., 302(214), 337
Leaderman, H., 75, 77(11), 79, 128, 92(68), 131, 159,162(74), 238
Lebedinskaya, M. L., 302(218), 337
Leben, L., 354(57), 374
Lee, B-L, 401(42), 445
Lee, C. C., 434(175), 451
Lee, L-H., 462, 465, 474, 486(29), 505
Lee, W. A., 21(38), 21(39), 34, 31(99), 37
Lees, J. K., 458(23), 465, 474(23), 505, 480(76), 507
Legge, N. R., 59(69), 66, 217(316), 251, 292, 294(143), 334, 397, 429(39), 444
Le Grand, D. G., 302(211), 337
Lepie, A. H., 162(95), 239
Levreault, R., 56(43), 64, 118(167), 119, 137, 189(195), 244
Levens, J. A., 480(79), 507
Lewis, A. F., 139(30), 236
Lewis, F. M., 411(85), 447
Lewis, R. B., 361(95), 376

Lewis, T. B., 382, 383(5), 387, 392, 401(19), 443, 388, 444, 402(43), 403, 435(43), 445, 456, 458(21), 504, 494, 495 (98), 508
Li, C. H., 433(174), 451
Li, H. L. 290(131), 333
Libby, P. W., 434(177), 452
Lifshitz, J. M., 162, 163, 164(91), 239, 428(145), 450
Lim, C. K., 122(185), 138, 422(131), 449
Lin, J. M., 471(53), 506
Lindley, P. B., 321(281), 340, 351 (37), 373, 361, 362(92), 375
Linhardt, E., 56(46), 64, 423, (133), 449, 497(112), 509
Lipatov, Yu. S., 425(138), 449, 425(139), 450
Lipatova, T. E., 425(138), 449
Liska, J. W., 343(10), 372, 353 (52), 374
Litt, M. H., 301(199,200), 307, 336
Livingston, D. I., 139(58), 237 198, 209, 210, 216(248), 247, 364(102), 367(111), 369(117), 376
Lloyd, B. A., 302, 303(220), 337
Lobanov, A. M., 217(331), 252
Loft, B. C., 181(158), 242
Lohr, J. J., 139(24), 236, 267, 284(25), 329
Long, V. C., 104(106), 133
Longworth, R., 100(100), 133
Lord, P., 139(55), 237
Loshaek, S., 23(53), 35, 52(32), 64, 97(89), 133
Lott, S. A., 139(21), 236
Lottanti, G., 177, 180, 181(149), 242
Loveless, H. S., 44(9), 62, 348, 351, 352(32), 373
Lovell, S. E., 171(130,131), 241
Lubin, G., 308(237), 338
Lucke, K., 228(381), 255
Lundstedt, O. W., 319(268), 339
Lyons, J. W., 160(79), 238
Lyons, W. J., 351, 352(40), 373
Lyons, P. F., 105(118), 134

M

McCarthy, R. A., 314, 315, 317(261), 339
McCormick, H. W., 273(43), 329
McCrackin, F. L., 121(183), 138
Mac Crone, R. K., 139(39), 236
McCrum, N. G., 81, 129, 167(119), 240, 186(170), 187(177,178), 201, 215, 217, 222, 225(177), 229(178), 243, 229(390), 255, 395, 424(37), 444
McEvily, Jr., A. J., 348, 351, 352 (29), 373
McGarry, F. J., 265(12), 328
McGeary, R. K., 382(4), 443
McGill, C. R., 434(177), 452
McGrath, J. E., 294(168), 335

McIntosh, J., 225(373), 254
McIntyre, A. D., 216(295), 250
McIntyre, E. B., 347(25), 373
McKee, A. W., 406, 411, 433(53), 445
McKenna, L. W., 187(186), 244
MacKenzie, A. P., 195(211), 245
MacKnight, W. J., 187(186), 244, 215(329), 252, 222(361), 253
McLean, D., 480(74), 507
McLoughlin, J. R., 84(31,34), 130, 94(80), 132
McMillan, J. L., 119(176), 138
McSkimin, H. J., 48(26), 63, 139(61), 238
Maeda, Y., 93(76), 132
Maekawa, E., 105(115), 134
Magagnini, P. L., 215, 222(325), 251, 224(367,369), 254
Magnusson, A. B., 278(61), 330, 280(70), 331
Maiors, I. Yu., 270(35), 329
Malac, J., 284(99), 332
Malkin, A. Ya., 52(34), 64, 170(128), 241
Malpass, V. E., 166, 240, 369(118), 376
Mandelkern, L., 23(55), 35, 30 (94,95), 37
Mann, J., 294(156), 334, 319(269), 339, 415(99,100), 416(99), 447
March, H. W., 48(23), 63
Marcucci, M. A., 362(99), 376
Margolies, A. F., 273, 275(44), 329
Marin, J., 47(13), 62, 89, 93(43), 130, 92(69), 131
Mark, H., 118, 119(165), 137, 343 (15), 372
Marker, L., 59(71), 66, 123, 138, 217(313), 251, 294(169), 335, 416, 428(106), 448
Markert, G., 191, 193, 209, 216(198), 244
Markovitz, H., 97(95), 133, 139(50), 237
Marks, M. E., 363, 367(100), 376
Markwood, Jr., W. H., 290(126), 333
Marsden, J. G., 409(80), 446, 409 (81), 447
Marsella, R. A., 498(116), 509
Marshall, I., 300(193), 336
Martin, E. V., 285(110), 332
Martin, G. M., 22(46), 34, 23(55), 35
Martin, P. I. A., 411(86), 447
Marvin, R., 139(49), 237, 172(134), 241
Mason, P., 164(101,102,105,106), 240, 177(152), 180, 242
Mason, W. P., 48(26), 63, 139(61), 238
Masuda, T., 161(81), 239, 172(135), 241, 386(13), 447
Matkovich, V. I., 406(55), 445, 496(107), 509
Matonis, V. A., 416(114), 448, 499 (119), 509

Matsumoto, A., 216(305), <u>250</u>
Matsumoto, T., 386(13), <u>443</u>
Matsuo, M., 216(299,308), <u>250</u>, 229
  (387), <u>255</u>, 313, 319, <u>320</u>(251),
  <u>338</u>, 429(160), <u>451</u>, 499(125), <u>510</u>
Matsuoka, S., 187, <u>188</u>, 205(180), <u>243</u>,
  202(273), <u>248</u>
Matsura, H., 206-208(285), <u>249</u>
Matusik, F. J., 219(346), <u>253</u>
Maxwell, B., 104(109), <u>134</u>, <u>139</u>
  (44), <u>237</u>, 162(87,92,93), 163
  (87,92,93), <u>239</u>, 285(111), <u>332</u>
  367(114), <u>376</u>
May, C. A., 110(137), <u>135</u>, 229(392),
  <u>255</u>
Mears, D. R., 270(27-31), 271(30),
  <u>329</u>
Medalia, A. I., 406, 411, 413(66),
  <u>446</u>, 413(91), <u>447</u>
Mehan, R. L., 453(2), <u>504</u>
Melchore, J. A., 343(15), <u>372</u>
Menges, G., 96(85), <u>132</u>
Mercier, J. P., 84, <u>113</u>, 114(40), <u>130</u>
  113(151), 116, <u>136</u>
Meredith, R., 93(75), <u>132</u>
Merriam, C. N., 218, 224(341), <u>252</u>
Merz, E. H., 95(82), <u>132</u>, 160(77,78),
  161(78), <u>238</u>, 171(129), <u>241</u>,
  272, 273, <u>317</u>(39), <u>329</u>, <u>284</u>(97),
  <u>332</u>, 294,318(163), <u>335</u>
Metelskaya, T. K., 474(60), <u>507</u>
Meyers, R. J., 284(98), <u>332</u>
Michno, M. J., 498(114), <u>509</u>
Mikhaylov, V. K., 355, 356(74), <u>375</u>
Miklowitz, J., 290(137), <u>333</u>
Milagin, M. F., 285(113), <u>332</u>
Mileiko, S. T., 480(73), <u>507</u>
Miles, D. O., 139(51), <u>237</u>
Miller, H. T., 162, 163(94), <u>239</u>
Miller, R. L., 26(75,76), <u>36</u>, <u>31</u>(96),
  <u>37</u>, 170(127), <u>241</u>, 188(190), <u>244</u>
Miyamoto, K., 83(21), <u>129</u>
Miyamoto, T., 212, 214, <u>217</u>(286), <u>249</u>
  395, 416, 428, 429(34), <u>444</u>
Miyata, S., 58(60), <u>65</u>, 214, <u>216</u>(289)
  <u>249</u>, 395, 416, 428, 429(35), <u>444</u>
Moacanin, J., 22(42), <u>34</u>, 229(391),
  <u>255</u>
Moehlenpah, A. E., 46(12), <u>62</u>, 265,
  267(17), <u>328</u>
Moffit, G. L., 285(112), <u>332</u>
Mohr, J. G., 454(5), <u>504</u>
Mooney, M., 381, <u>443</u>
Moore, G. E., 281(80), <u>331</u>
Moore, R. S., 90(56), 92(56,
  70), <u>131</u>
Moreen, H. A., 499(121), <u>509</u>
Morey, D. R., 17(14), <u>33</u>, <u>285</u>
  (110), <u>332</u>, 308, <u>309</u>(233),
  <u>338</u>
Morgan, H. M., 198(259), 200,
  <u>248</u>
Morgan, P., 354(4), <u>504</u>
Morgan, R. J., 139(41), <u>237</u>,
  195, 197(219), <u>245</u>, <u>215</u>
  (330), 218, 222(340), 226
  (330), <u>252</u>, 222(356), <u>253</u>,
  223, 228(365), <u>254</u>

Moriwaki, M., 83(19), <u>129</u>
Morley, J. G., 485(88), <u>508</u>
Morris, E. L., 81(16), <u>129</u>
Morrow, D. R., 352(48), <u>374</u>
Morton, M., 294(168), <u>335</u>
Moseley, Jr., W. W., 198(257,
  258), 199, <u>248</u>
Moser, B. G., 383(7), <u>443</u>
Mostovy, S., 17(18), <u>33</u>, 298
  (187,188), <u>336</u>
Mrowca, B. A., <u>48</u>(27), <u>63</u>
Mueller, A., 201(270), <u>248</u>
Mueller, E. R., 411(88), <u>447</u>
Mueller, F. H., 92(60), <u>131</u>,
  301(195,196), <u>336</u>
Mullins, L., 321(279,282),
  <u>340</u>
Murayama, T., 84(29), <u>129</u>,
  169(124), <u>240</u>, 175, <u>177</u>
  (140), <u>241</u>
Murphy, B. M., 301(203), <u>336</u>
Murphy, T. P., 486(91), <u>508</u>

                    N

Nagamatsu, K., 47(15), <u>63</u>, 83,
  114(23), <u>129</u>, 114(152), 116
  (152,156), <u>136</u>, 116, <u>137</u>
Naganuma, Y., 167(121), <u>240</u>
Nagasawa, M., 100, 101(104), <u>133</u>
Nagerl, H., 139(17), <u>235</u>
Nakada, O., 93(76), <u>132</u>
Nakagawa, T., 195, 225(230), <u>246</u>
Nakamura, K., 195, 225(230), <u>246</u>
Nakanishi, M., 195, 225(230), <u>246</u>
Nakayama, C., 139(32), <u>236</u>
Narkis, M., 406(46), <u>445</u>, 408,
  409(70), <u>446</u>
Nash, R. W., 139(26), <u>236</u>
Nason, H. K., 17(13), <u>33</u>, 262(5),
  <u>328</u>, 311(246),338
Natarajan, R., 301(204), <u>336</u>
Nauton, W. J. S., 351, 352(43), <u>373</u>
Nederveen, C. J., 139(18), <u>235</u>, <u>139</u>
  (23), <u>236</u>, 406, 422(60), <u>445</u>,
  405(68), 409(74), <u>446</u>
Neimark, I. E., 431(164), <u>451</u>
Nelson, J. A., 278(60), <u>330</u>
Nelson, L. E., 409(79), <u>446</u>
Nemoto, N., 83(19), 84(27), <u>129</u>
Nestlen, H., 360(90), <u>375</u>
Newberg, R. G., 293(148,149,152), <u>334</u>
Newman, S., 56(42), <u>64</u>, 139(33), <u>236</u>,
  170(125), <u>241</u>, <u>188</u>(192), <u>244</u>,
  273(49), <u>330</u>, 306(227), <u>337</u>, 343
  (12), <u>372</u>
Nicholais, L., 265, 301, 307(15), <u>328</u>,
  406(46), <u>445</u>, 408, 409(70), <u>446</u>
Nielsen, L. E., <u>33</u>-35, 37, 62-66, <u>128</u>,
  <u>131</u>-137, <u>236</u>-239, <u>241</u>-245, 248-
  <u>250</u>, <u>252</u>-254, <u>328</u>, <u>329</u>, <u>331</u>, <u>332</u>,
  <u>334</u>, <u>335</u>, <u>372</u>, <u>443</u>-446, <u>448</u>-451,
  <u>504</u>, <u>505</u>, <u>507</u>-509
Ninomiya, K., 100(101-103), <u>133</u>, 109
  (134), <u>135</u>, 157(68), <u>238</u>
Noga, E. A., 431(166), <u>451</u>, 462, 465,
  474, 481(27), <u>505</u>
Nolle, A. W., 48(28), <u>63</u>, 139(4), <u>235</u>

Nordby, G. M., 480(77), 507
Norman, R. H., 355(69), 374, 357(82), 375
Norris, F. H., 198(251), 247
Norton, Jr., J. W., 314, 315, 317(263) 339
Nowick, A. S., 228(380), 255
Nozaki, C., 216(299), 250
Nutting, P., 78, 89(12), 128, 158(72), 238
Nye, J. F., 39, 40(30), 62

O

Oberth, A. E., 409(75), 446, 431(163), 457
Oberst, H., 194(203), 245, 313(247, 248), 314(247,248), 338, 406(51), 445, 423(133), 449, 497(112), 509
Ochiai, H., 219(348), 253
O'Connor, D. G., 47(17), 63, 90, 92(52), 131
Odani, H., 83(19), 129
Offenbach, J. O., 116(155), 136
Ogawa, Y., 58(61), 65, 216(296), 250
Ogihara, S., 116(157), 136, 161(82), 239
Ohlberg, S. M., 317(265), 339
Ohta, M., 224(370), 254
Okajima, S., 202(272), 248
Okano, K., 185(160), 242
Oleesky, S. S., 454(5), 504
Oliphant, W. J., 89, 92(42), 130, 162(96), 239
Onogi, S., 83(22), 83, 113, 114(25), 129, 84(38), 130, 116(157), 136, 139(32), 236, 161(81,82), 239, 167(121), 240, 172(135), 241, 386(13), 443
Opp, D. A., 351, 352(41), 373
O'Reilly, J. M., 22(43), 34
Orlova, T. P., 217(331), 252
Orowan, E., 297(182), 335
O'Shaughnessy, M. T., 84, 92(30), 129, 118(173), 137
Oswald, H. J., 290(131), 333
O'Toole, J. L., 351(44), 373 351, 352(45), 374
Otto, H-W., 313(252), 338
Oue, T., 369(119), 377
Outwater, Jr., J. O., 469, 470(41), 506
Owen, A. J., 202(278), 249
Owens, D. K., 354, 356(63), 374
Oyane, M., 285(116), 333
Oyanogi, Y., 171(132), 172, 241
Ozaki, M., 100, 101(104), 133
Ozawa, Y., 187, 188(182), 244

P

Padawer, G. E., 496(109), 509
Padden, F. J., 27(86), 36, 281, 282(73), 283, 331
Pae, K. D., 270(27-32), 271(30), 329
Pagano, C. A., 411(83), 447
Pagano, N. J., 462(28,31), 464(31), 505

Painter, C. W., 139(53), 237
Palm, W. E., 347(27), 373
Papir, Y. S., 187, 229(176), 243
Parikh, N. M., 499(121), 509
Parkhomenko, V. D., 419(123), 449
Parrish, M., 285(121), 333
Parry, J. S. C., 270(37), 329
Parry, H. L., 434(176), 451
Parsons, G. B., 479(68), 507
Pascoe, M. W., 356(77), 375
Passaglia, E., 22(46), 34, 93, 120 (74), 132, 167(118), 240
Paterson, M. S., 22(45), 34
Patterson, D., 198(254), 247
Paul, Jr., J. T., 467, 505
Payne, A. R., 162(88-90), 163(88-90), 164(88-90), 239, 280(71-72), 331, 357(82), 375, 406(65), 446, 428 (143,144), 450
Pechhold, W., 223(364), 254
Pegoraro, M., 113, 114(149), 136
Penn, R. W., 83, 114(24), 129
Perry, E., 59(72), 66, 217(311), 251 428(150), 450
Peterlin, A., 27(85), 36, 281(75-77), 283(75-77), 300(77), 331, 305 (222,223), 337
Petersen, J., 225(374), 254
Petit, P. H., 388(23), 444, 455, 456, 464, 493(14), 504
Petker, I., 473(57), 506
Petrie, S. E., 105(112), 134
Pezdirtz, G. F., 224(372), 254
Pezzin, G., 105(116), 134, 171(133), 241, 195, 215, 225(229), 246
Philippoff, W., 139(56), 237
Phillips, D. C., 484, 485(86), 486 (89), 508
Piggott, M. R., 469, 506, 484(85), 508
Pinchbeck, P. H., 353(56), 374, 433 (169), 451
Pitts, E., 367(109), 376
Pizzirani, G., 224(369), 254
Plueddemann, E. P., 409(79), 446
Plazek, D. J., 47(14), 63, 84(39), 130, 108, 109(131), 135, 139(14), 235
Pohl, G., 177(155), 242
Polmanter, K. E., 26(70), 35
Pomeroy, C. D., 119, 120(180), 138
Porod, G., 27(80), 36
Port, W. S., 343(13), 372
Porter, R. S., 52(33), 64
Powles, J. G., 217(336), 252
Pregun, S. E., 308(243), 338
Prestridge, E. B., 413(92), 447
Prevorsek, D. C., 290(131), 333 351, 352(40), 373
Price, C., 229(388), 255
Price, F. P., 26(77), 36, 283(95), 332
Prins, W., 100(98), 133
Prot, E. M., 348(31), 373
Pu, S. L., 472(55), 506
Pugh, S. F., 295(171), 335
Pyankov, G. N., 341(6), 372
Pyrkov, L. M., 294(167), 335, 416(108), 448

R

Rabinowitz, S., 270(37), 329,
    292, 306(145), 334
Rabjohn, N., 278(58), 330
Radcliffe, S. V., 270(33,38), 329
Rademacher, H. J., 93(77), 132
Radford, K. C., 406(58), 445
Raff, R. A. V., 317(265), 339
Ranby, B., 225(374), 254
Ranchoux, R. J. P., 292, 294(144),
    334, 415(103), 448
Ranney, M. W., 411(83), 447
Rasmussen, D. H., 195(211), 245
Raumann, G., 197, 198, 202(235),
    246
Rawson, F. F., 290(130), 333
Read, B. E., 81(17), 129, 145,
    198(64), 238, 187, 201, 215,
    217, 222, 225(177), 243, 187
    (186), 244
Read, R. M., 47(21), 63
Reddish, W., 219(343), 252
Reding, F. P., 215(327), 251,
    224(371), 254
Reed, M. C., 347(24), 372
Reed, P. E., 301(204), 336
Regeta, V. P., 341(6), 372
Rehner, J., 296(175), 335, 431
    (162), 451
Reid, D. R., 90(49,50), 91, 92
    (49,50), 131
Remaly, L. S., 281, 283(81), 331
Rempel, R. C., 188(190), 244
Rhode-Liebenau, U., 23(51), 35
Rhodes, M. B., 27(78), 36
Richardson, M. O. W., 359(85), 375
Richmond, P. G., 406, 414, 422,
    425(44), 445, 496(102), 508
Riddell, M. N., 351(44), 373, 351,
    352(45), 374
Rider, D. K., 384(98), 332
Rider, J. G., 285(114,115), 287
    (114), 332, 290(130), 333
Rieke, J. K., 201, 202, 229(268),
    248
Riley, V. R., 469, 470(47), 506
Ripling, E. J., 17(18), 33, 298
    (187,188), 336
Riser, G. R., 343(13), 372
Rivlin, R. S., 321(276), 340
Roark, R. J., 44(8), 62
Robertson, R. E., 198-200(260), 248
    302(215,216), 337
Robeson, L. M., 118(170), 137, 195
    (226,227) 224(226,227), 246
    284, 318(104), 332, 314, 319,
    320(259), 339, 428(157), 451
Robinson, A. E., 406(64), 446
Robinson, D. W., 139(35), 236, 219,
    222(350), 253
Roder, T. M., 281(80), 331
Rodriquez, F., 139(20), 235
Roe, J. M., 139, 187(29), 236
Roe, R. J., 111(145), 136, 185(167),
    243
Roelig, H., 139(46), 237
Roesler, F. C., 297(177), 335

Rogers, E. A., 418(119), 448
Rogovina, L. Z., 96(84), 132
Rohall, P., 369(117), 376
Roller, M. B., 139(28), 236
Rollmann, K. W., 56, 57(50), 58
    (57), 65, 191, 193, 209, 216
    (199), 244, 216(300), 250, 429
    (161), 451
Romans, J. B., 473(58), 506
Ropte, E., 59(68), 66
Rosen, B., 297(181), 335
Rosen, B. W., 453(1), 469, 503, 455
    (8,17), 469(17), 504, 469(43),
    472(54), 506
Ross, J. A., 293(154), 334
Rotem, A., 162-164(91), 239, 428(145),
    450
Roth, J., 317(265), 339
Rouse, P. E., 76, 128
Rovatti, W., 434(175), 451
Roylance, D. K., 305(224,225), 337
Rudakov, A. P., 341(1), 371
Rudd, R. F., 96(83), 132
Rugger, G., 496(101), 508
Rusch, K. C., 81, 129, 294(159), 334
    301(201), 307, 336, 415(102),
    447, 416(115), 448, 421(128), 449
Russell, J., 229(383), 255
Rutgers, R., 381(2), 442
Ryan, J. D., 363, 367(100), 376
Ryzhov, N. G., 341(2), 372

S

Saba, R. G., 187, 198, 206(174),
    243, 215(324), 251
Sabia, R., 119, 137, 119(175),
    138, 409(78), 446
Sadowsky, M. A., 306(231), 338,
    472(55), 506
Sahu, S., 406(59), 409(59), 445
St. Lawrence, W. F., 406(62), 446
St. Pierre, L. E., 425(137), 449
Saito, M., 187(181), 244
Salee, G., 176, 177(145), 242
Salyer, I. O., 284(105), 332,
    423(132), 449, 497(111), 509
Samuels, R. J., 198(252), 247
Sands, A. G., 414(94), 447
Sands, R. H., 188(190), 244
Sardar, D., 270(33), 329
Sasaguri, K., 116(157), 136,
    283(87), 331
Satake, K., 292(142), 334, 362
    (97), 376, 415, 416(101), 447
Sato, M., 205, 206(280), 249
Sato, T., 83, 113, 114(25), 129,
    84(38), 130
Sato, Y., 394, 444
Sauer, J. A., 19(24), 34, 22(47,
    49), 35, 46(11), 62, 89, 92(42),
    130, 92(69), 131, 162(96), 239,
    187(171,173-175), 198, 206(174),
    215(171,175), 229(171), 243, 215
    (323,324), 219(323), 222(324),
    251, 217(335), 252, 222(352,
    355), 229(352), 253, 229(386),
    255, 260(2), 328, 270(28,30,31),
    271(30), 329, 343(11), 372

Saunders, D. W., 119, 120(179), 138,
    197, 198, 202(235), 246, 198(247),
    247, 202(269), 248
Savkin, V. G., 356(76), 375
Sazhin, B. I., 217(331), 252
Schael, G. W., 354-356(65), 374
Schaffer, M. C., 278(58), 330
Schaffhauser, R., 53(37), 64, 347
    (22), 372
Schallamach, A., 353(53,54), 355(71),
    359, 374, 359, 375, 433(172,173),
    451
Schatzki, T. F., 222(362), 254
Schell, W. J., 218(338), 252, 222,
    225(357), 253
Schlein, H., 195(217), 245
Schmid, R., 23(62), 35
Schmidt, H., 96(85), 132
Schmidt, P. G., 285(119), 333
Schmieder, K., 23(56), 35, 56(45),
    64, 139, 189, 219, 222, 225(7),
    235, 177(151), 242, 187, 215,
    219, 222, 225(184), 244
Schmitt, J. A., 294, 302, 306, 318
    (164), 335, 302, 306(212), 337
Schnell, G., 23(56), 35, 177(151),
    242
Schonhorn, H., 188(191,194), 244
Schoppee, M. M., 265(10), 328,
    301(197), 336
Schrager, M., 351, 352(42), 373
Schreyer, G., 58(64), 65, 216(301),
    250, 428(154), 450
Schultz, J. M., 281, 283(81), 331
Schwaneke, A. E., 139(26), 236
Schwarzl, F. R., 17(10), 33, 92(59),
    131, 157(69-71), 158(69,70),
    238, 393(31), 444, 406, 422(60),
    445, 406(61), 409, 411(74), 446
    419(122,124), 449
Schwertz, F. A., 343(11), 372
Schwippert, G. A., 422(60), 445,
    406(61), 446
Scott, J. R., 366, 376
Scott, W. W., 139(39), 236
Semenov, N. A., 341(1), 371, 341(2),
    372
Sen, J. K., 162(97), 239
Sendeckyj, G. P., 455(12,18), 504
Senshu, K., 84(32), 130, 113, 114,
    116(148), 136
Serafini, T. T., 265(9), 328
Sergeyev, V. A., 341(5), 372
Sergeyeva, L. M., 425(138), 449
Sewell, J. H., 21(38), 34
Shapery, R. A., 435(180), 452, 487(94)
    508
Sharma, M. G., 89, 92(45), 130, 92(73)
    132, 162(97), 239, 406(62), 446
Sharp, T. J., 293(154), 334
Shaw, R., 139(6), 235
Shen, M. C., 19(34,35), 34, 26(74), 36
    84(26), 129, 107(121), 111, 134,
    122(184), 138, 195(216-218),
    197(218), 245, 219(346), 253,
    422(129), 449
Sherman, M. A., 290(133,135), 292
    (133,135), 333

Sherrard-Smith, K., 92, 94(63),
    131
Shibayama, K., 110(139), 135,
    177(153,154), 181(156), 242,
    212, 214, 217(286), 249, 219
    (347), 253, 285(117), 333,
    395, 416, 428, 429(34), 444
Shindo, H., 219(348), 253
Shinohara, Y., 216(303), 250
Shishkin, N. I., 285(113), 332
Shito, N., 205, 206(280), 249
Shooter, K. V., 257(81), 375
Shreiner, S. A., 425(142), 450
Shroff, R. N., 139(38), 236,
    139(58), 237
Shteding, M. M., 341(4), 372
Shtrikman, S., 387(21), 443
Shuttleworth, R., 409(76), 446
Sillwood, J. M., 487(93), 508
Simeoni, R., 177, 180, 181(149),
    242
Simha, 22(41,42), 34, 105(117),
    134, 218(338), 252, 222,
    225(357), 253
Simon, R. H. M., 100(98), 133
Simunkova, E., 284(99), 332
Sinnott, K. M., 139(15), 235, 187
    (183), 188(189), 244, 229(389),
    255
Skelton, J., 265(10), 328, 301(197)
    336
Skinner, D. W., 351, 352(41), 373
Skinner, S. M., 434(175), 451
Slinyakova, I. B., 431(164), 451
Slonaker, D. F., 104(108), 134
Slonimskii, G. L., 96(84), 132
Slutsker, A. I., 302(208), 302
    (209), 303(208), 337
Smallwood, H. M., 386(15), 443
Smith, J. C., 139, 198, 204(31),
    236
Smith, Jr., K. J., 111(145), 136,
    185(167), 243
Smith, R. R., 292, 302(146), 334
Smith, T. L., 265, 267, 268(21),
    328, 267(22-24), 268(22-24),
    278-280(24), 329, 278(61),
    330, 280(70), 331, 406, 409
    (52), 445, 419, 425(121), 449
Smoluk, G. R., 68, 119(3), 128
Sogolova, T. I., 283(91), 331,
    474(60), 507
Soliman, F. Y., 479(71), 507
Solomon, D. H., 181(156,158), 242
Sone, T., 362(97), 376
Sookne, A. M., 273(41,42), 329,
    352(47), 374
Southern, E., 355(75), 375
Speerschneider, C. J., 433(174), 451
Spence, J., 198(244), 247
Spencer, R. S., 19(29), 34
Sperling, L. H., 122(186), 138,
    499(122-124,127), 510
Spurlin, H. M., 290(126), 333
Stachurski, Z. H., 187(187), 244,
    197, 198, 200, 204(238), 247,
    204, 205(275), 249
Stainsby, D. F., 139(21), 236

Starita, J. M., 499(126), 510
Stark, C. F., 308(243), 338
Starkweather, Jr., H. W., 281
    (80,84), 331
Statton, W. O., 26(72), 36, 283(96),
    332, 302, 303(210), 337
Staverman, A. J., 17(10), 33, 139, 219,
    222(9), 235
Stearns, C. A., 139(48), 237
Stearns, R. S., 197(233), 246
Stein, R. S., 27(78,79), 36, 113,
    119(147), 136, 123, 138, 198
    (245,246,251), 247, 283(85-87),
    331, 416(105), 448
Stephenson, C. E., 347(27a), 373
Sterman, S., 409(80), 446, 409(81),
    447
Stern, D., 47(21), 63
Sternberg, E., 306(231), 338
Stevens, D., 496, 497(106), 509
Stockmair, W., 167(116), 240
Stockton, F. D., 54(38), 64, 111(142)
    136, 185(166), 243
Stowell, E. Z., 47(18), 63
Stratton, R. A., 165(110), 240, 306
    (229), 337
Strauch, O. R., 414(95), 447
Street, K. N., 480(75), 507
Strella, S., 17(16), 33, 139(36), 236
    306(227,228), 337, 308(240), 338
Strong, J. D., 195(216,217), 245,
    219(346), 253
Struik, L. C. E., 14, 33, 157, 158(69),
    238, 224(368), 254, 393(31), 444,
    406, 422(60), 445, 406(61), 446,
    419(122), 449
Sumner, J. K., 284(98), 332
Sutherland, T. H., 19(26), 34
Sutton, W. H., 453(1), 469, 503,
    453(2), 504, 469, 505
Suzerki, Y., 110(139), 135
Suzuki, Y., 177(153,154), 242
Sviridyonok, A. I., 356(76), 375
Swanson, D. L., 348, 351, 352(32),
    373
Sweeny, K. H., 393(28), 444
Swift, J. D., 181(158), 242

                            T

Tabor, D., 353, 355, 356(66), 374,
    356(77), 375, 365, 367(104), 376
Takahashi, M., 53(37), 64, 84(26),
    129, 347(22), 372
Takahashi, Y., 216(294), 250
Takano, M., 200(266), 248
Takashima, A., 386(13), 443
Takayanagi, M., 58, 59(65), 66,
    139(60), 237, 187, 188, 225
    (185), 244, 198, 200(264),
    248, 229(387), 255, 397(40),
    445, 429(158), 451
Takemoto, T., 114, 116(152), 136,
    116(158), 137
Takemura, T., 114(152,153), 116
    (152), 136
Takeuchi, A., 202(272), 248
Tanaka, H., 216(305), 250

Tanaka, T., 181(156), 242,
    219(347), 253
Tarnopol'skii, Yu. M., 469, 506
Tawn, A. R. H., 107(120), 134
Taylor, D. J., 366, 376
Taylor, G. R., 278-280(59), 330
Taylor, J. S., 25, 26(66), 35
Taylor, R. B., 84(26), 129
Teitel'Baum, B. Ya., 341(3), 372
Telfair, D., 17(13), 33, 311(246),
    338
Temple, R. B., 198(250), 247
Terada, H., 187, 188(182), 244
Tetelman, A. S., 484, 485(86), 508
Tetreault, R. J., 215(329), 252
Thelin, J. H., 354-356(65), 374
Theocoris, P. S., 84(36), 130
Thomas, A. G., 321(276, 277, 279-281),
    340, 361, 362(92), 375, 416(112,
    113), 418(118), 448
Thomas, D. A., 96(86), 132, 122(186),
    138, 499(123, 124, 127), 510
Thomas, J. P., 435, 436(179), 452
Thomas, L. S., 290, 292(136), 333
Thomas, P. H., 357(81), 375
Thomas, R. L., 481(81), 491, 494(97),
    508
Thompson, A. B., 198, 204, 225(256),
    248, 300(193), 336
Thomson, J. B., 467, 505, 480(79),
    507
Thorne, J. A., 26(70), 35
Thurn, H., 19(27), 34, 423(134), 449,
    497(113), 509
Till, P. H., 27(82), 36
Timoshenko, S., 121(182), 138, 296
    (173), 335, 365, 376
Tobolsky, A. V., 4(6), 33, 53(37), 54,
    39, 64, 56(49), 65, 59(70), 66,
    75, 76, 79, 128, 84(26,28), 129,
    84(31,33,34), 90(47), 130, 94(80),
    132, 105(118), 107(121), 111, 134,
    111(140,141), 135, 113(147), 116
    (155), 119(147), 136, 118(64), 137,
    159(75,76), 238, 176, 205(144),
    242, 185(164,165), 243, 198(246),
    247, 217(314), 251, 294, 335,
    301(199,200), 307(199,200), 336,
    347(21,22), 372, 429(159), 451
Toggenburger, R., 273, 330
Tokita, N., 139(16), 235, 290(132),
    333
Tompa, A. S., 279(65), 330
Toor, H. L., 290(127), 333
Trachte, K. L., 263, 284, 301, 307(6),
    328
Trayer, G. W., 48(23), 63
Tregear, G. W., 294(170), 335
Treloar, L. R. G., 176, 198(142), 241,
    202(277), 249, 275(57), 330
Trementozzi, Q. A., 273(49), 330
Trivisonno, N. M., 139(48), 237
Tsai, S. W., 388, 444, 455(7,13),
    456(13), 504, 460(25), 462(25,31),
    464(31), 466(25), 505
Tschoegl, N. W., 122(185), 138, 422
    (131), 449
Tsuge, K., 187, 188(182), 244

Tsunekawa, Y., 285(116), _333_
Tsutsui, M., 369(119), _377_
Tuijnman, C. A. F., 187(184), _244_
Tung, L. H., 275(54), _330_
Turley, S. G., 58(63), _65_, 167(120),
    240, 216(309), _251_, 314(258,260),
    _319_(258, 260), _320_(260), _339_,
    428(153), _450_
Turner, L. B., _293_(149), _334_
Turner, P. S., 435(178), _452_
Turner, S., 90(53), 91, 92(61),
    92(53), 94(66), 114(61), 116,
    _131_, 92, 94(71), _132_, 118(171),
    _137_, 120(181), _138_, 479(69),
    _507_
Tyson, W. R., 469(42), _506_

U

Ueberreiter, K., 23(51,52), _35_,
    53,54(36), _64_, 177, 180(_148_),
    _242_
Ueda, A., 313, 319, 320(251), _338_
Uematsu, I., 185(161), _242_
Uematsu, Y., 185(161), _242_
Uemura, M., 187(181), _244_
Ueno, S., 369(119), _377_
Updegraff, I. H., 344(_18_), _372_
Ushirokawa, M., 83, 113, 114(_25_),
    _129_, 84(38), _130_
Utracki, L., 105(_117_), _134_

V

Valentine, R. H., 109(134), _135_
Van Brederode, R. A., 139(20), _235_
Vanderbilt, B. M., 409(82), _447_
Van der Wal, C. W., 139(23), _236_,
    406, 422(60), _445_, 406(61), _446_
van Duijkeren, M. P., 224(368), _254_
Van Holde, K., 90,92(48), _130_
van Hoorn, H., 275, 281, 317(53),
    _330_
Van Kerpel, R. G., 229(383), _255_
van Schooten, J., 275, 281, 317(53),
    _330_
Van Vlack, L. H., 499(120), _509_
Van Wazer, J. R., 160(79), _238_
Vasilieko, Ya. P., 425(138), _449_
Vernon, F., 229(388), _255_
Vickers, H. H., 355(70), _374_
Veith, A. G., 361(94), _375_
Vincent, P. I., 262(4), _265_(18),
    _328_, 301(198), _336_, 308(235,
    _241_), 309(235,2_45_), 311-315
    (235), _338_
Vinogradov, G. V., 52(34), _64_,
    170(128), _241_, 355, 356(_74_),
    _375_, 406(48_), _445_
Vokulonskaya, I. I., 425(142), _450_
Volkova, T. A., 425(142), _450_
Voyutskii, S. S., 341(4), _372_
Vrancken, M. N., 139(14), _235_
Vroom, W. I., 270(36), _329_, 354(61),
    _374_

W

Wada, Y., 84(37), _130_, 187, 188(182),
    _244_, 222(354), _253_, 314(256), _339_
Wagner, E. R., 314, _319_, 320(259), _339_
    428(157), _451_
Wagner, H. L., _474_(62), _507_
Wagner, M. P., 474(63), _507_
Wales, M., 283(90), _331_
Walker, R. W., 355(75), _375_
Wall, R. A., 187, 229(17_1_), _243_,
    217(335), 252, 229(386), _255_,
    406, 414, 422, 425(44), _445_,
    496(102), _508_
Wallach, M. L., _59_(75), _66_, 217(312),
    _251_, 428(151), _450_
Walters, M. H., 362(_98_), _376_
Wambach, A., 425(135), _449_
Warburton, B., 314, 320(_257_), _339_
Ward, I. M., 39(4), _62_, 92(72), _132_,
    187(187), _244_, 19_7_(237,238),
    198(237-239,_254_), 200(238), 201
    (237), 202(237), 204(238), _247_,
    202(276,278,279), 204(275), _205_
    (275), _249_, 225(373), _254_, 265,
    300(14), _328_, 270(37), _329_, 285
    (120,122,_123_), 290(122,_129_), 300
    (120,192), 301(192), _336_
Warfield, R. W., 270(34), _329_
Wargin, R. V., 279(64), _330_
Warnaka, G. E., 162, 163(_94_), _239_
Warren, R. F., 229(388), _255_
Warrick, E. L., 411(84), _447_
Warshavsky, M., 290(132), _333_
Waterman, H. A., 48(25), _63_, 139(62),
    _238_, 198, 204(262), _248_, 224(368),
    _254_
Waters, N. E., 351, 352(38), _373_, 366,
    367(105), _376_
Watson, M. T., _343_(9), _372_
Watson, W. F., 109, _135_, 162-164(89),
    _239_
Watts, D. C., 217, 225(333), _252_
Weaver, A. E., 188(190), _244_
Webb, R. S., 369 (120),_377_
Weems, D. A., 104(108), _134_
Weir, F. E., 110(137), _135_, 139(22),
    _236_, 229(392), _255_
Welner, S., 23, 24(_59_), _35_
Wen, P. R., 89, 92(45), _130_
Westover, R. F., 270(36), _329_, 354
    (61), _374_
Wetton, R. E., 139(40,55), _237_,
    217(332), _252_
Weyland, H. G., _164_(107), _240_
White, E. F. T., 202(277), _249_,
    301(203), _336_
White, J. W., _198_,200,205,206(265),
    _248_, 285(125), _333_
White, P. L., 499(1_20_), _509_
Whitman, R. D., 215(327), _251_,
    224(371), _254_
Whitney, J. F., _281_, 282(79), _331_
Whitney, J. M., 39, 40(2), _62_,
    455(11), _504_

Whitney, J. W., 198(242), <u>247</u>
Whittaker, R. E., 280(72), <u>331</u>
Wiederhorn, N., 113, 119(147), <u>136</u>
Wiinikainen, R. A., 359, 363(88), <u>375</u>
Wijga, P. W. O., 275(55), <u>330</u>
Wiktorek, R. J., 351, 352(41), <u>373</u>
Wilchinsky, Z. W., 198(249), <u>247</u>
Wiley, R. H., 19(23),<u>34</u>
Wilkes, G. L., 123, <u>138</u>, 416(105), <u>448</u>
Wilkinson, C. S., 139(47), <u>237</u>, 162(86), <u>239</u>, 347(20), <u>372</u>
Willbourn, A. H., 215, 219, <u>222</u>(319), <u>251</u>, 219, 222(350), <u>253</u>, 347(27a), <u>373</u>
Williams, A. J., 499(121), <u>509</u>
Williams, B. L., 354-356(65), <u>374</u>
Williams, G., 81(17), <u>129</u>, 187, <u>201</u>, 215, 217, 222, 225(177), <u>243</u>, 217, 225(333), <u>252</u>
Williams, J. L., 343, 344(16), <u>372</u>
Williams, M. C., 84(29), <u>129</u>
Williams, M. L., 76(10), <u>79</u>, 100, 109(15), 114(15), 122, <u>128</u>, 150 (66,67), 172(66), <u>238</u>, <u>422</u>(130), <u>449</u>
Williams, M. L., 297(184,185), <u>336</u>, 302, 303(220), 305(224,225), <u>337</u>
Winans, R. R., 308(237), <u>338</u>
Witnauer, L. P., 343(13), <u>372</u>, 347(27), <u>373</u>
Witsiepe, W. K., 217(318), <u>251</u>
Witte, R. S., 48(27), <u>63</u>
Woerner, S., 223(364), <u>254</u>
Wohlnsiedler, H. P., 344(18), <u>372</u>
Wohrer, L. C., 406(55), <u>445</u>, 496(107), <u>509</u>
Wolf, K. A., 23(56), <u>35</u>, 56(44,45), <u>64</u>, 139,189,219,<u>222</u>,225(7), <u>235</u>, <u>177</u>(151), <u>242</u>, 187(184), 189(196), 215(184), <u>219</u>,222,225(184), <u>244</u>
Wolfe, J. M., 92(72), <u>132</u>
Wolock, I., 290(133,135), 292(133, 135), <u>333</u>, 292(139), <u>334</u>
Wolstenholme, W. E., 84(35), <u>130</u>, 308(243), <u>338</u>
Wolter, F., 411(88), <u>447</u>
Wood, L. A., 26(67), <u>35</u>, 108(128-130), <u>135</u>
Woodbrey, J., 195(209), <u>245</u>, 224(370), <u>254</u>
Woodford, D. E., 162(85), <u>239</u>, 347(20), <u>372</u>
Woodhams, R. T., 431(166), <u>451</u>, 462, 465, 474, 481(27), <u>505</u>, <u>498</u>(117), <u>509</u>
Woods, D. W., 56(41), <u>64</u>, 170(126), <u>241</u>, 198, 204, 225(256), <u>248</u>
Woodward, A. E., 19(24), <u>34</u>, <u>22</u>(47), <u>35</u>, 187(171,173), 215, 229(171), <u>194</u>(205,206), 215(205), 222(205, 206), <u>245</u>, 201, 202(267), <u>248</u>, 215, 2<u>19</u>(323), <u>251</u>, 217(335,336), <u>252</u>, 229(386), <u>255</u>
Worf, D. L., 343(11), <u>372</u>
Work, J. L., 56(47), <u>64</u>
Wrasidlo, W., 167(114), <u>240</u>, 217, 218, 229(334), <u>252</u>

Wright, H., 202(277), <u>249</u>
Wrzesien, A., 487(92), <u>508</u>
Wu, T. T., 496(108), <u>509</u>
Wuerstlin, F., 19(27), <u>34</u>, 225(376), <u>254</u>
Wunderlich, B., 29, <u>36</u>
Wyman, D. P., 21(40), <u>34</u>, 273, <u>330</u>

X

Xanthos, M., 498(117), <u>509</u>

Y

Yamamoto, K., 139(32), <u>236</u>
Yamamura, H., 116, <u>137</u>, 219(348), <u>253</u>
Yamazaki, H., 369(119), <u>377</u>
Yanko, J. A., 273(47), <u>274</u>, <u>330</u>
Yannas, I., 195(210), <u>245</u>
Yano, O., 222(354), <u>253</u>
Yanovsky, Yu. G., 406(48), <u>445</u>
Yarmilko, E. G., 341(6), <u>372</u>
Yavorsky, P., 139(50), <u>237</u>
Yeh, G. S., 367(11), 369(117), <u>376</u>
Yim, A., 425(137), <u>449</u>
Yin, T. P., 171(131), <u>241</u>
Yokoyama, T., 206-208(285), <u>249</u>
Yorgiadis, A., 162(84), <u>239</u>, <u>350</u> (36), <u>373</u>
Yoshino, M., 139(60), <u>237</u>, 229 (387), <u>255</u>
Yoshimura, N., 58(59), <u>65</u>, 216(297), <u>250</u>, 293(150), <u>334</u>, <u>428</u>, 429 (152), <u>450</u>
Yoshitomi, T., 47(15), <u>63</u>, 114, 116(152), <u>136</u>, 116(158,159), <u>137</u>
Young, C. A., 278(60), <u>330</u>
Young, D. W., 293(148,1<u>49</u>,152), <u>334</u>

Z

Zahradnikova, A., 219(349), <u>253</u>
Zakrevskyi, V. A., 302, 303(221), <u>337</u>
Zaks, Yu. B., 302(218), <u>337</u>
Zapas, L., 139(50), <u>237</u>
Zapp, R. L., 361(96), <u>376</u>
Zaukelies, D. A., 283(88), <u>331</u>
Zelinger, J., 58(62), <u>65</u>, 216(298), <u>250</u>, 284(99), <u>332</u>
Zhurkov, S. N., 302(208,219,221), 303(208,221), <u>337</u>
Ziemianski, L. P., 411(83), <u>447</u>
Zihlif, A. M., 290(129), <u>333</u>
Zilvar, V., 351, 352(46), <u>374</u>
Zimm, B. H., 76, <u>128</u>
Zikek, P., 58(62), <u>65</u>, 216(298), <u>250</u>
Zubov, P. I., 425(142), <u>450</u>
Zupko, H. M., 188(193), <u>244</u>

A

Abrasion, 359
Anisotropic materials
  definition, 39
Anisotropy of fiber composites,
  40, 454, 519
Antiplasticization, 195
ASTM standards, 3

B

Biaxial orientation, 264, 290
  definition, 42
Blends of molecular weights,
  100
Block polymers
  creep of, 121
  dynamic properties of, 208,
    428
  modulus of, 394
  modulus-temperature curve,
    58, 213
  solvent effects, 122, 213,
    428
  stress-strain tests on,
    292, 415
Branching
  viscosity, effect on, 104

C

Coefficient of friction, 353
Coefficients of thermal expansion
  filled polymers, 434, 487
Cold-drawing, 282, 299
  theory of, 299
Complex moduli, 12, 139
Composite materials, 379, 453
  creep of, 418, 479
  dynamic mechanical properties,
    422
  hardness of, 433
  heat distortion temperature of,
    431, 481
  impact strength of, 430, 483
  interfacial adhesion, effect of,
    409, 471, 483
  interpenetrating networks, 499
  modulus of, 387, 454
  particle size, effect of, 392, 411
  strength of, 405, 465
  stress relaxation of, 421
  stress-strain tests, 405, 465
  thermal expansion, 434, 487
  thick interlayers, 497
  wear of, 433
Conversion factors, 513
Cracks, 295

Craze cracks, 301, 430
Crazing
  stress-strain tests, effects on, 281
  creep, effect on, 96, 122
Creep
  biaxial, 121
  block polymers, 121
  composites, 418, 479
  conversion to dynamic properties, 157
  copolymers and plasticization,
    effect of, 118
  crosslinking, effect of, 106
  crystallinity, effect of, 111
  fiber-filled composites, 479
  models, 70
  molecular weight, effect of, 95
  Nutting equation, 78, 89
  orientation, effect of, 119
  polyblends, 121
  pressure, effect of, 93
  stress dependence of, 87
  temperature, effect of, 84
  tests, 4, 67
  thermal treatments, 94
Crosslinking
  creep, effect on, 106
  dynamic properties, effect on, 174
  modulus of rubbers, 176
  stress relaxation, effect on, 106
  stress-strain tests, 274
Crystallinity, 26
  creep and stress relaxation,
    effect on, 111
  dynamic properties, effect on, 181
  modulus, interrelation to, 182
  stress-strain tests, 274, 280

D

Damping
  advantages and disadvantages, 142
  creep, relation to, 158
  definitions, 12
  fatigue life, effect on, 351
  filled polymers, 422
  interrelations, 16
  mechanisms, 147
  molecular weight effects, 171
  rolling friction, correlation with, 354
  stress relaxation, relation to,
    159
  swelling ratio, effect of, 175
Damping peak
  shift with frequency, 143
Deflection temperature under load,
  341, 345
Dewetting, 409, 483
Distribution of relaxation times,
  75, 154

Distribution of retardation times, 75, 155
Dynamic mechanical instruments, 139
Dynamic mechanical properties, 11
  chemical heterogeneity of copolymers, 190, 209
  composite materials, 422
  copolymerization, effect of, 189
  crosslinking, effect of, 174
  crystallinity, effect of, 181
  molecular weight effects, 170
  orientation, effect of, 197
  plasticizers, effect of, 189
  polyblends, block and graft polymers, 208, 428
  stress amplitude effects, 161
  temperature and frequency effects, 143
  thermal history effects, 165
  time-temperature superposition, 150
  viscosity, relation to, 160
Dynamic mechanical tests, 11
Dynamic properties to creep conversions, 158
Dynamic properties to stress relaxation conversions, 157

E

Einstein coefficient, 381, 391, 458, 459
Elastic modulus
  anisotropic materials, 39, 454, 491, 519
  composite materials, 387, 454
  conversion factors, 513
  definition, 9
  dynamic, 12, 143
  isotropic materials, 39, 387
  measurement of, 43
  rubber theory, 176, 275
  temperature, effect of, 48, 143
Entanglements, 97, 271

F

Failure envelope, 268
Fatigue, 348, 480
  fiber-filled composites, 480
Fatigue life, 349
  damping, effect on, 351
Fatigue tests, 348
Fiber-filled composites, 453
  creep of, 479
  fatigue, 480
  heat distortion temperature, 481
  impact strength, 483
  modulus, angular dependence, 459
  modulus of, 454
  randomly oriented fibers, 474
  strength of, 465
  strength of laminates, 474
  stress-strain tests, 465
  thermal expansion, 487
Filled polymers, 379

Flake-filled composites, 496
Flex temperature, 347
Foams
  modulus of, 394
  stress-strain tests on, 416
Fracture mechanics, 298
Fracture theory, 296
Friction, 353
  factors affecting, 354

G

Glass transition, 515
  copolymerization, effect of, 26, 193
  crosslinking, effect of, 23, 177
  molecular weight dependence, 22
  plasticizers, effect of, 25, 193
Glass transition temperature, 18
  chemical structure, relation to, 20
  intermolecular forces, effect of, 205
Graft polymers, modulus-temperature curve of, 58

H

Hardness, 363
Hardness of composites, 433
Heat distortion temperature
  annealing, effect of, 343
  fiber-filled composites, 481
  filled polymers, 431
  stress, effect of, 344
Heat distortion tests, 18, 341
Hertz hardness, 365
Hookes' law, 10

I

Impact strength, 308, 430, 483
  composites, 430, 483
  crystallinity, effect of, 317
  dynamic properties, correlation with, 320
  fiber-filled composites, 483
  instruments, 308
  notches, effect of, 309
  orientation, effect of, 314
  polyblends, 318
  temperature, effect of, 313
Impact tests, 17
Indentation tests, 363, 365
Interlaminar shear strength, 473
Interpenetrating network composites, 499
Inverted composites, 394

K

Kinetic theory of rubber elasticity, 176, 275

L

Laminates, strength of, 474
Logarithmic decrement, definition, 14

M

Master curves, 80, 83, 86, 101,
    114, 122, 150, 172, 268
Maxwell model, 68
Melting point, 515
    copolymerization, effect of, 30
        193
    molecular weight, effect of, 30
    plasticizers, effect of, 30, 193
Models, 68, 70, 148, 258
Molecular weight
    dynamic properties, effect on,
        170
    creep, effect on, 83, 95
    rheology, effect on, 97
    stress relaxation, effect on,
        95, 101
    stress-strain tests, effect
        on, 271
    viscosity, effect on, 97
Modulus
    conversion factors, 513
    crosslinking, effect on, 176
    crystallinity relation, 182
    definition, 9
    fiber-filled composites, 40, 454,
        519
    intermolecular forces, effect of,
        205
    kinetic theory of, 176, 275
    measurement of, 43
Modulus of block polymers, 394
Modulus of composites, 387, 454, 491
    errors in, 401
    thermal stresses, effect of, 402
Modulus of filled polymers, 387
    interfacial adhesion, effect of, 393
    particle size, effect of, 392
    viscosity, relation to, 386
Modulus of foams, 394, 416
Modulus of inverted composites, 394
Modulus of polyblends, 394
Modulus of ribbon-filled composites,
    491
Modulus-temperature curves, 48
    block polymers, 58
    copolymerization effect of, 56
    crosslinking, effect of, 52
    crystallinity, effect of, 54, 181
    molecular weight, effect of, 51
    plasticization, effect of, 56
    polyblends, 58, 209

N

Non-Newtonian suspensions, 384
Nutting equation, 78, 89, 158

O

Orientation
    creep and stress relaxation, effect
        on, 119
    dynamic properties, effect on, 197
    impact strength, effect on, 314
    Poisson's ratio, effect on, 120
    stress-strain tests, effect on, 285

P

Packing fraction, 381
Penetration softening temperature,
    347
Phase inversion in composites,
    394, 428
Poisson's ratio
    definition, 10, 42
    orientation, effect of, 120
Polyblends
    creep of, 121
    dynamic properties of, 208,
        428
    impact strength of, 318
    modulus of, 394
    modulus-temperature curve of,
        58
    stress-strain tests on, 292,
        305, 415
Polymers, chemical structure,
    511

R

Relaxation times, 70, 75
Retardation times, 71, 75
Rheology, 95, 380
    suspensions, 380
Ribbon-filled composites, 490
    moduli of, 491
    strength of, 493
Rolling friction, 354
Rubber elasticity, kinetic
    theory of, 176, 275

S

Scratch resistance, 359, 362
Secondary glass transitions, 215
    liquids and plasticizers,
        195, 219
Shear modulus of filled polymers
    388
Softening temperature, 341
Strain, definition, 9
Strain dependence of stress
    relaxation, 92
Strength, theory of, 296
Stress concentrators, 294
Stress, definition, 9
Stress dependence of creep, 87
Stress relaxation, 5
    block polymers and polyblends, 121
    composites, 421
    conversion to dynamic properties,
        157
    copolymers and plasticization,
        effect of, 118
    crosslinking, effect of, 106
    crystallinity, effect of, 111
    model for, 68
    molecular weight, effect of, 101
    orientation, effect of, 119
    pressure, effect of, 93
    strain dependence of, 92
    temperature, effect of, 84
    thermal treatments, 94

Stress relaxation tests, 5, 67
Stress-strain models, 258
Stress-strain tests, 5, 257
  block and graft polymers, 292, 415
  branching, effect of, 274
  composite materials, 405, 465
  compression and shear, 260
  copolymerization, effects of, 283
  crosslinking, effect of, 274, 275
  crystallinity, effect of, 274, 280
  failure envelope, 268
  fiber-filled composites, 465
  filled polymers, 405
  flexural, 261
  foams, 416
  heat treatments, effect of, 283
  hysteresis, correlation with, 280
  molecular weight, effect of, 271
  morphology, effect of, 281
  orientation, effect of, 285
  plasticization, effect of, 283
  polyblends, 292, 305, 415
  pressure, effect of, 270
  rate of testing, effect of, 265
  ribbon-filled composites, 493
  rubbers, 275
  spherulites, effect of, 282
  temperature, effect of, 262
Superposition principles, 77, 79
  Boltzmann, 77
  time-temperature, 79, 267
Suspensions, rheology of, 380

T

Tearing, 320
Time-temperature superposition, 79
Toughness, definition, 258
Transcrystallinity, 188

V

Vicat softening temperature, 347
Viscosity
  complex, 13
  conversion factor, 514
  dynamic properties, relation to,
    13, 160
  molecular weight, effect on, 97
  plasticizers, effect of, 104
  shear rate dependence, 160
Viscosity of suspensions, 380
  shear modulus, relation to, 386
Viscoelasticity
  definition, 2
  molecular theories, 76

W

Wear, 359
  composites, 433
W-L-F superposition, 79, 82, 102,
  150, 172

Y

Yielding, theories of, 299
Young's modulus, definition, 9